Coromandel!

JOHN MASTERS

Coromandel!

THE VIKING PRESS · NEW YORK

For Susan, My Daughter

Coromandel!

Chapter One

The girl leaned out of the casement, the leaded panes and all her face dark in the shadow of the overhanging thatch. The clock in the church tower struck twelve.

The cracked notes dropped slowly, one by one, into the moonlit well of the green, and ran about the lanes of the village and crept down in softer echoes from the slope of the Plain beyond. The churchyard lay below the girl's window. The gravestones shone silently with the pale fire of the night, and the shadows of them knelt in square blocks, like patient mourners, on the humps of the graves. The wind moved warm from the valley to the Plain, and summer was nearly gone.

The girl sighed and rested her weight heavily on her elbows and waited. She was naked, warm, and kindly. She heard nothing, and thought of nothing but her waiting, although the wind made music in the thatch so close above her head.

* * *

The young man moved slowly under the edge of the Plain, in the shadow of the last hedge. He moved as though watchers lay in wait for him in the moonlight. He paused at a tussock of grass, and again in the shadow of a group of elms, and looked ahead, to right and left, and behind; then he moved on. He heard music in the silence and saw men where he knew there were none; so he had forgotten the girl and her waiting.

The Vale dipped down to his right. There, lying in the moonlight, the wheat was cut and the fields were bare and the orchards heavy. He was moving along the border between the cultivation and the Plain. He liked best to prowl that line, especially at night, because the fields made him think of people, but the Plain was empty and full of lonely music, and he needed both to build substance for his dreams.

He stopped and looked about him with a frown. It was good to summon phantoms from his mind to go beside him and so make the

3

familiar strange. But he must not do that all the time, or soon he would not be able to tell which things he had made and which God had made. In truth this was only one night of a thousand he had known like it, only a summer night. The owl screeched from the firs in Bellman's Hollow above him, but that was its habit. The wind stirred the grass of the Plain as it had always done. The farm slept behind him, and the village in front of him slept, and only one light shone in the Vale, far and yellow among the woods, and he knew that light. It lived in the iron lantern that hung from the oak in front of the Green Man in Shrewford Admiral. He'd heard the Pennel clock strike twelve, and soon the lamp would go out because Mistress Dalton stumped out of her back room at midnight every night and made a great noise with her stick on the beams in the kitchen and drove the last drinkers out. Any minute now the crew of them would be grumbling in the lane outside the Green Man— Joe the tinker, and Peter, and Jonas, and Tom Devitt who had sailed with Drake, and the other Tom, Long Tom Bolling from Pennel.

But the rest of the world was asleep. The cattle were asleep in the fields, and the people were asleep in their beds—his father in his wide bed (but cold, because his mother was dead and his father had no wife now), his sister Molly in her narrow bed, Sir Tristram Pennel in his high bed, Old Voy the poacher in—but no one knew where Voy slept from night to night. The horses were asleep in the stables, heads hanging and three legs stiff and one leg bent. Parson was asleep in the rectory, and all the dead people in the ground, and—Mary was waiting for him.

He started and began to move with quick, quiet steps toward the Vale.

If he met anyone they might ask where he was going at this time of night. But now there was a dim footpath under his shoes, and it was no crime to tread a footpath. The Pennel gamekeepers might think he was poaching, but he wasn't. It was good to creep along and be afraid, when you had, yourself, in your head, made the people you were afraid of, the ones who were hunting you. It wasn't right to be afraid of real people though, if you could help it. He was twenty, and he could use bow, sword, sling, and halberd. He had fired guns and lain with girls. He could sing a madrigal and tune a fiddle; he could dance the Moorish dance at Whitsun and join in the Ring at the harvest fair. He could drink to King Charles in ale or brandy or wine—just as he wished. He could ride a horse and milk a cow and

4

plow a straight furrow with two oxen at the plow. Sickle, billhook, and scythe wrought comfortably in his hands, and his fingers could hold the bull by the nose. He could not read or write.

He was a man. Boys played at make-believe; for a man, it was silly. Perhaps it was even sinful, but he couldn't help it.

He said to himself, "It is an ordinary summer night," and tried hard to see only what his eyes showed him. But really, nothing was ordinary. Up there on the Plain, where the wind blew close to the earth and at night the larks started out of their shelters at your feet, there were long, quiet humps, and they were not ordinary. A plow-man had turned up statues and stone arrowheads there not long ago. Across the Vale, above the Wansdyke, a farmer digging his well had found a man's spine with a rusted sword broken off in it, and bones that turned to powder when he picked them up. By Shrewford Ring two stones stood ten feet high in the middle of nothing, and a third stone lay flat over them. The three stones made a bulky and danger-ous shape up there, and in the broad sunlight of daytime he could not guess what they were for. At night, sometimes, he could—but he dared not tell anyone what he guessed, because it was dark and full of animals and witches. As a boy, he had asked his father about the stones, but his father couldn't answer him. As a youth, he'd asked Parson, and Parson had said, "Romans, Jason. Romans and heathens and Druids, Jason. Have you learned your catechism, Jason? Have you had any sinful thoughts?" Parson was sly and fat and liked to make fun of the farmers because they could not read.

Jason groaned. There was so much to know, and he knew nothing except to be a farmer's son in Shrewford Pennel, in the county of Wiltshire, in the year of Our Lord 1627.

The church clock struck a single note. Half-past twelve? Or one? He'd kept Mary waiting a long time already. He walked quickly down the path and soon came to a stream ten paces wide. It ran noisily now, at night, over its stones. A heavy plank bridge crossed it in two parts, one from the near bank to a big stone in the middle, and one from the stone to the far bank. As Jason crossed, a fish swirled suddenly upstream. The lash of its tail flicked a spray of water into the moonlight and sent circles of ripples under the bridge and out to the banks. Jason watched the ripples till the sparkling shallows broke and swallowed them. Slowly he dropped to his stomach and lay on the plank, peering into the water.

"Oh, I see you," he muttered, "and I could catch you too."

5

He glanced round. Sir Tristram's keepers might have been watching him come down from the edge of the Plain. They might be watching him now. Then he'd get a beating, or worse. The law didn't allow any such thing, and most of the squires didn't allow it either. But the Pennels were ginger-haired and had narrow heads, and Sir Tristram was jealous of every fish in his streams and every rabbit in his warrens. His men had caught Jason half a dozen times already. Then Sir Tristram would curse him and swear he'd die on the gallows, and his father would get into trouble again, for not keeping him in order, and Parson would make a joke about it in his sermon next Sunday, but not pleasantly.

But—he could catch that fish. He rolled back the sleeve of his shirt and stretched his arm down into the water. He half clenched his fist and slid his hand slowly along under the overhanging bank, moving his fingers and gently stirring the water, just as a trout's tail would do.

Ah, and what does the fish see? It will be green and dull and swirly, all that he sees. People are nothing but shadows that pass across the light, and they don't look like people; they are bent and short the way a stick is when some of it's in the water and some isn't. A man walking is a *thump-thump* on the earth, which makes a noise in the water, but not a noise you hear, a noise you feel, like when they fired the big cannon over at Amesbury and Jason felt it here. And the swirling and the blunt shape, greeny-bluey and gently stirring—that's not Jason's hand, that's another trout—not a pike, for the pike moves fast, turns quick . . .

His hand cupped under the belly of the trout, and he moved his fingers up and down, tickling, touching—a pound, a pound and a half. Flip him out, and then a fire of dry wood; wait till the wood turns to red coals. . . .

The clock struck two. It must have been half-past one he'd heard before. Mary was waiting. He didn't know why she'd become his girl when she had been all but betrothed to George Denning, but so she had, and his father told him it was time he got married so that when his sister married the fool Ahab Stiles she had got herself betrothed to, and went away, there would still be a woman to cook the food and keep the chickens. He'd have to get married sometime, and then it wouldn't be right to stay out late at night. *Clang, dang,* the old clock would go, and about eight every night he ought to be home, and the trout would swim unseen in the Avon, and the broad leaf gleaming in the bush would never be a golden helmet, but only a leaf.

He walked down the lane, dry and hot and deep, that ran between the churchyard and the back of the Bowchers' cottage. The moon shone full on Mary's window now. He was a fool to be so late. Two hours ago he would have climbed in shadow. Now any inquisitive old fool in the village could see him if she chose to look. The casement was open, and that was the sign that nothing was wrong. Mary was a good girl. For a moment, standing with one hand on the ivy, he thought of her. She was kind, and when she smiled it was slow and didn't hurt, and her hands were hard as his, but her thighs were soft and her lips wet. He was very fond of her.

He looked up at the wall. Now the best way was to use the ivy to the right of her casement. Old Bowcher slept with his wife on the ground floor at the other side of the cottage. Jason needn't fear disturbing them unless he fell off, and even then— He could hear them snoring, and smiled.

He'd never tried climbing the ivy on the left. There was a gap of four feet, nearer five, between the ivy and the casement up there, but he could swing across that and catch hold of the sill. He'd been up on the right so often that it wasn't exciting any more.

He began to climb on the left. He went up easily and quietly, hand over hand. It was fine, his muscles easy and strong and moving the way he told them. This was how Tom Devitt had climbed the side of the Spanish galleon in Cadiz harbor, he said—the moon was a lamp swinging at the masthead as the great ship rocked. The water lapped far below, the glowing water, warm and full of light. Winged golden fish scuttered across the surface, leaving sparks of water-fire behind. The crew paced the deck with bare feet. They challenged one another in their strange language—"*Raval push millowo?*" "*Groton smahooken! Ta mien? Hellog she varam!*" A sharp steel sword swung naked at Jason's belt, and the next man hung on the rope below him, and the little boat waited with muffled oars, and it was full of their dark, eager, bearded faces, and the English ship lay hidden in the mist beyond. . . .

It looked a long way to the casement. He reached out as far as he could—short by two feet. The ivy was not so strong on this side either. He could go down again easily enough, and climb up the other side.

One of the Pennels had captured Alton Castle for King Harry this way, swinging in from a tree to an arrow slit and strangling the sleepy soldier on guard there.

He leaned back, moved his feet until the ivy stopped creaking, and

7

jumped. His hand grasped at the window ledge, and his head hit the casement with a bang. As his fingers gripped, he heard a gasp from inside the room. He drew himself up, suddenly tired now that the excitement was over and it was only Mary Bowcher's window, and only Mary leaning out to pull him in.

As soon as he was inside she whispered anxiously, "What happened, Jason? Are you hurt?"

She wouldn't understand about Drake and Alton Castle, so he muttered, "The ivy nearly gave way." He didn't like to lie, but people often forced him to, because they wouldn't accept the truth. To them a lie was often truer than truth—like the time when he didn't go to catechism and told Parson he'd been thinking about the three stones at Shrewford Ring, which was the truth, but Parson had called him a liar. Next time he said he'd been drinking beer in the Cross Keys, and Parson believed him.

Mary was strong and short, with big breasts and sunburned arms. Her hair was thick and straight and hung down in a brown cloak over her shoulders and breasts and back. Beyond her he saw the bed in the corner, under the slope of the roof. You had to stoop there, and one of the boards groaned when you trod on it. Mary was twenty-two, and she slept naked because her father was only a laborer on the Pennel estate. In the winter she slept in her shift. The blankets were coarse and dark, and the only other pieces of furniture in the room were a short bench, a square table, and a big chest of drawers. The heavy smell of night-scented stock came in through the window, mixed with the acid tang of bruised ivy and the sharp, cold smell of the gravestones; but Mary noticed only the good smells of the cows, which she knew, and of the flowers, which she knew.

A cock crew in the village. The earth turned over; the moon swung. Jason caught his breath, for the gravestones stood so tall and white above the shadows. Again the cock crew. From the close-woven night, from under the moon on the Plain, another answered it.

*   *   *

She peered at him with a kind of exasperated lovingness. He had a queer, foreign smell, of hawthorn and dew and wild animals, and he came crashing in at her window two hours after he'd said. The line of his jaw was hard and dark, and he was tall for a farm boy; his face was long, his hair dark, and his eyes pale, pale gray, sometimes empty as a stone, sometimes flashing and shining. He had thin lips

8

and a wide mouth that turned down at the corners, and ears set far back on his head, and a long neck and narrow nostrils. For the sake of a peculiar sparkle in his eyes she had left George Denning. Now she'd got Jason for her man, and they were almost betrothed, but she didn't know what to make of him. She was wildly happy with him, and then for long periods vaguely ill at ease. She thought slowly, watching him: I'd like to be sure, one way or the other. Oh, I'd like to be sure, but with Jason will I ever be?

She settled on her side and stretched out her arms to him. "Come into the bed to me, Jason," she whispered. She heard her mother snoring downstairs and felt a little sleepy herself now. She wished he would come quickly to her and wake her up. Or that he would go to sleep in her bed, and then she could curl her arm over him and feel she knew where he really was, asleep, under her arm, in her care.

Jason stayed at the window, looking out. When she spoke he turned and said, "I thought to bring you a trout, Mary."

She said, "You'll get into trouble again, Jason, with your poaching." He'd hang on the gallows because he was wild and strange. They'd cast him out like a witch, and if they couldn't do that they'd make him do something they could hang him for. He wasn't like any of the rest of them. "Come to bed," she whispered.

Jason swung quickly, went to her, and knelt beside her bed. He put out his arms, caught her, and whispered, "Will you be happy with me, Mary?"

She didn't know. That was the question she had just been asking herself. Would he be happy with her, or any woman? She didn't know. After a time, when she lay with her head pressed against his shirt, she said again, "Come into bed." He slipped quickly under the blanket and made love to her.

*   *   *

Jason wished he knew whether this was good or bad, of sin or of heaven. He seldom looked forward to it or imagined it, but when her arms came up round his neck and her lips opened below his, then the little room began to disappear and the patched moonlight turned into wonders—not Romans in gold helmets, not the stone shapes on the Plain or the magically soughing grass; but, mounting from the grass, the laverock, wildly turning, the land bursting in great circles, wider below its little rapid wings; and the peewit, black and white, sweeping up with silent beats and crying aloud to her, "Come, come,

9

Mary!"—to those places, to see those marvels—"come!" But she only groaned with love and whispered his name.

He lay back on his arm, beside her. This time he'd seen the Golden Fleece. It was hung on a barn door in a steep valley. He could have described it to her, every golden curl of the wool, but the Fleece wasn't so important as the waves of effort that had carried him up the valley, past many discoveries; and he couldn't tell her about those because he didn't know the words. It was like being a dog or a baby, looking and whining and knowing but not having the words. Perhaps the Fleece was another of Parson's jokes. He'd found out that it was Parson who had chosen his name, Jason, for him; and after he grew up Parson would sometimes ask him if he'd found the Golden Fleece yet. It might be a joke, but if it was, it had failed, because he had found the Fleece just now, and at other times, in other places. Suddenly he hated the Parson, and Sir Tristram Pennel, and Hugo Pennel, and everyone who knew words and writing, because he did not.

The clock struck three. He said, "Mary, when we are married shall we go away?"

She asked, "Where can we go?" Then she said, "What do you want to go away for? We can have your room in the farmhouse, and when Molly marries Ahab I'll keep the house for you and your father. Oh, but Molly's never going to, Jason. She'll keep that old Ahab waiting till crack of doom before she'll leave you."

Perhaps it was true, what she said. That would be another reason for going away. He repeated his question.

Mary whispered, "Where could we go to? There's the Plain on the south, all the way to Salisbury. On the north there's the Downs. There isn't a piece of free land in the Vale between here and Pewsey, and that's four miles."

Jason said, "We could go to Aleppo."

Mary did not speak. . . .

Aleppo had a rich and spicy smell. He didn't know where he had first heard the name. It was white and gold there, and hot. The desert wheeled up to the window of a house—his house, his window. He saw the window and a woman's dark eye at the lattice as he rode in on a camel from the desert. A hundred bells tinkled, and a thousand horsemen cantered in the dust behind him. No one knew he had gold, frankincense, myrrh, and spikenard in one saddlebag, and turquoise, onyx, alabaster, jade, ruby, emerald, and a grain of mustard seed in the other. His diamond saber jerked at his side, or at the camel's flank, in a scabbard. What size was a camel, what color? Ivory, perhaps. His ship lay in the harbor, and he had only to fight through the crowd to it, and swim out. The girl would wait till he came back. He would come back in another ship, the pennant streaming out from the stern and St. George's Cross flying high.

"Where's Aleppo?" Mary said.

"I don't know."

"Jason, how can we go there if you don't know where it is? It's time you went home. You'll be tired, and your apples aren't in yet, are they?"

"Apples?" he repeated vaguely. Why didn't she see that Aleppo was a place you didn't have to know about? He had thrown his jerkin off somewhere, and now he tripped over her clothes before he came to it.

"Shhhh!" she said. "Father will hear you."

"Not with your mother snoring so loud." At the casement he turned back suddenly and kissed her on the hand, though she held up her lips for him. She was so happy with him sometimes that he was sure he'd better marry her. He didn't think he'd be the same person after that, but perhaps she'd like him better for the change. He said, "I'll come again, night after next, early."

She began to say something, but he was on the ivy and away.

The trout were not moving under the bridge, and he did not stop there. He walked quickly along the footpath, crossed a field, bore left, and cut up toward the shoulder of hill that separated the village of Shrewford Pennel from his father's farm. It was late. Lying with Mary made the moment splendid, but for a time afterward there was never anything in his head but facts. On this journey back, the Romans had gone, and the shadows were only sleeping cows, and the smells were just of grass and dung.

At the crest of the rise he saw the light thatch of the farm below, less than half a mile away. He had begun to hurry down to it when three men jumped out on him from the shadow of the hedge.

He rolled silently to his back under the weight of them and lashed out with fists and shoes. Three! The Pennels only had four gamekeepers, and, of the four, Hammond was in bed with colic and Sale had gone to Amesbury. His fist jabbed into one of the men's stomachs, and he heard a gasp. Another muttered, "Young polecat! Stand away, Tim." A heavy stick whirred down and thudded into the side of his head.

He lay quiet for a moment after the darkness went away. His head hurt, and before he said anything he wanted to know who the third man was. He listened to their voices above him. The third man was Hugo Pennel, the squire's son. He heard Hugo ask, "Who is it?"—so he could not have been hovering for long out of his senses. One of the others answered, " 'Tis young Jason Savage, master. We've caught him at it before."

Hugo asked, "Has he got any game on him?"

Jason stood up unsteadily, and the keepers jumped to grab his arms. He said, "I haven't been poaching, master Hugo."

"What are you doing here, then?"

Hugo was a tall young man, and even in this light you could see his clothes were richer than any of theirs. They all spoke the same broad Wiltshire—knight's son, gamekeepers, and yeoman boy. Hugo was twenty-two. When he was fifteen his father had sent him up to London to be a page at the king's court.

He repeated his question. Jason did not answer.

"You've been poaching, Jason," Hugo said threateningly.

"No, I haven't," Jason said.

"You have!"

Hugo wasn't a bad young gentleman. He used to be obscene-minded and a little cruel when they were boys together, but they'd had good fun birds'-nesting and snaring rabbits and talking of ships and girls and the king. Perhaps Hugo would like to forget all that now. Hugo wanted him to answer, but he wouldn't. It was none of Hugo's business.

"He's been poaching, master," the head gamekeeper said. "He has a trout or a pheasant or a couple of rabbits hidden down there where he can get 'em tomorrow."

"Have you?"

"No."

"We'd better give him a taste of stick, master," the head keeper said. "He's going to live here all his life. He'd better learn now not to—It's no use to kick, Jason."

"I'm not going to live here all my life!" Jason cried, suddenly stung to furious, impotent tears.

The keeper laughed curtly and twisted his arm. With that pain Jason got himself under control. He saw that Hugo didn't want to beat him. Perhaps Hugo was afraid he'd make a complaint to the sheriff. But the keeper meant to see that it was done.

After a pause the keeper said, "If he can poach, master, all of them will. The law's not strong enough."

"Beat him, then," Hugo said; and angrily: "It's your own fault, Jason."

But the head keeper meant to fix it in the young master's heart that he was a squire's son, and grown up now. He gave Hugo the cudgel and said, "We'll hold him. Lay on hard, master."

Jason faced Hugo, and the yellow moon sank into the Plain. The wind got up. Jason's eyes bulged, and he struggled round to keep his face to Hugo, but the men were too strong for him. They forced his head into the fork of one's thighs and pulled down his breeches.

The stick droned and struck harder as Hugo gathered vengeful anger that Jason should have forced him to do this. After a dozen blows Hugo threw the stick away, panting. He gasped. "There! Now run and complain—but you'll get the same next time. Do you understand?"

Jason felt cold trickles of blood running down the backs of his legs. He hauled up his breeches and fastened them. The blood wouldn't show through. His sister Molly would wash them for him later. He'd have to tell her. She'd be thrilled and horrified and angry, and would blame him and be sorry for him all at once. There wasn't anybody he could talk to the way he could talk to Molly.

He didn't answer Master Hugo Pennel, but turned and walked on the way he had been going, while the three stared at his back.

"Don't you forget what the young master said," the head keeper called after him, and he heard the other man say, "He's a bad one, master, a real bad one."

His buttocks began to ache and burn so that he ground his teeth together to stop himself from moaning. In the pain, though, the power to get away came back to him, and even as he walked down the long slope he was gone. The afterglow of the moon arched up from behind the bare hill, and it was the light from the Golden Fleece—or the brilliance from campfires glaring in the desert outside Aleppo, or a cave of Indian jewels. It was not Hugo and the keepers who had beaten him, but nobler, stranger enemies.

He stopped and struck his palms together and whispered, "Speranza Voy!" God's wounds, it was Voy they'd been after—Old Voy, the poacher, the strange talker, the seller of nostrums and teller of stories. The fools had been hiding up there on the edge of the

13

Plain to catch Old Voy, but they'd caught him instead, because Voy was too smart for them.

He began to laugh. His window was on the ground floor, and he climbed in through it.

*   *   *

The boat rocked on the sea, and the spar where he lay cut hard into his buttocks. He clung on with one hand and shaded his eyes with the other. The low land lay like a bar of gold, and thin trees waved over the white and blue line of the shore. The boat lurched; the spar swung him on a long arc, far out over the waves.

"Wake up, wake up! Jason, can't you hear the cows? Father will be angry."

He slipped out from under the blanket and stood, yawning, on the rushes. The light was gray, and a cow was mooing on the other side of the thorn hedge. A chilly wind blew in through the window, and he felt tired. He remembered last night and went for his clothes, but Molly was quicker and had his breeches in her hand, holding them out to him. Then she saw, and cried, "Blood! Turn round, Jason."

He didn't want to explain just now. He said, "Give them to me," and grabbed the breeches from her hand and put them on. He met her eyes, defying her to be angry with him. She was his twin, a tall girl with his thinness of body and neck and nostrils; but a woman's lips and a woman's eyes, darker gray than his; and small, tight breasts.

"Who did that?" she asked.

"Gamekeepers."

"Were you poaching?"

"No."

She said, "I'll kill them! They have no right to hurt you." He pulled on his jerkin, looking down to avoid the blazing heat of her eyes.

She turned on him. "It's your fault too. Why do you go creeping about in the middle of the night? Why don't you take Mary into the woods on Sunday afternoons the way everyone else does? Is she so hot under her shift, for you to go there every other night? You treat her as if she's a king's whore and you a—a prince, a knight! She wishes she was safe back with George Denning, I can tell you!"

He didn't speak because it was no good answering Molly when she was in this mood. He kissed her, letting his lips cling for a moment to her ear, and went out.

He let the cows into the byre and began to milk. "Get over, Daisy," he muttered, and butted his head into the cow's flank. She moved comfortably over for him. Her side was warm, and the dew steaming off her made a sweet smell in the byre. The milk spurted ringing into the jug, with rhythm like music, like the handbells of the young men at bell practice. "Sweet Daisy." He nuzzled his head against her, turning it round and rubbing her with his hair. She champed loudly on the hay in the stall. Through the low window at the back of the byre, when he raised his head, he saw the sun rising.

He could not sit down comfortably. Tomorrow night he'd flip that old trout out of the Avon, and as many more as he could. Hugo had no right to disbelieve him. He'd never told Hugo a lie. He picked up the stool by one leg and went over to the next cow. Susan wasn't a good cow. He couldn't talk to her at all. She was just a cow.

The light darkened, and his father stood in the low doorway. "When you've finished, Jason, clean out the yard."

"Yes, Father."

"Then trim the hedge up below the Plain."

"Yes, Father."

"You should have done that hedge yesterday, Jason. Daisy went through and onto Squire's land, on his twenty-acre."

"I'll do it today, Father," Jason said, but he thought: Good Daisy, clever old girl, you'll go and find out, won't you, with your big inquisitive face?

His father went out—heavier than Jason, and hunched. Jason couldn't remember his mother. She had died with another baby when he and Molly were five. Through the door he watched the morning sunlight edge down the ribs of the Plain. His hands slowly stopped their squeeze and release. The distracting music of the milk ceased.

After a while he shook his head and hurried to the end of his task, hurried through the cleaning of the yard, dumped the manure and mud and straw on the pile outside the byre, took his billhook, hurried up to the farthest hedge. Once there, he began to whistle. The closer to the Plain his work lay, the better he felt. Little pieces of the Plain had been plowed, and here and there men kept sheep on it, but the Plain was not farmland and never could be—not enough water, and the soil crumbly and chalky. Or perhaps the dark men of his dreams, the men with the stone arrows, wouldn't allow it. The wind blew in gusts and bent over the tassels of the rye grass, and a rabbit sat up in the white mouth of its burrow to watch him.

15

He saw Old Voy coming along the other side of the hedge, before Voy saw him. He swept short strokes with his bill, cut and bent and tied back the living fence, and from the corner of his eye watched the old man coming. Voy was small and blotchy-faced, and his dirty gray hair hung down on his shoulders. Jason didn't think he was quite as old as he looked, because after dark he seemed to change and move like a young man. Perhaps he was sixty. His teeth were good, but for three missing at the top front. He always carried a gentleman's sword and wore a velvet doublet with puffed, slashed sleeves. The doublet was old and very dirty. A sack dangled at his right hip, from a leather strap across his left shoulder, and Jason chuckled when he saw it. The keepers had been inside that sack twenty times and never found anything but books and papers and medicines. Old Voy also wore a sleeveless leather jerkin that bulged mysteriously over his stomach and hid a might of queer things, but never a rabbit or a partridge that anyone had looked and seen.

Voy stopped opposite Jason on the other side of the hedge and for a minute silently watched the work. Then he said, "You're a good boy, Jason. *You* didn't tell the rascals anything, did you?"

Jason lowered the billhook and looked at a thorn in his hand. So Voy had been watching, last night. He must have been close. He said, "I'd nothing to tell."

"I'm not a gamekeeper, Jason."

"I'd nothing to tell, didn't you hear me?"

"What were you doing there, then?"

Jason spat out the thorn and picked up the bill. "None of your business."

Voy said, "Ah, a girl. Hugo was a fool not to believe you."

Jason said nothing, and after a while Old Voy said placatingly, "You come down the spinney tomorrow night, and I'll show you how my ferrets work. They're from France, Jason."

"France?" Jason lowered the bill. "Have you been to France?"

"France? Of course I've been to France—and Rome, and Damascus, and everywhere."

"Have you been to Aleppo?" Jason asked anxiously.

"Yes, I've been to Aleppo, Jason."

"You have, really?" Jason glanced up and down the hedge. He'd done enough for the time being. He could go on after eating his dinner. He took a pace back, vaulted over, and landed on hands and knees beside Old Voy. He said eagerly, "Do you want a piece of

16

my bread? Tell me about Aleppo. And I've got two eggs and two potatoes and an onion."

"Beer?" Old Voy was looking at him, reading him.

Jason unslung his leather bottle and passed it over. They sat down on the sunny side of the hedge there, the sun high over the Plain and all the lanes and byres and cows and church towers behind them, beyond the hedge. Jason said, "What's it like? Where is it?"

Voy looked narrowly at him, took a bite out of a potato, and said, "You want to leave Wiltshire, Jason?"

Jason remembered that Voy must have heard him last night when he shouted at Hugo that he wasn't going to stay here forever. But now he only said, "I don't know about that. How can I leave?"

"Going to be wed soon, eh? And then there's the farm to look after. And your sister, what will—?"

Jason said angrily, "If you don't want to tell me anything, you go away, see? I asked you about Aleppo."

Voy eyed him all the time. When he answered he spoke in a dreamy, distant voice as though he were remembering things from a long way back. "Aleppo is in the East, Jason, on the edge of the desert. It belongs to the Grand Turk. There aren't any poor people in Aleppo—least, not poor Englishmen. English people go there for the Levant Company, and they make a fortune, every one. They stay there a few years, then come home rich."

"How do they get rich?"

"Buying and selling, of course."

"Oh." Jason was disappointed. After a moment he asked, "How rich? Richer than Sir Tristram Pennel?"

"Much richer. Why, Jason, the streets are paved with gold there, and in the bazaar—that's what they call the market—there's gold lying out in big blocks ready to buy. The women wear jewels in their noses, and gold and silver ornaments from head to foot, and ride on camels. There's wine all the time, and sherbet they sell ice cold."

"Where does the ice come from?" Jason asked quickly. Old Voy was supposed to be a great liar. Jason didn't want to believe that, but he didn't want to be laughed at for a simpleton either.

"Why, they send trains of camels and horses out to the mountains—the mountains there are to the north of Aleppo, where the Old Man of the Mountains lives. Ever heard of him?"

Jason shook his head. The Old Man of the Mountains! That's who had the Golden Fleece. It must be!

17

Voy said, "They get the ice there in winter and cut it and store it in holes in the ground. Then in the summer—in the summer in Aleppo it's hotter than you'd believe—they send the camels up to bring the ice down."

Jason nodded. You couldn't catch Old Voy out in a story any more than Pennel's men could find a trout in his bag or a bird under his jerkin. Voy helped himself to the beer, and when he handed the bottle back it was nearly empty. He said, "I've traveled everywhere, Jason. I've been to Tartary. The men wear long robes made out of sheepskins, and ride all day on little ponies. It's like the Plain there, only big! Why—"

"Like the Plain?" Jason said incredulously. "Do they have the standing stones and the earth walls like Shrewford Ring?"

"Of course! Why shouldn't they? I tell you, Tartary is like the Plain, only it goes on for a thousand leagues—ten thousand—to the end of the earth. After ten thousand leagues you come to a big wall, and demons and dragons guarding the wall."

"Have you seen the wall?"

Voy hesitated, then said regretfully, "No, I've never seen it, Jason. I—I was captured by robbers before I got there. They held me prisoner for three weeks in a cave. I was a prisoner with a dozen beautiful girl slaves they'd captured at—"

"Has anyone ever been over the wall?" Jason cut in eagerly.

"No one."

No one. Then no one knew what was behind the wall. There might be cities of amethyst and sapphire and topaz. The Golden Fleece might be there. But no, the Fleece was near Aleppo, where the Old Man lived in the mountains. Jason hardly noticed Voy taking the other egg.

With his mouth full, Voy said, "The only place I have not been to is the best place of all. There's treasure in that place. The people —ah!" He paused.

Jason said, "Yes? What are the people like?"

Old Voy began slowly, "Why, they're tall. And they have fair skins, boy, and golden hair and shining helmets. They're nothing like the Tartars, who are small and yellowish and have eyes like this." He pulled up the corners of his eyes.

"What is this place called where the treasure is?" Jason asked.

"Coromandel!"

"Coromandel. Coromandel! Where is it?"

"It's in India, near Golconda."

"Can anyone find the treasure? Is it lying about? Or do you have to dig it up? Will the people with the shining helmets help you or fight you if you go there for the treasure? How do you get to Coromandel?"

Voy sucked his raggedy mustache, eying Jason. Then he said, "Can you read, Jason?"

Jason answered sullenly, "No."

Voy said, quickly cheerful, "That doesn't matter. You'll learn, won't you?" Feeling in his sack, he carefully drew out a book and shook it, and out fell a folded sheet of paper. He said, "Here's a map of Coromandel, Jason." He spread the map out flat on the grass and brushed off the long-legged field spider that began to walk across it.

Jason gazed breathlessly at the map. He could not read, but this map hardly needed reading. There were pictures. There were the blue waves of the sea, and a row of thin trees with feathery tops. There was a big dark red stain in one corner, and writing every-where. Voy ran his finger along a blue line and said, "Here's the river of Coromandel. These humps are mountains. This is where the treasure lies, and here's the name of the mountain—Meru. It has two peaks, see?"

Old Voy's strangely clean and uncallused finger wandered over the map, and his voice was hoarse in Jason's ear. "The Coromandel Coast. The City of Pearl, by the sea. And then you go up the river, a long way. Right up near the source, there, that's the Castle of the Holy Monks. From there it's a hundred leagues to the mountain Meru, and—"

"What's that red mark?"

"Blood. 'In the cave, forty-eight paces below the eastern peak, toward the north, a countless treasure lies hid.' That's what it says."

There were horsemen galloping over the empty spaces on that part of the map, and waving spears in the air. Devil faces blew wind over the sea. It was a blue and black map on yellow paper, with the bloodstain in a corner.

Jason said, "How can a man travel to Coromandel?"

Voy said, "In a ship from London, Jason. You go south to the Cape of Storms in Africa, and then east. It's a long, hard voyage, Jason—but think what's at the end of it, for you!" Old Voy's blue eyes gleamed, and his hand squeezed Jason's shoulder.

Jason said with a sudden renewal of suspicion, "Why don't you go and get the treasure yourself? It's marked on the map."

"Me?" Voy shook his head so that his gray hair swung out clear from his shoulders. He laughed throatily. "I'm too old. This is young man's work. But you can go. I'll sell the map cheap to *you*, because I like you."

Jason was thinking—not thinking, but sinking, under a torrent of ideas: Tartary, horses and the sea racing together, snow on the mountains—though he'd never seen a mountain—camels. Mary—she wouldn't want to go to Coromandel. How far? How long to wait? How much? The map might be a fraud. Farm boys were always losing their money to gypsies and chapmen who sold charms and nostrums and curses, none of them ever any good.

He said cautiously, "How much?" trying to sound uninterested.

Voy said, "I wouldn't sell this map to just anyone who wanted to buy it. What's the use of letting a man have this map who'll send out an expedition and get the treasure for himself without ever stirring a foot from Wiltshire?" He busied himself in a careful stowing away of his belongings as he spoke. He squeezed the leather bottle, squirted the last of the beer down his throat, and handed the bottle back.

Jason waited eagerly. He said, "I haven't got much, mind."

Voy wiped his mouth with the back of his hand. "Jason, *you* can have it for forty shillings."

Jason hesitated. For all the years he'd been putting a little money aside he had got only forty-six shillings and three pennies and two farthings.

He said, "I'll buy it."

"You've got a bargain," Voy said cheerfully and folded up the map and handed it to him. "But mind, don't you show that map to anyone, and don't go talking about it, or you'll find someone else has got there ahead of you and taken the treasure."

Jason held the map carefully and said, "But I haven't got the money with me. I keep it in—I haven't got it here."

Old Voy nodded approvingly. "That's a wise man. Don't you tell anyone where you keep your money. The world's full of thieves these days. You treat that map as if it was money itself. Take it. Pay me any time. I trust you."

Jason's heart swelled up, with the map inside his jerkin and Voy trusting him for forty shillings. He mumbled, "Thank you. Tomorrow night?"

Voy nodded. "Early. At the spinney." He jerked his head toward the floor of the Vale.

Jason nodded, stepped back, and again vaulted over the hedge onto his father's land. He felt inside his jerkin to make sure the map had not fallen out. Then he picked up the billhook and began to work. Old Voy waved his hand in a courtly gesture and shuffled away along the line of the hedge, his head downcast and moving from side to side as he peered at the ground. "No runs along there— I've looked," Jason called after him with a grin. Old Voy shook his long hair and shuffled on and at last out of sight.

Coromandel!

God's blood, this hedge never grew right, and every year he was back up here, early spring and end of summer, getting thorns in his hand. The hedge was like a wall, like a prison, only he could look out over the top, and that made it worse. When he'd done here, he had to go down to the orchard. The wasps were thick on the trees now. He'd get stung a couple of times, as usual.

Coromandel!

He put down his bill and got out the map. There was the word. He remembered where it lay in relation to the bloodstain. It was written in fine wavy black writing, but bigger than any of the other words, all along the land inside the blue line where there was a ship with a high stern. He couldn't see any flag on her. Perhaps the map-maker hadn't painted one in. Perhaps ships did not fly flags on the Coromandel coast. Tom Devitt said ships always flew flags, but Tom had never been to Coromandel—at least, he had never mentioned it.

He could ask Tom about Coromandel and how long it took to get there. No, he couldn't, because the map was a secret.

He must ask Voy about the bloodstain.

He must learn to read.

Here was the place where the hills stood all around and the men were galloping on small horses under the mountain Meru. To get there he'd have to cross the sea at least as far as to America. The sea was to the south, beyond the Plain, beyond Salisbury's tall spire. Men went to sea and came back like Tom Devitt, with funny clothes and funny words, or a wooden leg. The sea was cold blue and ended in a pit with big gray birds circling and crying over it. He'd seen the seagulls driven even here in hard winters, their cry like babies left out on the Plain, the birds standing in the fields when the icicles hung from the thorn bushes and the mud crackled under the cart-wheels and the oxen breathed steam in the shafts.

"Jason!"

He scrambled to his feet, quickly folding the map away and picking up his bill.

"What have you got there?"

"Nothing, Molly."

He wanted to show her the map, perhaps tonight, but not here in the field. Molly changed so much. By day, when the sun shone, she could be very like Mary. At night in the house, best of all when the south wind blew from the Plain and the rain hissed in the thatch, she was like another piece of himself, a piece that was lost from him when they were apart; then they huddled together in his narrow bed and told stories of ghosts and made up pictures in words about the men and women who had raised Shrewford Ring long ago and set up the three stones.

Molly said, "It is something, liar!"

He said, "It's a map. I'll show it to you tonight."

Molly said, "A map! I saw Old Voy up here. So did Father. He's going to give you trouble. You know what he thinks of Voy."

Jason knew. His father thought the same as Parson and Squire Pennel and all the other steady people. Old Voy was good for nothing. His real name was Potts, and he came from somewhere east, almost to London. Voy himself had let that out when he got drunk in the Cross Keys one day, but he drew his rusty gentleman's sword if you mentioned it, and insisted his name was Don Speranza Voy—a Spanish nobleman's bastard. Voy lived like a gypsy, and told lies and poached, and slept out winter and summer, and sold charms to love-sick milkmaids. In the summer Voy lit bonfires on the edge of the Plain and sat round them with tinkers and poets and actors. He was supposed to be a confidant of the robbers on the Plain.

And had Voy really ever visited foreign places? Or had he talked to so many people that he could pretend he had? Jason shied away from that persistent thought. He had paid forty shillings for the map, and Coromandel was a magic word, like a spell.

"Look at that hedge," Molly said in exasperation. "What have you been doing? What's that going to be like when it grows across the tree next year? Here." She seized the billhook from him and began to cut and slash, mending his mistakes. He stood watching her and

22

wondered whose head she wished she were cutting off—his, or Ahab Stiles'.

When she had finished they walked down together to the farm and began to gather apples. The orchard stretched up to the front of the house, and he saw a fine big horse tethered there near the wall.

"Squire's here," he said.

"It will be about you that he's come," Molly muttered. "Are you sure you weren't poaching last night?"

They worked up close to the house. It was late afternoon, and the windows were open. When Jason climbed into the apple tree nearest the door and began to unload the heavy branches, his father saw him through the window, but Sir Tristram had his back turned. Jason admired the squire's red silk doublet and the white cloth showing through, and went on picking apples.

Soon his father called him. "Jason, come in here. Squire wants to talk to you."

Jason winked with bravado at Molly's anxious face and went into the house. He pulled his forelock to Sir Tristram, who regarded him sternly and said, "Hugo tells me he caught you poaching last night, Jason."

"I wasn't poaching," Jason said.

"Come, now, don't lie to me." Sir Tristram's long face reddened.

"I wasn't poaching, and I'm not a liar," Jason shouted suddenly, the heat whirling up in his neck and a cold hollow forming in his stomach. A sword—if he had a sword he'd be entitled to whip it out and demand satisfaction. His hands shook, and his fists clenched and unclenched.

Sir Tristram, taken quite aback, stammered, "Y-you weren't—why, eh, what—?" and his father said sharply, "Don't shout at Squire!"

Sir Tristram got up, the tip of his scabbard clanking on the stone floor. He said, "You're going to the bad, Jason. You'll finish on the gallows."

Jason said angrily, "I was not poaching."

"What were you doing out at three in the morning, then?" Sir Tristram asked. "Stealing?"

Jason held on to himself with a huge effort and did not speak.

The squire's face hardened. He said, "Go on out, then, to your work, Jason. You have become a liar as well as a poacher and a gypsy. You will have to mend your ways in the future. If you attack my keepers again, you'll go to prison."

23

44694

Jason turned and went out and walked blindly through the orchard. Hedge. Apples. Milk the cows.

He opened the gate, let the cows into the byre, and roped them in their stalls. He went back to the kitchen and picked up the earthenware jugs from the corner. Molly was there, lighting the fire for supper. She glanced at him silently, and her eyelashes were wet, but Sir Tristram's voice still snapped through the house from where he sat on his great horse outside the front door, talking to their father.

Jason went into the byre, jerked the milking stool into position with his foot, and dug his head into Daisy's flank. Daisy moved over and flicked her dung-smeared tail across his face.

❋   ❋   ❋

He lay quiet in his bed until all the sounds of the farm were stilled and the doors bolted and his father's footsteps had creaked up the stairs. The ceiling was whitewashed, and the beams ran like thick iron bars across it. The moon would not be up for another hour and a half. Tomorrow night, rabbits in the spinney with Old Voy's French ferrets. A couple of nights later, and he'd take the big trout under the Avon bridge. He used to tell himself that he would stop poaching when he was married, but now he knew that he would not. They could only beat him.

But it was a poor man's right to take trout and rabbits. All the other squires allowed it, or at least didn't do anything to prevent it. Why not go poaching with a few of the young men, and, when the Pennel keepers tried to stop them, fight?

Because the young men wouldn't go with him, that's why. They grumbled at Sir Tristram's selfishness, but they obeyed.

The Pennels meant to send him to prison. He'd never let them take him. He'd use his knife and run away and join the murderers and sheepstealers who lived on the Plain. He'd be sorry for Mary and sad for Molly, but he couldn't help it. He'd do it rather than be locked up.

They had no right to disbelieve him. They had no right to tell him he was going to be here all his life, because then his dreams, being impossible of coming true, would be like a madman's. If he was really to be here until he died he could not, even in his mind, ride deserts and sail oceans. He could not use his power to make the sounds of the night blur until they became anything he chose. He could not turn silence into music and his thoughts into poetry—such

24

poetry as Old Voy learned from his strange friends and sometimes shouted aloud in the woods. He could not make new stars out of an old moon or change the midday sun into a fresh dawn or the fields into a foreign shore—the strand of Coromandel.

Coromandel!

The map was better than a night's dreaming, far better than Mary's female warmth. He slid out of bed and felt behind the casement, where he kept a candle. He made a light, lit the candle, and stood it on the floor. He pulled up a loose board in the corner of the room and from the hole beneath drew out a book and the map. He had found this book eight years ago in the lane near Shrewford Admiral, lying on its face and all muddied. He did not know what the name of the book was, or who had written it, or what it was about. He put it aside now, after stroking the leather binding and turning over a few of the crackling leaves. He spread out the map beside the candle and lay flat on his stomach to study it.

He heard the soft footsteps before they reached his door, and shaded the candle with his hands as Molly came in. She slipped down beside him.

She whispered, "Is this the map? How much did you pay for it?"

"Five shillings," he said.

"Five shillings! You are a fool, Jason. It's not worth a groat. Old Voy made it up himself and just waited for some donkey to come along who would buy it. Look at those horsemen! It's beautiful, Jason. What are you going to do with it?"

It was night, and the vast world had become enclosed in the circle of candlelight, and they two were alone there. He said, "I'm going to Coromandel to find the treasure. I'll come back here and buy a bigger place than the Pennels'. I'll give you diamonds and cedar wood, Molly, and ten thousand pieces of eight." He felt the ecstasy of giving her those things, and in the dark corners the floor creaked under the weight of the golden coins. It had happened, and now what should they do? He said, "You won't have to marry Ahab Stiles."

"No! We'll go to London and find a prince and a princess to marry."

"I think Mary wants me to marry her," he said slowly, feeling less exalted.

"She did a month ago," Molly said heatedly, "but she doesn't now that she knows you better—knows you less, *she*'d say."

Jason considered. His sister was probably right, but all the same he

25

must ask Mary to marry him. Otherwise he might hurt her. He said aloud, "I don't hate her, as you hate Ahab."

"Ahab!" Molly snapped. "Miserable, creaky old thing, always looking at me like a dog that's just been beaten. Forty years old, and foul-smelling as a badger."

Jason hardly listened. He was thinking: What will Mary Bowcher do with a big house where all the wardrobes are full of pieces of gold, and tame lions and peacocks stroll up and down in the garden, and twenty huge blackamoor servants with great swords bring her cider at dinnertime?

Molly got up suddenly. "It's all pretend, Jason, isn't it? Isn't it? The map's worth nothing, and you paid more than five shillings for it. We're twenty years old, and we're going to be here forever. What's the use of pretending? A little bit of real happiness that you can touch is better than any dream."

Jason whispered furiously, "Go back to your own room, Molly. I don't want to talk to you. Leave me alone."

"You're going to be a farmer here," she whispered. "And I'm going to be a farmer's wife in Pewsey. Isn't Wiltshire good enough for you? Why do you make everyone who loves you uncomfortable when they're with you? And then angry, because they think they're missing something you can see and they can't? Why don't you leave us alone?"

Jason breathed almost silently, "I'm not going to give up anything. If they send me to prison I'll kill them. If I can't even think of going to Coromandel I'll be a murderer instead."

Molly said as softly, "God's blood, I hate you, Jason. If you ever leave Wiltshire I'll leave too. Do you hear me? I will! I will!"

She slipped out. After a while Jason turned back to the map. Soon the moonlight crept across the corner of it, but he did not blow out the candle. A vixen yowled crazily for her dog under the Plain, and the hens mumbled and the cock blared and the bull struck his horn against his crib, but Jason had fallen asleep with his head on the map.

*   *   *

The next evening he lay down, fully dressed, on his bed, pulled the blanket up to his chin, and was quiet, thinking, for nearly two hours. Then he got up, raised the loose floorboard, brought up a bag of silver, and counted out forty shillings by touch. The moon had not yet risen, and the night was astir outside the black casement. He wrapped the forty shillings in a cloth and tucked it into his jerkin. From the same hiding place he got out his sling and tucked it through his belt. He had made it three years ago, and each leather thong was a yard long. Then he waited, crouching by the window, until the moonglow reached out round the side of the byre and up from under the earth toward Pewsey. Then he slipped out of the window.

He lifted some loose straw that lay against the outer wall of the byre and selected half a dozen round stones from the pile that had been hidden beneath, put them in his scrip, replaced the straw, and set off up the sloping field. It was another warm night, with a slight wind from the southwest, and the distorted moon low over Shrewford Down.

Old Voy was waiting for him at the corner of the spinney where they had agreed to meet. Jason saw his hair like a patch of dirty snow under an oak, where the moonlight fell in sprinkled rain through the heavy leaves and the acorns glinted in a thousand tiny points of fire. He went up close and muttered, "Voy?"

"Of course. Follow me. We're going up to the Windline."

"Why?"

"Master Hugo has put the head keeper on the other side of the spinney here. He's there now. Hammond's not well, but Hugo has dragged him out of bed and sent him over to Hangman's Copse. Sale's back, and he's on the Avon, by the good pools below Pennel Church. Granger's over between Hatchard's and the Cross Keys. There's no one on the Windline. I've left the kit up there. Come on."

"Is Hugo out as well?"

"Yes, with Granger. The young cockerel means to catch someone tonight. But not Speranza Voy, not Old Voy, he won't!"

They worked south along the edge of a root field and over the sheep pastures on the edge of Shrewford Pennel village. Soon the towering elms of the Windline began to climb above the horizon of the distant Plain. It was a bank of trees, half a mile long and thirty yards wide, running down from the lip of the Plain into the Vale below, and ending at the border of the Pennels' home farm. After twenty minutes of quick and silent movement they came to the lower end and began to work up the hill under the trees. Jason knew now where they must be going. There was a big warren quite close ahead, out on the sheltered eastern side, at the edge of a sheep run.

27

A few yards short of the warren Voy stopped and squatted at the base of an elm. Jason helped him pull pegs, nets, hollow spade, bill-hook, line, and muzzle cords into the open. The ferrets squeaked in their bag, which was hung in a bush to one side, and the air was feral with the acid smell of them.

"Now, quick, lad," Voy said. Jason took a handful of nets and pegs and began covering every hole of the rabbit warren. He stretched the little nets tight and forced the pegs into the chalk with the heel of his hand. They wouldn't send him to prison, to be shut in and given food like an animal. He slipped his hand round and felt the blade of the short knife at the back of his belt.

When he had finished, he and Voy looked carefully over the whole warren, found three holes they had missed, and netted them. Voy brought the ferret bag and opened the mouth a couple of inches. A long, quivering nose poked out and sniffed the air; then the head followed, and the little pink eyes glittered.

"He's a white 'un," Jason whispered.

"All the French ones are white," Voy answered. "Careful of him, he's sharp with his teeth." He grabbed the ferret by the back of the neck, slipped it under one corner of a net, and replaced the peg. The ferret turned its long body round and round in the mouth of the hole and stuck its nose through the meshes of the net, trying to get back. Voy flicked its nose with his finger, and it turned round again, a furred snake, slow-moving, the pink eyes burning in the moonlight, and went slowly out of sight under the ground.

"Stand the other side now, and quick, Jason!"

Jason waited, crouching like a runner in the edge of the tree shadow, watching the moonlit hummocks of the rabbits' home. The supple murderer was down there now, sneaking on, half blind, his teeth gleaming and his eyes like coals glowing in the black tunnel. Oh, the blood of Jesus, to be a rabbit down there with the burning eyes at the end of the tunnel, to thump the ground with your legs, jerk them down, and turn and run, crazy-mad with fear, the strong waves of the ferret stench rolling with you, and the eyes and teeth snaking on and on and on behind you, earth crumbling over you, in front of you, to burst out at full jump into the poured moonbeams, into the net, kicking the net, all silent.

He shook his head. He was a man. He'd like to pull off the nets and go home, but it was always the same. Times, when he'd set a running noose on his father's land and left it out at night, he'd lie awake on the bed and could not sleep until he managed to wrench his thoughts away from the moonbathed hedge and the dead shape of fur, stinking of fear and cold as it died.

He heard the *thump-thump* deep under the earth. A long minute passed, and a rabbit dashed out of a burrow into a net. Jason threw himself on it, all thought gone, hauled it out by the back legs, ran his fingers down its jerking neck, felt the place, squeezed, and bent. He dropped the rabbit, reset the net, dived on another. Voy darted from side to side, and the white bellies of the dead rabbits gathered in the moonlight.

After ten minutes no more rabbits came out. Nor did the ferret. "He's sucking," Voy said. "Get the line."

Jason walked into the trees. The ferret had killed inside the warren and was gorging itself deep underground. Now they must line another ferret, send it after the first, measure how much cord it dragged after it, and then dig down for them both. He wanted to get it over quickly so that they could go down into the copse below and knock a few pheasants off their roosts with his sling. Sometimes the birds perched so low you could grab them by the legs and pull them down. Voy would have sulphur matches to burn, which made them giddy.

Searching about in the trees for the ferret line, Jason found he had come to the wrong place. There was nothing here but a big stick leaning against the bole of an elm. He took it curiously in hand as he walked across to the other tree, thumping it on the ground and thinking it must be Voy's—and *clang,* a low shape bounded out of the earth at his feet, snapped the cudgel from his hand, and fell back with a groan. The cudgel stood there, upright of itself beside him, and his wrist ached, and he was biting his lips to keep down the fierce yell of fear.

Voy hurried over. "What was that? What? Whose staff is that? Don't move." He knelt and peered at the earth. He said softly, "A man trap, it is. I've heard of them—in Prussia, not in England. Oh, the whoreson pigs!"

The cold sweat burst out on Jason's forehead. Tremblingly he took hold of the thick cudgel and pulled. It came free with a small creak, for the serrated teeth of the trap had bitten through all but a sliver of the wood.

Voy said, "You didn't have a stick? Not mine, either. Don't get excited, Jason. They won't have a man here as well as a trap. Besides, they don't have any more men. But walk carefully. Where did you find that stick?"

"There," Jason said, "against that tree." His heart still hammered, and his lips twitched. Oh, the pigs, the devils! He walked round the tree, his hands out, into the black shadow there where a bush grew close to the trunk. His side brushed into something soft, and a breath of exhaled air touched his face. He whipped round, seeing nothing—but already imagining the keeper's grinning, triumphant anger and, behind it, the dank prison walls.

"Keeper!" he muttered, and stabbed down with his knife. The shape screamed and turned under his blow. Miss. He hit out with his fist, and Voy was with him, trying to hold back his knife hand; but the time had come, and he ripped the knife up where the stomach ought to be, in and up, underhand. Thick cloth tore, and the blade sprang up. Missed again. Why didn't the knave step forward and fight? He steadied himself to kill, and the dark shape slowly fell out of the shadow, fell through the clinging arms of the bush, and fell, thumping, to the ground.

Long hair spread out on the earth there, light red, rippling and stirring in the ground wind. Her face was pale, and her eyes were closed and her arms bent beside her. Her stomacher was ripped apart, and a thin scarlet line threaded up the center of her belly and stained the torn edges of her shift.

Voy said, "Mistress Jane Pennel—the daughter."

"Have I killed her?"

He had never wanted to kill Jane Pennel. He had known her all his life, though never so well as he had known Hugo, of course. Everyone knew her. She rode about on a little cob and was friendly with the wives of farmers and laborers, but she looked down her nose even while she tried to be pleasant, and people said she was overproud for a maid of seventeen.

Now he'd killed her, and she'd never ride the lanes again. She was dead, and he was a murderer, her blood on his knife. The worms would eat that white belly before long, before the red cow calved, and the worms were himself, because he had killed her. It was he who crawled in the earth to devour her, and she used to play the spinet and know how to read from books. Jason turned away and retched dreadfully to cast up the worms of death in his throat, but they would not leave him. He must go, run through the night, across the Plain, take ship, go.

30

His retching came to an end. He had talked to himself of killing, but now he had done it, and it was more terrible than any of his dreams.

Yet there was something else, a distant, growing spark of light in the tomb. Everything had conspired together to keep him here—the farm, his father's age, Molly, Mary. Now it would be the other way. The hands that had held him would push him away. The voices that had said, "Stay," would now shout, "Go."

His mouth drooped open as the spark grew, became a lamp of gold, and he realized the approaching shape of freedom.

Old Voy said, "She's not dead. You scratched her pretty skin for her. She's fainted from fright and a knock on the head."

Jason's knees trembled under him. He wasn't a murderer, and he wasn't free. He looked down at her, his lips working. She was a thin girl, and her breasts were small and round and high. He was glad he hadn't killed her. The door to Coromandel would open some other way for him. He didn't have to buy the key with the life of this rich girl.

"We can't go away and leave her," Voy said. "She saw us. She'll say we attacked her and then ravished her."

He knelt beside the girl, set light to a sulphur match, and waved it back and forth under her nose. After a moment she stirred, then sat up, then looked down and around, then grabbed the sides of her stomacher and joined them over her nakedness. She whispered, "Are —are you going to kill me?"

"Kill you, Mistress Jane? Of course not," Voy said in a soapy voice. He was supporting her shoulders with his arm.

"I don't know why we shouldn't," Jason snarled, suddenly remembering. "Setting that devilish trap and then standing over it to see a man lose his leg."

"If you do you'll hang for it, Jason Savage," she said with a burst of spirit. "Hugo says you'll hang someday."

"Why all this talk of hanging?" Old Voy said. "We were on our way back from Pewsey Fair, and we found you lying in the wood. What were you doing here? This is no place for a maid at night, and alone. There isn't a man with you, is there?" he finished, suddenly suspicious.

"My brother told me to come here, in case," she said. "There was no one else. He gave me a bell to ring if a poacher got caught in the trap. And—and you were poaching. I saw you." Her voice shook.

31

"Why, that was very cruel of your brother," Voy said, looking more intently at her. "Real poachers might have done you a mischief, bell or no bell, when they saw one of their friends with his leg off and blood everywhere and him screaming and bits of broken white bone splintered in his boots."

The girl said, "Don't! Oh, I was frightened." She burst into tears, and her long hair, disheveled and dirty and stuck with leaves, shook on her shoulders. "I didn't want to do it. I hate that trap. Hugo made me. He said it would be exciting, but it was lonely and terrible."

Jason said, "Cheer up, Mistress Jane. No one's been hurt, and we'll look after you." He gave her his hand and pulled her to her feet. He'd danced the Harvest Ring with her once three years ago, and although she was only fourteen then they had almost won the prize. Proud she was, but she thawed out of that when something excited her. She'd asked him that time to take her out plover shooting when next he went with his bow and arrow to the Plain. But when the time came and he'd gone round to Pennel Manor for her, she'd come to the door and flushed and made an excuse—remembered who she was, perhaps, or been reminded by her father.

She looked at him now, almost ready to smile, and Old Voy said, "Of course you were frightened, and it's your brother's fault. He had no right to send you out here."

She said, "Hugo's bad sometimes."

"And you've not seen any poachers at all," Old Voy continued. "You set off the trap by mistake with your stick—here you are—and then you went back to bed."

The girl eyed them surreptitiously, in turn. Her green eyes were large and rather prominent, like her father's.

Voy said pleadingly, "That was the way of it, Mistress Jane, wasn't it?"

Jason saw that she was looking at him. She wanted him to plead too. He had so nearly killed her. She had so nearly set him in Coromandel. He said gently, "We were poaching, Mistress Jane—rabbits. Here." He picked up two rabbits and gave them into her hands.

She said, "I like rabbit pie. I'll say I got them out of my snares, though really I never catch any. I've set two up here. Look."

She led him to the edge of the warren and showed him two running nooses of wire attached to sticks set firmly into the earth. Jason said, "You'll never catch a rabbit there. That's a vole run." He pulled up the sticks and pushed them in again a few paces to the right, where several rabbit runs led into the Windline. "I'm sorry I cut you," he said as he stood up. "I thought you were a keeper. Doesn't it hurt?"

"A little, now," she said. "I'll put some salve on it when I get home. Isn't it wonderful out here at night? Father and Hugo never let me go out to see. How did you kill those rabbits just now? I got so excited while the ferret was in that I almost forgot to be afraid."

In the shadow of the wood behind them Old Voy was gathering up his belongings. Jason looked at the girl with surprise. She was really interested. She could read, and had rich clothes and a great manor house and a big garden of flowers, but she liked to set snares for rabbits, and obviously she wished she knew more about the wild animals of wood and field. He showed her how to kill a rabbit, and she said, "Hugo hits them on the back of the head with his hand, but I never seem to be able to hit hard enough. Take me home now, please—and don't you ever dare to poach on the Pennel land again, or I'll have to tell my father." She stood away from him, clasping her stomacher. Jason thought: She's remembered again, and just when she was having a good time.

He said curtly, " 'Tis only your father, of all the squires, who calls it poaching."

They walked down the Windline, one behind another. Jane went slowly down ahead of the two men, holding up her wide skirt to keep the hem off the ground. They passed by fields lying still under the bell of the sky, and cottages asleep under their thatches, and heard no sound except their own.

When they came near Pennel Manor and could see its twisted chimneys ahead, Voy took the girl's arm and pointed. There was a small rabbit warren here, and Jason saw that the rabbits were out at play in the moonlight. For a moment the three stood close together, watching the rabbits hop and skip and the young ones roll together in their games. Fifty yards away, across a narrow pasture, a thick hedge bordered the stables and chicken runs at the back of the manor house.

Suddenly, *thump-thump*, a rabbit struck the ground with its hind legs. Everywhere the white tails scuttered up and darted down the holes. In five seconds the field was empty. Jane Pennel drew in her breath to speak, but Jason put his hand across her mouth, and Old Voy leaned tensely forward. A tender breeze blew from the manor house toward them.

A red dog fox came to the edge of the covert twenty paces to their right and stood a moment, silent there, in the spotted moonshade. Jane Pennel had not seen it and still peered straight ahead. Gently Jason took her neck—it was soft and downy and thin in his hands—and gently turned it so that she saw the fox. Now from the fowl house just inside the Pennels' hedge they heard the subdued clucks and indignant murmurs of the hens stirring in their places.

Jason pulled the sling from his belt and felt in his scrip for his biggest stone. A bow and arrow would have been better for this; but the fox might come a little closer as it crossed the corner of the pasture. He could see no gap in the hedge opposite, but there must be one, and the fox would head for it.

Carelessly the fox trotted out into the moonlight, neither hurrying nor dawdling. Jason leaned back and turned his shoulders. He wouldn't miss, not with Jane Pennel watching breathlessly beside him. He had never missed a step in the dance with her as his partner.

The fox crossed from right to left, directly in front of them and thirty feet away. Jason swung the sling twice; he had to be quick or the fox would see the movement of it. Then he threw with all his force. The stone hissed through the air and struck the fox on the point of the shoulder. It stumbled forward with a low, quick snarl, whipped round, and bit angrily at the place, and Jason ran out with the girl's big stick in his hands. As he reached the fox it sat back on its haunches, its white teeth bared and fierce. Jason swung the jagged stick and hit it once on the head.

He picked it up by the tail and brought it back to the others. Jane ran out to meet him, clapping her hands and crying, "Jason! That's the fox who's taken ten of my hens!" He gave her the warm body, and she held it for a moment in both hands, her eyes sparkling at him.

He smiled slowly and said, "We'd better take and bury him, Mistress Jane. You can't say you caught *him* in a snare." He took back the fox and slung it over his shoulder.

Jane said, "I could never catch him. The keepers tried too. But you did it! I saw it! Well—" She stood a moment, glancing from them in their moleskin breeches, with the smell of earth and night on them, to the black tall shadows and the shining windows of Pennel Manor. "I must go back."

She hurried across the field. Voy called gently, "Eh, Mistress Jane!" He gave her the stick and the bell and the two rabbits.

"Thank you," she said quickly, and turned again.

When she had gone Jason said, "Do you think she'll tell on us?" She was nice, but when daylight came she would have to be Mistress Pennel again. He remembered that he had promised to go this night to Mary.

Old Voy said, "Not she. You know, she thinks you're the greatest man in the world now—except when she remembers that you're only a farmer's son."

"What do I care what she thinks?" Jason said, but he knew he did care because of how nearly he had killed her. "That cut in her belly will smart soon, and then she'll tell on us."

Voy said, "I knew a poet in London once—or was it Paris? He said to me—mind, he was drunk—but he said, 'If you want to make a man your friend, allow him to do you a favor!' She's seventeen. Come on away. Did you bring the forty shillings, lad?"

*　　*　　*

It wasn't many days before he saw her again. He was passing the Cross Keys, driving a bull calf his father had sold, when he saw her riding toward him on her horse. They came together slowly. He thought she was going to pretend she couldn't see him, but when they came closer he saw that she was blushing furiously. As they passed he touched his forehead and said, "Good morning, Mistress Jane." The acknowledgment seemed to release her from her confusion. She stopped the horse, bent down, and muttered, "The rabbit pie was very good." She smiled down on him from the horse, then looked nervously about to see if anyone was watching, but the lane was empty. She looked beautiful and rich on the shining horse, and her white hand hung down, and he saw that it was trembling a little. The bull calf reached up its head to sniff the strange horse's nose.

Jason remembered that time, three years back, when her breasts were just growing, and she'd hung around him at the fair, and they could have been in love, only she was just a girl and a Pennel, and he was a young man and a Savage. In the interval he had forgotten that time, but he knew now, looking up at her, that she had not forgotten. She had nursed it close in her memory, and now she was a woman, and the secret they had shared in the Windline was not the only secret.

He went forward to her on the horse, wondering, remembering the red scratch he had slit in her skin, and feeling her nervousness, and her eyes on his strong forearms. He took her hand, and kissed it. The hand pressed against his mouth and then pulled away as the horse started forward under the jerk of her thighs and heels, and the bull calf started back with a bellow of fright; but from thirty yards on she looked back at him and waved the hand that he had kissed.

It was another day, and the wind blowing from the west, wet and soft in the steady procession of days. Gently it carried to Jason in his byre the thin wailing of the pipes and the thumping of the tabors and the shouts of the whirling dancers. He looked affectionately at the red cow, pulled her ear, and said, "Not this afternoon, will you, please?" The cow stood restive, with her four legs spread and her flanks bulging in tight drum-circles, and looked at him.

Jason went out and spoke quietly to the young man who was sitting on the wall and counting his thumbs. You had to speak quietly to Softy Turpin or he ran away. Jason said, "Softy, you'll go into the byre now and stay there, won't you?"

"Yes, your grace, yes, yes, yes, I'll go away," Softy said, pulling his long hair.

Jason said, "That's good, Softy. If she starts, you come running to me in the church field, eh?"

"No, no, I won't come to the church field, your grace," Softy said, giving his forelock another tug. Jason patted him on the shoulder and walked, frowning, toward the gate.

It was easier to make himself a trout under water than Softy in a world turned upside down. Softy called farmers and laborers "your grace" and "squire" and "sir," and the dirtiest tramp, "your majesty." Sir Tristram he called "Pennel," and Mistress Jane, just "Jane." You had to tell him straight what you wanted him to do, and if he understood he answered crooked. Did Softy see him, Jason, in velvet slashed doublet with a sword and a horse? And Sir Tristram in moleskin? Was it all blurred, like what the trout must see, through water, of the land? He didn't know. He could only be sure that Softy did

36

not see the same as other people did; but no more did he himself. But Softy was off his head.

The music tinkled distantly in his ears. He found he had stopped at the gate of the farmyard and was staring at the wall of the byre a foot above Softy's shoulder. Softy was looking at him, the big china-blue eyes and slack mouth smiling overwidely. Softy said, "I'll go away, your grace."

Jason shook his head and hurried over the hill.

Already they were shouting inside the Cross Keys as he passed it, and several of the village rascals were rolling in the hedge and singing and waving their jugs of ale. All the drunkards had come here from the Green Man in Admiral, too, for the harvest fair. This was where he'd kissed Jane Pennel's hand. The church field was close now, and the noise loud. He wondered suddenly if one of the young gentlemen who rode over to the manor from Admiral and Chirton and Pewsey on their stallions was Jane's man. If it were true, would anyone in the village know? How could anyone know what happened in that big house? He walked on, frowning.

But of course people would know. The maidservants and the cook would. They were all village people. They'd know, and they'd tell quick enough. They hadn't said anything, so Jane Pennel didn't have a man.

What did it matter to him? Except that he'd kissed her hand and looked into her eyes. He remembered how she had marveled at the night when they were coming down from the Windline. She had been excited then, and now he was. He began to whistle and pushed through the gate into the church field.

Tomorrow was the Sunday of Harvest Home, and Parson should have been busy with Lady Pennel and all the old besoms, decorating the church; but Parson was there, near the gate, talking to a knot of sniggering old men.

"Good afternoon, Jason," Parson said. "Come to look for the Golden Fleece?"

Jason touched his forehead as the men laughed. What were the fools laughing at? he thought resentfully. They'd never even heard of the Golden Fleece, let alone touched it in their dreams.

The rough, sloping field was full of people. There were even a few faces he did not recognize. From the three Shrewfords everyone was here, but people had come too from Chirton and Alton and Bishop's

37

Cannings, and even from Pewsey and Challbury. They'd come for the cockshies, the archery, and the horseshoe throwing, and the dancing, and the black home-brew in the Cross Keys.

He wandered idly on. He didn't have much money to spend today, but he had a map. He was supposed to meet Mary. She'd be about somewhere. He'd find her.

He saw a knot of men grouped together against the far hedge and strolled over toward them. As he came closer he heard a familiar hoarse voice droning in a half-shout, half-whisper, "To Rome I've traveled, and France and Paris and Aleppo. To everywhere on this globe I've journeyed, and everywhere the surgeons and noblemen make use of this nostrum. This nostrum is used by the Pope of Rome himself to ward off the colics."

"To hell with the Pope!" a voice murmured dutifully.

"To hell with the Pope, you say, and so do I, so do I. But have you thought, how does that Anti-Christ keep alive with so many thousand good men giving him the bad wish? Can you answer me that? Does he drop dead?" Voy paused a long moment and looked round the crowd. "He does not. And is there not one of you here who thinks there might be someone wishing him ill at this moment, using the pins on him, like? A wife, by chance—it may be a shrewish wife? A girl who mistook your meaning when—?"

A laborer called out hastily for a bottle of the nostrum. Other voices joined in. Jason walked away, crossing himself nervously. God knew who would want to make a wax figure of him and stick pins into it, but such witchcraft did work evil, and there was no defense against it, certainly not in nostrums. Perhaps praying and crossing yourself was the only way, as Parson said.

Nearby he saw Molly with Ahab Stiles, and turned away to avoid them. Molly was loaded down with knickknacks and cheap finery. Ahab must have bought them from the chapmen's stalls for her, but her expression showed that she didn't want them, she hadn't asked for them, and she wasn't going to be softened by them. Her head was turning this way and that, and he knew she was looking for him; but he didn't want to be reminded that Mary Bowcher was also looking for him, so he turned his back and went over to the cockshy. He threw a dozen shies at the Aunt Sally, and paid his penny. He used the bow and arrow, and paid his penny. He wandered aimlessly round, searching.

At last he saw Jane Pennel talking to one of the fiddlers. She must have just arrived, because he had looked in that place several times already. He began to walk toward her, having no idea what he was going to say, and simultaneously heard his name called. "Jason! Jason Savage!"

It was Mary. He hesitated, then turned to her. She took his hand, smiled up at him, and said, "Oh, you look well." She squeezed his arm.

He watched Jane Pennel. The fiddler was tuning his fiddle. The members of the Club were almost ready to dance the Oak and Horn, the last dance before the Ring Competition. The Club was all the married men, and they were called that because only they could dance the Oak and Horn at harvest time, just as only the unmarried young men could dance the Moorish at Whitsun. Both groups used the same costumes and masks, but the Club had an extra mask, of a bull's head, which the young men weren't allowed to use.

Mary was saying, "I'd like some cider, Jason."

Unwillingly he turned his eyes away. He walked quickly with her through the crowd to the stall where Mistress Bolling sold the rough cider by the jug or the mug. He took two mugs, shook out the old lees, had them filled, drank his own, and stood waiting impatiently for Mary to finish hers.

But Mary sighed comfortably and settled down on the grass with her legs tucked under her. "It's good to be off my feet," she said. "My new shoes hurt. Aren't they pretty, though?"

She stretched out her strong legs and showed him the new black shoes with silver buckles. He noticed that they were the same shape as Jane Pennel's, but much heavier.

"Hurry up, Mary," he said. He was full of impatience now.

"What need is there to hurry?" she asked.

"I want to watch the Oak and Horn."

"Oh yes, it's almost started. Do you think you'll be in the Club to dance it next year?" She smiled up at him a little doubtfully, finished her cider, and got to her feet. They went to the edge of the circle of spectators, and Jason forced through to the front, careless of the scowls cast at him.

Jane Pennel was sitting at a big table under the great oak that stood in the corner of Church Field. All the Pennels were there— Sir Tristram, his lady, Master Hugo, and Jane. Jason stared and stared directly at Jane, because the taste of her hand was in his mouth, because she had books all round her and could sit in a high chair reading them, because . . . Mary was afraid of him—afraid, rather, of the future with him. He felt it in her big strong hand. She was trying now to pretend that all was well between them. There must be some way out of this, he and she being so affectionate to each other, but not truly in love.

At last Jane Pennel's restless, wandering glances met his stare. For a moment she looked at him; then she lowered her head and seemed to speak at random to her brother lounging beside her.

"Mistress Jane is beautiful, isn't she?" Mary said, sighing. "Look at her lovely shoes. Seeing them makes me want to throw mine away. But what's the use? I don't have her little feet."

"She's not beautiful," Jason said hoarsely, cut by a sharp edge of shame at hearing his Mary so downcast. Mary hugged his arm, and that was worse.

The Oak and Horn began with a ruffle and a double stamp.

He watched and became absorbed, because he saw that, as they danced, the men became like him in his dream journeys. They were no longer here in Shrewford Pennel, King Charles was not their lord, they were not farmers. They kicked their feet, and the head masks spun. The bull nodded and lifted his heavy horns. The white crossed garters on their legs snapped and spun, the feet of the watchers jigged on the grass, the men's eyes bulged, the women's lips drooped, wet. The dancers waved their boughs of oak, and the bull a peeled oak yard. Check and spin, stamp and spin—there were Roman helmets watching, amazed, under the oak tree where the Pennels sat. Head down, head up—kick, kick, kick, they danced under the three harsh stones on the Plain, round and round inside the earthen banks agleam with spears. It was dark on the Plain, and the wind whistled. Men in the skins of animals danced, their stone ax-heads catching the firelight. (But here were the tight-drawn eyes and the smell of cider and trampled grass, and the church clock's warning: *Sin! Sin! Sin!*) Parson's reading was no armor now; fear quivered in his chops; and the Pennels stood close-knit as Romans, watching; but for the dancers the lark burst up spiraling, ascending, climbing into the sun's eye.

Jason held Jane's eye steady, the bull prancing between them. In her vacant, stunned submission to his stare, in the reaching out from his loins to her, the Oak and Horn overthrew them.

He turned away, Mary following him. He had to get out of Jane's presence and control himself. As soon as the pipe and tabor stopped, the spell began to fade. He told himself the Oak and Horn was only a harvest dance, and Jane was a Pennel. In the black pit of his belly it made no difference. They were overthrown. Meantime—he didn't want to talk to anybody.

"Let's go and listen to Speranza Voy," he said. "He's always worth hearing. And you can watch him selling useless medicines to fools. But I shall have another mug of cider first."

The crowd round Voy was as thick as ever. As they came close they heard him. "You'll not regret it, master. Here, put it away; don't show it to your friends, even. You don't want anyone else to find the treasure, do you?" Jason saw Voy hand a piece of folded paper to a gawky youth from Shrewford Admiral. At the same time Voy saw Jason, and his voice faltered, but he hurried on. "Hide—hide it till you can fit out your own ship. Of *course* you'll find the gold where it's marked on there. . . ."

Jason felt sick with a sickness of disgust, a hopeless, dead nausea. Voy was, after all, only the agent of those who feared him. At Voy's hands they had set a bowl of cold, rotting tripes before him, and now watched to see him eat it.

The crowd drifted away. Jason said bitterly, "I thought you were my friend."

Old Voy looked at him for a while, as if trying to find words. Jason thought: He is mean and weak. He pretends to himself that he's a gentleman-adventurer, but he's only a liar called Potts.

Old Voy's eyes began to water, and he said, "Jason! You think I sold *you* a useless map? That boy only paid five shillings for his, and even that may be valuable. The seas are full of sunken Spanish galleons. I have to live. But that doesn't mean your map is no good, does it?"

Jason was silent. It certainly did, really, but he could not afford to believe that there was no Coromandel. If there wasn't, he would do better to go up at once to join the robbers on the Plain, before the people of this place walled him into prison.

Old Voy said earnestly, "As sure as I'm standing here, it's a true map. You're my friend. Do you think I'd take forty shillings off anybody for a worthless piece of paper?"

"Forty shillings!" Mary gasped. "Jason, you didn't—?"

"Oh, be quiet, Mary!" he shouted desperately.

Old Voy said, "You want to know where I got that map? Listen. 'Twas in the desert, a league and a half outside Aleppo—nearer two.

41

Come closer, I don't want anyone but you to hear. In the desert outside Aleppo"—he took a quick draft from the jug of ale beside him—"I was riding on a camel, returning from a visit to the King of —ah—Balgallum, who lived out there; he's not a big king, you understand, but he's rich. I'd been making a secret treaty with him for the Levant Company. Then, in the distance, I saw a man staggering toward me across the sand. He was thin as a rake, lad, and starving, and his hair was white as swansdown, though he wasn't old, and there were dried wounds and marks of the lash crisscross on his chest. I slid down from my camel . . ."

Jason listened. His doubts and anger slowly, willingly, fell away. Robbers; thirst; the Grand Turk's cavalry; men on small horses; mountains and snow and circling eagles; rivers, caves, and tigers—all for the sake of the map, his map.

Voy leaned back with a sigh, and Mary said, "I don't believe a single word of it! Forty shillings! Jason, you're madder than Softy Turpin!"

"It's all true," Jason shouted. "Voy's my friend. You don't know. You don't understand." She was a country girl, and she'd lain in his arms on the dry leaves in the spinney with the moon at quarter, and she'd stood beside him atop the silent earth walls on Shrewford Down—but she didn't understand. She couldn't see that there *must* be a road to Coromandel.

She tried again to ask him about the map, but he hauled her so fast across the field that she didn't have the breath. Near the oak tree Parson was clapping his hands and calling one and all to choose their partners and join in the dance of the Harvest Ring.

"Well, here's a chance to get your money back, and more," Mary said crossly. "There's a big prize this year. Squire's giving forty shillings, and a heifer in calf by his young bull. It's that light heifer with the liver markings."

Jason stared at the Pennels, hunching his shoulders and daring himself to do what he meant to do. Affection wasn't enough. He was in love with Jane Pennel. He was a selfish, heartless man. He'd have to be quick. Mary expected to be asked to dance. His sister Molly was coming toward him, old Ahab Stiles trotting behind her like a ram with thoughts of tupping on his mind.

Jason said, "I'm going to ask Mistress Jane to be my partner."

Molly had arrived. She cried, "Jason!" But Jason knew that she understood, knew that the whole meaning of what he said had come to her in a flash as she heard him speak.

He left Mary's frightened murmurings behind him and walked up to Jane Pennel. He touched his forehead and said, "Mistress Jane, will you dance the Ring with me? I think we'll win."

Sir Tristram frowned, and Hugo said coldly, "Certainly not."

Jason said tensely, "I was asking Mistress Jane, Master Hugo."

He held out his arm. Jane rose slowly to her feet and came to him. Together they walked into the ring. Tom Devitt, Drake's old sailor, noisily cleared his throat and cupped his hands to his mouth. He was drunk as a fiddler's bitch by now, but Tom could call the Harvest Ring unconscious. He usually did.

Jason held both Jane's hands and looked steadily at her until her head came up and her eyes met his. He pointed his left foot, and she pointed hers. The caller would call only once in each part of the dance, because it was a competition. After that the dancers had to remember the turns, but Jason knew no one was going to miss a step today. The prize would be won by the grace of their turns, by the poise of the movements and the pointing of the toe and the straightness of the leg.

Tom Devitt called, "The maidens in the middle and the men outside. To the left, to the right, dance the Old Wife's Pride." Jason and Jane began to dance.

After ten minutes Jane whispered breathlessly to him as they turned back to back in the sixth change, "There are only two other couples left."

He muttered, "Don't look at them." She must not even think of the other dancers, or hear the singing of the drunkards outside the Cross Keys, or notice the amazed surprise in Parson's smug face, or her father's strange look, or Master Hugo's black disapproval.

But he himself could not help seeing the Parson call one of the other couples out of the ring, and noticing their disappointed, sweating faces on the side. Now they'd be saying to each other, to console themselves, that he was still in there because his partner was Jane Pennel. Let them say. He and she were the best dancers in the ring.

The other couple was good too. But he must not think of them, only of the shape of the dance, and the moves as fluent as the Avon flowing. Tom Devitt began to call the changes faster, until they were having only a single round of each. "Benjamin the Fiddler, call him down; Back-a-back and ride to town. . . . Green grass grows in the field, and turn. . . . Alton Chimes. . . . Meadowsweet, meadow-sweet . . ."

"Oh, Jane," he whispered. Her eyes shone like large green stars. "Oh, Jane!" he reached out his hands, and she caught them and held fiercely. They couldn't put a foot wrong or miss the grip of their fingers forever and ever.

"Come to the spinney tomorrow afternoon."

She muttered, "Yes."

Something caught at his sleeve, and he brushed it off, not thinking, not taking more notice of it than of a fly.

Again it caught him, but harder, this time nearly pulling him off his balance. Angrily he glanced round, and Parson was shouting, "Go away!" It was Softy Turpin, frowning ferociously beside him and ludicrously swinging round after him so that all the people rocked and screamed and slapped their thighs with laughter. Softy bawled, "She'm not started yet, your grace. She'm not started. No need for you to hurry!"

Jason stopped. It was no use. All the power of movement flowed out of his legs, and he could only stand there, trembling. He saw his father, hunched and dark beside the church wall, with three of his cronies. He saw Jane's huge, soft eyes.

He muttered, "The red cow's calving."

He left her standing in the middle of the ring and ran off. Mary was running after him across the field, and Molly was trying to stop her, but as soon as he got into the lane he left them both far behind.

*   *   *

Ten days later there was no moon, and it was a thick night, compounded of darkness and autumnal rain that flowed in a soft black stream over the Pewsey Vale. The wind had changed with the new moon, and blew this night quietly against his cheek as he hurried across the shoulder of the Plain on his way to Pennel Manor.

He came to the spinney and went carefully through it. He stroked his hand against the body of an ash as he passed it. The Oak and Horn had brought Jane here on that Sunday in the hazy afternoon, to lie down together with him here, so that afterward they could look speechless into each other's faces. Twice more they'd found an hour to come here. He had asked her to bring a book and teach him to read. She had, and had shown him the letters of the alphabet. Then she had read aloud to him from the book, but haltingly, for the words were long and strange. It was a book about a man's travels in foreign countries, and as he lay listening he thought: When we marry we'll have to go away to escape Sir Tristram's anger. He saw her standing on the deck of the ship, her lips parted and her pale red hair streaming out behind her in the wind. They would search over the rim of the world for all marvels, for whales, cachalots, and dolphins, for flying fish and the magic lights turning in the waves under the ship.

But she stopped reading soon, and, when he began to talk longingly of those voyages as if they were reality, she shook her head impatiently and wanted to be told about ferrets and fitchews and how to set a snare, and she told him that he smelled of the farm, and reminded him that she could marry anyone she chose, even the king's son, because she was Jane Pennel—but before the reading, when they first saw each other under the trees, she hadn't thought of how he smelled or what he wore, but only ran breathlessly into his arms. The making love ended her love, but began his.

He came to the edge of the pasture, where he had killed the fox. The manor hedge was fifty yards ahead in the darkness, and the rain dripped off the homespun hood he wore on his head. The hounds knew him, because each time she came to the spinney she had pretended to be walking two of them, and they'd cocked their big heads and whimpered while he kissed her.

He crossed the field, slipped through the hedge, and worked past the outhouses until he stood under the wall of the manor. He'd been here once or twice, but at the side door, waiting with a basket of eggs or a ham that the Pennels had bought from his father. The house was built all of new small bricks, and the windows had many leaded glass panes. It looked new, raw, and ungainly, but he thought it must be comfortable inside. Once, when Jenny the serving maid opened the door to him, he had seen only the big kitchen. Another time the door beyond the kitchen had been open, and through there it was different from anything he had ever seen. There were oak paneling in big carved squares from floor to ceiling, and tapestries hanging, and a whiff of beeswax polish coming out over the smell of cooking in the kitchen, and he had seen a table with carved legs, and two big globes standing on it, and through there the floor was made of little oblong wooden blocks. Then Jenny gave him a saucy remark and he had to slap her round buttocks, and someone shut the inner door.

He found the small window open, as Jane had promised, and climbed through it. Now he had to remember what she had told him. The staircase was on his right, and, directly opposite him, the great hall and fireplace. On his left there was a passage with two rooms leading off it. That passage ended in the door he'd seen from the kitchen. One of the two rooms was a store chamber, and the other a room full of books.

He was a little early. Perhaps Jane wouldn't be expecting him yet. Perhaps her tirewoman was still hanging round before going through the upstairs door that divided the Pennels' rooms from the servants'.

Thousands of books, she'd said.

He turned left and carefully opened the second door. A faint beam of light fanned out in the widening gap as he opened it, and in fright he held his hand steady. Hugo might be in there—but Hugo didn't do much reading, and Sir Tristram was visiting Lord Henry in Admiral. He peered cautiously round the door. The room was empty. The light was coming in through the windows from the carriage lantern that hung over the front door of the manor. He slipped into the room and closed the door behind him.

There were the books. His heart bumped loudly. There was a smell of paper and leather, and the rows of leather backs swept up to the ceiling and round the four walls. He saw another globe on a table, and parchment, sand, ink, and quills beside it. But—the books! He took one out at random and carried it like a jewel to the window.

He opened it and stared at the print. It wasn't even English. He knew the alphabet now, and this was different. He put it back and got out another. All writing, and he could not read.

He found a book with pictures on nearly every page. He burst out laughing with delight, and quickly hushed and listened, but no one moved in the big house. He was looking at a wondrous animal with a tail at each end and four, five, six men, carrying spears, in a box on its back. The animal had—he looked more closely—God's blood, it had great teeth like a boar's, only ten times bigger and curving down instead of up. He looked at the ceiling. That animal could not fit into this room. There was writing in the book as well as pictures, and he could not read it. Still, the pictures were more marvelous than shooting stars. He turned the pages greedily.

Pennel Church clock clanged loud and close, the cracked bell notes shaking the glass panes in the window and thudding to silence among the leather books. Jason started and stared nervously around him. What was he doing here? Jane Pennel.

The back of the chair was damp where he had been sitting in his wet jerkin. He slipped out of the room, taking the book with him. He crept up the wide staircase. The third door on the left. He made a little scratching on it with his fingernail and waited. He heard a stir in the room and stepped to one side, in case it might after all be the wrong room that he had come to. The door opened an inch and, used now to the darkness, he saw a slice of Jane's face. She opened the door, let him in, and shut it quickly behind him.

She whispered, "Where have you been? Why are you so late?" He said, "I was looking at this book, Jane. It's full of pictures. Look." He opened the book at random and said excitedly, "Look at that!"

She whispered furiously, "I don't want to look at pictures. You gave me a terrible fright!" She was trembling as she stood beside him. He began to explain that the book was like a key to heaven, but she said, "You're wet. You smell of cow dung."

Jason sniffed carefully. He did smell strong. The rain always did that, and the smell seemed even more powerful in this faintly scented bedroom. He took her in his arms and kissed her. That was what she had wanted most from him, ever since the Oak and Horn. She was dressed only in her shift, and she pressed her spiced mouth against his. He opened his eyes to look past her head through the window as they kissed. The first leaves were beginning to fall; they looked like tiny flying ships of air as they sailed down in the light of the outside lantern. He ought to have told Mary he couldn't marry her; but he hadn't seen her since the harvest fair.

He stood back from the girl and whispered, "Jane, we must go away. We'll go to Aleppo and see all the animals in the book." He picked up the book and opened it.

*   *   *

For a moment she stood watching his face. Already he was absorbed in the book, and she standing here in her shift trembling for him—and she her father's only daughter. And he—he did smell of cow dung. But she ought not to have said that just now. It was cruel. He couldn't help it. She couldn't help what she was doing, either, because his eyes sparkled when he looked at her, and she had felt the same helpless weakness years ago when she was only a little girl and hadn't then really known the difference between a Pennel and a

Savage. So because he had been her first love then, and she had not dared to tell him, she was here and he was here.

She was wicked, and Hugo would kill her if he knew. But Jason would protect her. He had a short knife, and his arms were sinewy and sunburned. The line of his jaw lay hard against the light from outside.

She took the book gently out of his hands and put it down on the bed behind her. She sat down on the edge of the bed and, as he turned, put up her arms and her face to him and closed her eyes.

She felt his breath by her ear, and then his whisper. "Will you marry me, Jane? If you will, we'll go away, and then we can discover everything together."

Not now, not now, don't talk of it now when I am helpless, because now I must listen lovingly to everything you say, and it seems good and wonderful, but I know it isn't. Talk of it later, when this is done and you have assuaged me, and then I will know it is madness and I will tell you again that you smell of the farm.

She whispered, "Jason, Jason!"

He forced her gently back on the bed, and she sighed, but he sat down beside her and said again, "Will you marry me, Jane? We'll find men who know the way, and we'll go with them to Coromandel. Old Voy told me that's the best thing to do. I will make you happy all your life if you will."

The dim yellow light, diffused and rain-blurred, washed his dark face as he leaned over her. He said quietly, "It's no use just lying together every time you want to forget that I am a farmer's son, dear Jane. Do you love me, Jane?"

Because he had held off she was helpless against the truth. She did love him, but oh, it was wicked and impossible. She muttered, "I do love you, Jason."

She heard her own words and faced them. The memory of every time she had ever seen him came upon her, all at once and together, and swept aside the obstinate remnants of her pride. If her father could be made to agree to the marriage he would give them land and send them to London for Jason to be made into a gentleman. Hugo would be furious—but she didn't like Hugo. She was afraid of him, that was all.

She said, "I'll marry you, if my father will agree."

She felt herself shaking with relief and anxiety. She had found the truth at last, and now it became the most important thing in the world that Jason should agree and somehow find a way to make her father agree.

Ah, she could have married anyone, but she would marry Jason. They couldn't live in Wiltshire, but her father owned land in Dorset too. They would go there when Jason had learned to be a squire. He'd be a small farmer-squire, like Master Yeoford and Master Ingle here in the Vale. It would be all right, and she and he would— He had gone limp beside her, and a sudden access of panic sent her arm jerking out to seize his elbow. "What is it, what's the matter?"

Surely he couldn't refuse now, to go and follow his crazy dreams, his mad books. He only wanted to go away because he was not treated as he deserved, but that would all change when he was a squire in Dorset. What more would he want or expect?

"What is it?" she whispered.

The door opened, and light flooded the room; light sparkled on the sheets and the high canopy and the red Turkey carpet and the stone walls, and on her clothes in the open wardrobe, and on the book beside her white legs. She rolled over and up with a cry, her hands pressed to her face. Jason jumped to his feet and turned. It was her brother Hugo.

Hugo put down his lantern on the table, and the light from it flashed down the long blade of the rapier in his hand. He was fully dressed—crumpled riding boots and spurs, silk breeches, red doublet, wide white ruff, his head bare, long hair wet on his shoulders, empty scabbard swinging against his legs as he stepped forward, the sword drawn back.

She cried, "Oh no, Hugo, no! I love him. We're going to be married!"

Her brother looked only at Jason and muttered, "You whoreson knave," and lunged out.

The rapier slid down the light, the sparks slid up the blade, and the point flickered past Jason's side as he bent and jumped in. The men met, breast to breast, in the center of her bedroom, their left hands locked above their heads, the rapier snaking back and back, but it was too long. Jane felt the night air cold in her teeth and saw the poacher's knife in Jason's hand, and saw it strike down into her brother's back. Hugo's eyes widened, and Jason caught him and eased him to the floor. What was the matter with him? But Jason's hand glowed red as nightshade berries, and the blade of his knife dripped red onto the red carpet, and the pool of red widened under

49

her brother's back, and his eyes stared, amazed, at the carved ceiling.

Jason bent and put his hand on Hugo's heart. He straightened up and said, "I've killed him." Then, slowly: "Better him than you. Did I have to kill him?"

He shut the door with care. She said, "Hugo, my brother." She knelt down and looked into his face, and put out her hand to touch him, but dared not. It was her fault too that he lay dead on her carpet, because she had been wicked enough to fall in love with Jason and to wish that Jason would protect her against Hugo's anger.

She felt wild, deep breaths of air fighting down into her lungs, and the room and Jason's face and Hugo's dead eyes blurred together. Then Jason's hands were on her wrists. He said, "Be still, darling Jane. We can reach my father's farm in twenty minutes. Molly will help, and we can get the horses ready in ten more. By morning we can be past Salisbury if we ride hard. If you have any money, get it. Dress quickly, my dear love. We'll take the first ship."

How could he speak of that now? Everything was changed, and her hopes lying as dead as Hugo at her feet. She saw the poverty of Jason's clothes, and behind him the silk dresses in her wardrobe. She blurted, "Jason, please, please don't tell them I asked you here." She burst into a passion of tears.

She heard Jason speaking gently, insistently, to her, as though she were a child who had not understood. "We're going to get married as soon as we can. But we must go away quickly now."

Slowly she collected herself. Being almost numb with shock, she spoke her thoughts clearly and simply. She said, "I don't want to go away with you. I love you, but I don't want to live under a hedge all my life."

Jason was silent for a long time, still holding her wrists. There was blood on her now, but she could not pull her hand away. She watched him, and he seemed to be looking round her room—into the wardrobe, aglitter with the fold and drape of brocade; out of the window, where, hidden in the night, her father's land lay wide under the rain. At last he said, "Would I give up this for Coromandel? When you said you'd marry me if your father agreed, I felt suddenly as though you'd given me a heavy weight to carry. Then Hugo came in—and I murdered him."

She found her eyes fixed now on Hugo's face. She said, "Not murder. He was trying to kill you."

Jason said, "I could have disarmed him, wounded him. But I killed him—as I nearly killed you. So now I *have* to go. Am I mad to think it happened like that?"

She looked up, startled, and he said quickly, "Give me an hour. Then scream and tell them Hugo found me robbing your room. Tell them it was a fair fight, though."

She felt his lips on her eyelids, then watched as he picked up the wonderful picture book, opened the door, and left her.

She sat down slowly on the bed and looked at her brother. Even now she could go with Jason into the rainy world if she had the courage. His eyes glowed before her, the fire of his strange enthusiasms warmed her, his lips searched hers. Even now . . . She rolled over on her face and began to cry deep in her chest—the tears of a woman, not of a girl.

*   *   *

Jason thought briefly of Hugo. He was sorry he had killed him, but the deed did not seem so terrible as the thought of Jane's unhappiness. Had he caused that too? He could not think of it now.

He must go now to Mary, because she had been kind to him. He ran quickly down the lane beside the churchyard wall in the rain. He came to the Bowchers' cottage, grasped the ivy firmly—on the left-hand side—and began to climb. He flung himself headlong across the gap, easily reached her window, and climbed in. He moved strongly and felt more alive than ever before. He had made no sound, and now he bent over the bed and shook her by the shoulder.

She awoke slowly, stertorously, unafraid. No one was going to harm her in her cottage, or ever had. She was different on the Plain or in an unknown place. Then she'd jump and scream if thistledown came on the wind to touch her cheek.

She said, "Who is it?"

"Jason."

She said, "Jason! You never said you were coming tonight."

He said, "I've killed Hugo Pennel. They'll be after me soon. I'm going to Coromandel. Will you come with me?"

After a time, when she sat quiet in the darkness, she said, "I can't marry you now, Jason. I promised myself to George Denning—this very day. I waited for you, and— I did right, didn't I, Jason?"

Jason said, "Yes."

She'd be happy. George Denning was a good man, a slow, bull-like fellow a year or two older than Jason. Everyone had thought

Mary was surely going to marry him until she ran off after Jason. George had just waited.

She was sitting up in the little bed, and the warmth in her strong fingers steadied him. She said, "How will you get to—that place?"

"I don't know," he said, "but I will. I'll go and ask Voy. He said I had to take a ship from London. I must go, Mary."

She stood up and took him in her arms with an extraordinary strength of longing, and he hugged her in a passion of affection. "Good-by," he muttered. "Remember me."

He slipped over the sill and down the ivy. Looking up for the last time he could see nothing in the dark and the rain, nothing at all.

He headed east, a little higher up the hill than would lead directly to the farm. Old Voy was living these days in Bellman's Hollow, a clump of small firs that filled a round dip in the downward slope of the Plain.

At the edge of the wood Jason softly called Voy's name. There was no light, no sound but the drip of the rain, and Jason had a sudden moment of panic lest Voy should not be here. He had to see Voy; Voy had sold him the map; Voy knew about ships and sailors and Aleppo and Rome. Without Voy's help now, it was hopeless to think he could reach Coromandel.

But Voy answered quietly from close by, and they went together under the dripping boughs into the tiny shelter that Voy had made himself among the firs.

Jason said, "I was with Jane Pennel, and I killed Hugo. I'm going to Coromandel. You said the ships go to Coromandel from London. Tell me quick, where are the ships in London? How can I get passage on one, without money? I'm not a sailor."

Voy was rummaging about in his larder. He lived like a shrike, and Jason knew there were bits of smoked ham there in the forks of the trees, and pigeons cooked in clay and left like that till wanted, and roasted rabbit legs skewered on sharp pine twigs.

"Tell me," Jason repeated impatiently.

"In a minute. Jason, are you sure you can't stay here? Suppose that map was no good—through nobody's fault, mind? Then you'd have no reason to go. *Could* you stay? And marry Jane? I saw you in the spinney with her Tuesday."

For a moment Jason thought he should heed the hint in Old Voy's voice and ask point blank whether the map was true or false. It might still be just possible for him to go back and tell Sir Tristram the whole

52

truth and perhaps marry Jane—but only if the beacon of Coromandel could go out forever.

He said, "No, I can't go back. I can't stay. Tell me how I can find a ship in London."

Old Voy said, "London, now? At the docks, boy. That's where the ships are."

"But how can I get on board? Will they take me as a sailor?"

Old Voy said, "Take you as a sailor? Why, I don't know. It depends, Jason."

Jason's fingers tightened. The damned old fool! He was helpless. Perhaps he'd never been to London or seen the sea, and didn't know what a sailor was any more than Jason himself did! But that didn't mean the map was useless! There were plenty of ways a man like Voy could come into possession of a real, true map. But the man himself was no good. Jason had depended on him and told himself he could do nothing without Voy's help. But he'd have to.

He said abruptly, "Thank you. I'll find my way. Good-by."

Old Voy sighed and pressed a sack into his hands. It was the one he always wore over his shoulder. "Take it," he said, "and when you fill it with the treasure of Meru, remember old Speranza Voy."

Jason crept out under the branches and ran full tilt down the slope toward his father's farm.

Time was passing, but he hardly thought about that. Had the hue and cry been at his heels, he could not have left out one of these last visits. He scrambled quickly in through his window, gathered his sling, his book, his map, and his last few shillings, and stuffed them all into the sack Voy had given him. Now he had two books, one full of writing and one full of pictures. He had found the first muddied in the road, and the second he had just stolen from Pennel Manor. Perhaps it would be all right to think Jane had given it to him.

He went silently into Molly's room and bent over to awaken her. She had heard him and was awake. For the third time he said, "I've killed Hugo Pennel. I'm going to London to take ship for Coromandel."

Molly was calm, but that did not surprise him. He had expected her to be. She said, "Can I come with you? Are they after you yet?"

He said roughly, "No," and, "No," and, "Good-by, Moll." For a moment they clung together like lovers. (But there must be a woman in the world for him, who was not his sister.) He broke away.

As he reached the door she said, "Wait! Which way are you going to London?"

He had no idea. He said, "Pewsey, I suppose."

She said, "That's the straight road. They'll be looking for you there. Don't go that way. Go across the Plain to Amesbury and up from there. As soon as you've gone I'll put on some of your clothes, take the mare, and ride through Pewsey, and on until I'm caught."

Jason said, "But they'll say—"

She leaped out of bed and whispered furiously, "Will you go away and do what you're told, you helpless booby? And as soon as I can I'll run away too. I told you I would. Oh, Jason!" Again she clung to him, then broke away with a violent jerk and turned her back.

All that she had said, both then and all their lives, stayed a long time with him as he hurried south through the rain.

For a time he would be safe on the open Plain, especially in this darkness. He climbed fast and did not look back until he was near the crest, where the hummocked circle of Shrewford River dominated the slope. His father's farm was the nearest building to him then, and he saw a faint point of light in that direction, and knew that Sir Tristram's men had reached the farm to look for him. He watched the light for a minute and wondered whether he ought to be thinking of his father, and whether Molly had got away to carry out her plan. The rain was only a thin spatter now, and, because he knew it so well, he could see the Vale spread out below him like a quilt, and fit each field into its place, and name each pouring copse, and hear the rain on every roof—all known, all unseen. He turned again.

He stretched his legs and swung on with long strides. There were no hedges or ditches to worry about on the Plain, only the rabbit holes, and usually you could see them by the whitish blur of the chalk the rabbits threw out in digging them. The wind veered steadily from west to northwest, the rain stopped, and it became colder. Clouds hurried close above, low over the long roll of the Plain, and the wet grass shimmered like a mist about his feet. Some light illumined his way, but whether it filtered down from above the clouds or came up through the chalky earth he did not know. He felt hungry and pulled out a rabbit leg and gnawed it as he walked.

The Avon ran south through the Plain in a deep and narrow valley to his right. The roads from Devizes and Pewsey, going toward Salisbury, joined each other just north of Challbury, which stood at the entrance of the valley. The wind blew from that quarter now, and

54

he heard the drum of hoofs and saw a lantern moving like a will-o'-the-wisp southward along the road. "Fools!" he muttered to himself, "I could hear them a mile off if I was on that road, and get off and let them pass." It was comforting to talk to himself as he hurried on.

But that meant that the chase was spreading out in all directions. The majority might be following Molly through Pewsey, but they were taking no chances. Sir Tristram must have sent men to warn all the squires around. The watches would be out in the villages, but horsemen would be his greatest danger. There might be twenty or thirty of them in the lanes by now.

He stopped suddenly and listened—only the wind; but he thought he had heard again the dull beat of hoofs, now on turf, and somewhere in front. He lay down and put his ear to the earth. Quite clearly he heard the *thud-thud*. He turned right and hurried diagonally down the slope toward the Avon. Horsemen were spreading over the Plain. Someone had guessed he would go on foot across the Plain rather than on horseback up the Vale—probably his father.

He came to the Avon and stopped a moment to collect his thoughts. Men would be watching the river if they had had time to get here. They could have done that only on horseback; so he should hear the horses stamping and breathing before he saw the men. They might be on either side of the stream, or both.

He began to walk very slowly southward on the left bank. The rushing of the water drowned the *shush-shush* of his shoes in the grass, but the same noise would hide the sounds made by men and horses. Challbury was on the hill up there to his right. If men had come down to the river they would probably be hereabouts, where a cart track led from the village to the stream.

It was not the horses he heard first but a man coughing close ahead of him. He stopped and crouched. A voice from the opposite side of the stream muttered, "Hold your coughing, Peter." That was Phineas Granger who spoke—to Peter Sale. They were two of Sir Tristram's men. They knew this water as well as he did.

Jason took off his shoes and dropped them into his sack. He stepped into the river, crouched low to the surface, and moved forward, feeling with his toes for his footing as he went. The river was twenty feet wide here, no more.

The enemy lurked about him, and there was a vital message in his sack. He was carrying it to his captain. The Turks lay in wait, and

Coromandel was beleaguered. He had a bloody knife in his belt. . . .
But there used to be a pair of moorfowl that nested every year in the
old snagged tree that had blown down when he was a little boy.
The tree lay in the middle of the stream, not quite straight across,
leaving only a foot or two clear between each end and the bank. He
reached out his hands and felt the smooth dead wood He could see
Peter Sale now, a shape to his left in the blackness. He sank under
the water and crawled forward on his stomach, holding his breath,
below the arch of the tree. He came up and breathed out with a gasp,
but he heard the changed sound of the water and knew he was dam-
ming it with his body. He heard Granger call in a low voice, "See anything in the river, Peter?"

Sale said, "Nothing. It's as black as pitch."

"I heard something."

Jason kept creeping forward. The wind blew through his clothes,
and he shivered with the cold of it. The water dripped loudly from
him into the rush of the stream. God's blood, his map and books
would be wet! He moved one foot forward, dragging it along, testing
the bottom, put it down, put his weight on it, dragged up the other
foot. He climbed carefully out on the right bank. There was a big
black hole under the overhang where he could put his foot. A pair
of water rats used to live in there. Once he'd seen the dog rat eating
the moorhen's eggs.

He struck southwest, up and away from the river, and moved at a
trot. The valley was too narrow to be safe by daylight; it could be
searched too easily. He knew where he was heading, and an icy light
lay low along the eastern horizon.

It was somewhere here, a little to the right or left, on this swell of
Compton Down. He knew the place, but he'd never had to find it in
the dark before. The three stones by Shrewford Ring stood away
from the earth now, a black finger-sign across the valley, and the
dawn spreading behind them.

He sighed with relief and dropped into a shallow chalk pit. It was
not more than ten feet long and a couple of feet deep. The turf above
was so thick, and its roots so strongly bound, that it projected a foot
or more over the edges of the pit. Jason lay down, frowning. He'd
found this in a midsummer's game of hide-and-seek with Hugo and
other lads long ago—the ponies tethered on the road to the east, and
the girls playing silly girls' games, and himself hiding here—and the
boys had never found him.

He got out his books and map and saw with amazed relief that they were hardly wet. Voy's sack must be almost waterproof. He ate some more rabbit and wished he'd remembered to take a drink before he left the Avon. The hurrying had warmed him inside, and down here he was out of the wind, but if the sun didn't break through later he would be cold. He chewed the tough meat, cautiously raised his head above the level of the turf, and looked around. No one in sight —only the Plain, a distant thorn, a lonely bank of firs, daylight, thinning cloud.

He felt his freedom as the physical lightening of a load—but some of that load had been comfortable and warming to him. "Home" had been in a certain direction; now it was in no direction, or in every direction. "Molly" had been his sister, who lived in the Savage farmhouse; now she didn't live there, and she was not his sister because they had parted forever. "Salisbury" had been a far town; but it was close, and where he was going was farther than the stars. All his horizons had vanished, and nothing was fixed any more. For a moment he cowered before the empty vastness of his freedom. Then he said aloud, "Coromandel!" and burrowed a place for himself under the overhanging turf at the edge of the chalk pit.

He thought for a moment about what he would do if they found him. He drew his knife, hefted it in his hand, and pricked the point through his clothes until it hurt. Then, with the knife in his fist, he curled up and went to sleep.

When he awoke it was midday and the sun was out, but it had rained again. Now he must wait at least six hours before it would be safe to move. He began to study his map of Coromandel. But soon he knew it by heart and put it carefully away. He ate a piece of ham. His lips were dry in spite of the damp, and long before dark he began to shiver. It was cold and lonely there on the Plain; he was lost by the world. He looked at the picture book but put it away when he found he could think only of the wind in the grass, and Molly, and his father, bitter and lonely at the farm. He shivered more violently and, to stop himself from weeping, stuffed his hand into his mouth and bit hard on it and cursed at himself with all the foul language that he knew.

*   *   *

When it was dark he stepped out of the pit, stretched, and began to move. He hurried down to the river and took a drink, then headed south by west as hard as he could go, across the Plain. The rain blew down in the wind, and, in fighting against it, he recovered his courage. He knew where he was going, and they couldn't catch him in this driving murk. To forget that he had wept from loneliness he summoned jewels into his sack and a curved sword to his side. The raging Turks gnashed their teeth behind him, having found their leader dead and the prisoner escaped; but they would never catch him.

A road. The deep ruts stretched across his path, half full of water. He stopped, looked north into the black rain—nothing. South—a dim lightness, and the spears of rain slanting down to pierce the earth; no one. He crossed the road and strode on. Men could get lost on the Plain, but not he. He could look at the sky and feel the wind, and walk and know where he would arrive. Aleppo stood dim above its battlements behind him; his camel moved fast across wet grasslands. What did you feed a camel? It would probably be a difficult animal to ride, being shapeless. The dark, mysterious girls in the houses were secretly laughing at him. A horse, then, it had better be, a stallion galloping toward distant, half-seen mountains. . . .

A voice called sharply, "There, left." Jason stopped dead. A light sprang out thirty yards to his right.

"Damn your eyes, I tell you something moved!"

Jason crouched, still as a hare in the rain. The lamp came toward him, and he saw two pairs of wet boots striding and two big cloaks swinging, and the blade of a sword. When they reached within ten paces of him he bounded to his feet and ran on south as fast as he could. He heard the gasp, the shouts of "Stop, stop!" The rainy wind drummed on his hood, and his heart pounded.

Quick! They'd run after him for a few paces; then they'd find they couldn't catch him because of their big boots—riding boots; horses. They'd go back for their horses and start to ride him down.

He turned sharp left and ran till his lungs were ready to burst. He lay down and put his ear to the wet grass and heard the horses galloping, not close. He didn't want to get into Amesbury itself, but to circle it and then head toward London. He'd better make for Stonehenge. He turned a point west and went slowly, every minute stooping to listen against the earth. The rain squall blew away, and the stars crept out.

He plodded south for another two hours and began to feel achingly tired, but he knew he was near now. He bore left and lay down to make a horizon. Staring, for a time he could see nothing. It was very quiet on the Plain, and no one was at his heels.

Gradually, striding slowly like giants out of darkness, the stones of the Henge advanced upon him. He lay lower against the wet earth and pressed his clenched fingers down until the chalk gritted under his nails.

The pillars of stone filled the Plain about him, the nearest not twenty feet away, and he heard their old voices and saw them sway and move, and felt the earth groaning under the weight of them. Alone—they for endless thousands of years, he now for the first time; and now the dawn was coming in green wedges of light under the altars.

He jumped up and ran back across the Plain. He heard himself shouting, but no one answered and the great stones did not move. Oh, God, let them catch me and lock me up and hang me, but never leave me.

He stopped running.

But this that he had run away from was Coromandel. This was the substance of his dreams—to travel with men he did not know and share their wonders and their awes. If he could walk by Stonehenge in the hour before dawn and feel nothing but the presence of wet grass and sleeping curlews, what would await him in Coromandel? Nothing.

He turned and walked slowly eastward into the spreading light, until once more he stood in the center of the Henge. In a minute he was afraid again, but this time with a fear that he had searched for in the past and found. He saw ten thousand men around him, and priests under the stones, and smelled blood and burning wood and felt the ecstasy and terror of the multitude, of whom he was one.

There was something else here for him too, some message that seemed to give him a vague comfort and warmth; but he could not properly catch it to understand it. For the moment it was enough that he had been afraid. Fear faded, the people were swallowed up, he opened his eyes and began to stride east across Knighton Down.

He'd seen Stonehenge. Now for Coromandel. And after that, Meru. He would get there somehow. He didn't have any money, and he wasn't a sailor, but he'd get there.

Chapter Two

The man in front of him on the horse pointed down the muddy lane that led off to the left and said, "There's my road to Islington. Are you sure you have somewhere to go to in the city? It is a wicked place for young men from the country."

Jason slid over the horse's fat rump into a puddle and said, "Thank you, sir, I am going to a friend's."

The man, who had been a stranger this morning, waved his hand and turned his horse's head into the gathering darkness of the December afternoon. Jason swung up his bundle, hitched his sack onto his shoulder, and began to trudge eastward.

He had somewhere to go. The letter was folded away in the bottom of his sack, and he would have liked to tell the man about it because it was exciting—but the people who had given him the letter had been insistent that he mustn't even talk about it, let alone show it to anybody.

Christmas Eve. He'd never thought, when he set out from Stonehenge, that it would take this long to reach London. Well, if he'd hurried he'd never have worked for the carters in Reading, and if he'd never worked for them he'd never have gone to the Caversham Tavern, never have had enough money to drink a lot of sack one night, and, after drinking, danced, and . . .

Brrr! The sleet blew into his face. Through half-closed eyes, he could see the lights of a village glowing dimly ahead. Strong on the wind he heard bells, near bells and distant bells, tenor bells and alto bells—Christmas Eve, and his knuckles blue with cold. His two books weighed heavily in the sack. Twenty times he had thought of throwing them away, but he had never been able to bring himself to do it.

He blew on his nails and walked faster. The letter was addressed to Master Dick Lanthard, but the hosts of the Caversham Tavern always called him Dick o' the Ruff. Dick o' the Ruff knew everybody in the whole of London, and in the whole of London everybody knew Dick o' the Ruff. Dick o' the Ruff was gay and generous, wise and clever and strong and brave. Dick o' the Ruff knew sailors and merchants and shipmasters. Jason would be on a ship to Coromandel before he could say "Dick Whittington," and all because he could dance the Old Wife's Pride.

But God's blood, there'd been some strange women at that Caversham Tavern o' nights! And the drinking and the gambling and the fights!

He was in a village; a river ran to his right, and the road was a deep trench of mud and sleet along the edge of the water. A man came hurrying toward him, the wind at his back billowing out his cloak. Jason stopped, lowered his hood, and said, "By your grace, sir—" The man glanced up, hurried past.

At the third attempt he was answered. An old, bent woman gathering sticks in the river mud said, "London? This is Chelsea. Keep straight on. You can't miss it. Mind your footing. A man lost his cart in the road last week. Five miles." She shook her head mournfully and returned to her search.

Jason turned again to face the sleet. Five miles; then he'd meet Dick o' the Ruff, and there'd be a warm fire and mulled ale and smiling, welcoming faces. The village sank into the river of night behind him, and fields and lone trees edged up close to the road. Cold water sloshed about in his shoes, and thin ice tinkled at every step, and for a mile he struggled, up to his knees in half-frozen mud. After a long time he saw clustering lights ahead, but they never seemed to come any closer. He waded a stream and stumbled on, his teeth chattering, his eyes all but shut. The sleet froze slowly on his clothes so that they became stiff and crackly as he moved.

Suddenly the houses opened out, closed in, and folded him in smells and light and warmth. People in wet clothes loomed, talking in the street, so that he had to crowd narrowly between them and the walls, muttering apologies; but he might have been a mouse creeping frozen past them, for all the notice they took.

I'm here, I'm here, he thought; all the way from Stonehenge to London. London! . . . The windows were steaming yellow squares, he saw rooms inside, a woman with a skillet, two men with long clay pipes, long black hair on their silk shoulders, silver and blue brocade, scabbards and sawdust, he walked on, beggars' eyes beside him at the windows, a troop of soldiers clattering on the cobbles, and he pressed back into a doorway, the sleet turned to rain here and poured down from the leaded gutters, in the flaring lights he saw designs and crests on the square drainheads, the roofs pitched steeply up into the dark, a girl in a white collar looking down from the shelter of her casement, a great palace of a house down a street, women crying in a singsong chant that he could not translate, wide baskets sheltered in their cloaks, and then a wife came out of a house, and they lifted the cloaks, to show her what they had, it was fish and meat, live chickens trussed, wet sparkling heads, one orange eye imprisoned, fiercely glaring, bigger circles of orange fire round the light on the corner, the feet of the people tramping, coming together, parting under the houses, the walls leaned in over him, they were timbered and old, the city smelled of ordure, of the baking fish and the burning pine, of men's sweat and women's lavender pressed last summer, closet lavender in their wet clothes, and the clean silver fish glittering in the orange tunnels of the city at night.

He saw a man peering in at a window and said, "Sir, can you tell me—?"

The man moved on.

"Mistress, do you—?"

The woman glanced warily at him and crossed the street.

"Maiden, will you—?"

The girl laughed and did not stop her hurrying. He caught her arm and shouted, "God's blood, where is Chain Street?"

She said, "Well! Here's a brave little country cockerel! Let go, or I'll call my friend, do you hear?" She lifted her other arm and smacked Jason across the cheek.

He muttered, "I'm sorry, but please tell me where Chain Street is."

She looked at him curiously and said, "Up there, pretty boy. A furlong and a half. Whose house in Chain Street?"

Jason hesitated. But he had to ask the way sometime. He said, "I seek Master Dick Lanthard."

She said, "I've never heard of him."

Jason said, "I think he's called Dick o' the Ruff."

The girl started. "Dick o' the Ruff! Master Lanthard—is *that* his name? Well, who'd have thought?"

Jason said, "Please, mistress—I'm cold. Can you tell me how to recognize the house?"

She said, "Yes. It has a blue door and leans out more over the street than the others near it. It's on the left. But what—?"

"Th-thank you, thank you," Jason stammered, his teeth rattling, and ran down the street.

Soon he came to the house with the blue door. He hammered on the knocker and stood waiting. The sleet blew straight into the door-way, and for a long time no one came. He knocked again.

The door opened sharply. An old woman with a billowing skirt, a clean white collar, and a sharp blue eye said, "What do you want, you?"

Jason said, "Master Lanthard—Dick o' the Ruff, mistress—does he live here?"

"You want to see him?"

"Yes, please, please."

"He's not in." She slammed the door. Jason beat on it and shouted, "But mistress, I have a letter—from Master Fowler, host of the Caver-sham Tavern, near Reading."

The door opened again, and the woman popped out. She said, "Come in. Here." She led up two narrow flights of stairs, knocked on a door, and called, "Emily, there's a man here who says he has a letter for Dick. You talk to him. I've got other things to do." She stumped off down the stairs.

From inside the room a woman's voice called, "Come in." Jason opened the door and stopped dead, the water from his clothes drip-ping off him in a steady small tattoo. A girl with a mass of brilliantly golden hair falling down her back was sitting at a table near the curtained window, wearing only a silk shift. Her pink skin glowed through the material and her strongly muscled legs stuck out boldly underneath; her feet were stuffed into bright satin shoes.

The girl turned to examine him. She had round, dark blue eyes and a broad forehead and painted cheeks. She said, "Well, you look like a drowned rat, you do."

Jason frowned in his effort to understand her. This London accent came very strange to his ear. She said, "What's the matter? Sit down. No, don't! You're soaked. 'Steeth, shut the door; that draft's as cold as charity. What's this about a letter?"

Jason said, "It's addressed to Master Lan—Dick o' the Ruff." He be-gan to shiver uncontrollably, and his hand shook so violently that he could hardly get the letter out of his sack to show it to her. He felt that her eyes were on him, and when he looked up, the letter at last in his hand, she was staring at him with open curiosity. She took the letter and held it in her hand but did not open it. She said, "What's your line, my bully?"

Jason stuttered, "I d-don't unders-stand. I c-c-come f-from W-w-wiltshire."

The girl sprang up. " 'Steeth, I can't abide this—and Christmas too! You're giving me the cold just to listen to you. Here, get those clothes off. Put this on." She rummaged in a closet and threw him a red-lined woman's cloak. "Take the blankets off the bed, wrap up, sit down. Go on! Don't tell me you've never undressed in front of a woman before, even if you do come from Wiltshire. But no tricks, mind!" Her voice hardened and grew shrill. "You try any tricks, and I'll give you more than you bargained for."

Jason turned his back and began to undress. This woman Emily was a funny one. In fact, nothing here was quite as he had expected. He wished Dick o' the Ruff would come soon.

The girl stepped negligently past him, got out a bottle of sack, and poured a big glass for him and another for herself. When he was sitting, warmly wrapped, on her bed she said, "What *are* you doing here? How did you meet the Fowlers? Why did they give you a letter?"

Jason gulped down the sack, but it might have been water for all its effect on him. He said, "I am going to Coromandel, mistress."

The fair-haired girl faced him fully, her mouth pulled down in astonishment. She said, "Where in damnation is that? Here, I'd better read this letter."

Jason thought enviously: So she can read. Perhaps that's because she's a Londoner. The room smelled of burned hair, and there was a small pair of tongs heating in a little charcoal fire beside her. Her black velvet stomacher lay on the bed beside him, its red lacing unloosed. There were all kinds of pots on her table, and a beautiful red skirt, with white patterns of lilies on it, hanging from a nail on the wall. He put out his hand to touch it, it was so beautiful, and, without looking, she reached out and rapped his knuckles with the hot tongs. "Keep your hands to yourself!"

She looked up suddenly. "I'm sorry, Jason. That's your name? You didn't mean any harm, did you?" She finished reading the letter and put it down on the table.

She said, "Fowler doesn't say anything here about that place—Coromandel."

Jason sat up angrily. He said, "He must. That's a letter asking Dick o' the Ruff to help me get ship to Coromandel." Perhaps the woman couldn't read after all, and was only trying to show off.

She looked at him and said, "Can you really dance? This letter says—"

The door opened, and a man came in with a curt "Hurry up, Emily! The lordlings don't like being kept waiting. By God, who's this toad in the hole?"

Jason got up with difficulty. He said, "I am Jason Savage, sir." He ought to have resented being called a toad, but he didn't want to quarrel with anyone while he was wearing a woman's cloak and nothing else. The man was about his own age and height, beardless, with a long pointed jaw and a long thin nose coming down to meet the jaw, thin cheeks, black eyebrows arching over brown eyes, and a clear, dead skin. He was foppishly dressed, with laces and ribbons hanging from his doublet and the sides of his breeches, but the most noticeable article of his clothing was his ruff. It was enormous, twice the depth of any that Jason had seen before, and three inches wider, and meticulously starched and ironed. It stood out like a crinkled white millstone round his neck. Above it his white face and ringed eyes looked like a corpse's head on a plate. Jason thought: He's vain, he's like a rat in a ruff; he's sharp and cruel, and I wish he'd go away.

Emily said, "This is Dick o' the Ruff, Jason."

Dick examined his fingernails with a show of carelessness and said, "Yes. Perhaps you have heard of me?"

Jason said slowly, "You? You're Dick o' the Ruff?" Of course he must be, with that name and that ruff. But—Jason's heart sank—he didn't like Dick. He watched unhappily while Dick read the letter.

After a moment Dick glanced up and said to the girl, "It might be worth trying, if he's as good as Fowler says. Your last partner was as much use as a stoned jellyfish. Let's see the two of you dance now. I'll keep the time." He began to clap his hands and hum, nasally and off key, a tune that Jason did not know.

Jason said, "I don't feel like dancing now, sir. I'm tired and I'd like to go to bed. Tomorrow I'd like to ask you about how to get to Coromandel."

Dick stood away from the wall, where he had been leaning. He put his left hand on his sword hilt and took a slow pace toward Jason. He said, "I tell you to dance, you dance, capon!"

Jason stood up—oh, to hell with this cloak, and the blankets falling off him, and his hands busy holding it all together. He was getting dully, exhaustedly angry. He said, "I do not want to dance, and I won't dance. And don't call me a capon."

Emily hurried between them. She said, "Don't be angry, Jason.

Please dance with me, will you? I'm to be your partner, you know." She smiled at him and put out her hands and pressed his arms.

Jason glowered at Dick and mumbled, "I can't dance without my breeches. Besides, there's not room enough in here."

Emily said, "This is all the room we'll have in the Cockpit. Dick, lend him some of your clothes. Then we'll practice a bit here, Jason, and then we'll all go together to the Cockpit Tavern. You haven't eaten any supper yet, have you?"

"Nothing all day, mistress," he said. He felt her hands trembling slightly on his arms, and thought: God's blood, she's terrified of this swine Dick Lanthard. Poor girl, if I don't dance with her she'll get into trouble. He has some hold over her. She was looking at him beseechingly, and he could smell a sweet perfume from her skin, and the shift was very thin. But why did they want him to *dance?*

She said, "Good. We'll have a great dish of stewed eels, then, with mulled ale, and you'll never pay a penny. And tomorrow Dick and I will have a talk about your visit to Coromandel."

"Jesus' bones, what's all this hogswill about Coromandel?" Dick said. "Where is it? Who owns it? Do they have women there better than mine?"

"Never mind now," Emily said quickly. "Lend Jason some clothes. Well, damn you for a fool, Dick, how can he dance without any breeches?"

"Very well," Dick said thinly, "I'll lend him some clothes for tonight. But he'd better learn to keep a civil tongue in his head while he's talking to Dick o' the Ruff. This way, capon."

*　　*　　*

Jason gaped at all the bottles and barrels they had against the wall in the Cockpit Tavern. He had never seen so many, nor heard such a noise. And the people! You would think they were all so jammed together they could not move, but somehow they did, and there were even tables, some in alcoves and some ranged against the wall, and people unconcernedly eating at them. The Cross Keys used to get as crowded as this sometimes, but in Wiltshire men stayed in one spot, drinking and having the jugs passed to them over the people's heads under the rafters, and the jokers took a swig out of each jug as they handed it along. In Wiltshire men drank where they stood, until they fell down or staggered out to sleep more comfortably in the hedge.

66

He and Emily were sitting at one of the tables. Dick o' the Ruff had disappeared. "Sir William Benson, that is, over there, with the pimples on his face," Emily whispered in his ear. "Lord Openshaw. . . . Mr. Charles Fitzjames. . . . The one with the round hat, he's a poet. He never has any money. He drinks here every night until no one will pay for him any more. Harry Levoller . . ." She knew everybody.

Jason listened half-heartedly. It was interesting enough, learning who all these people were, but now that Dick had left them alone at the table he wanted to ask her about the letter and about the dancing. They had danced together for five or ten minutes up there in the house in Chain Street, and Emily was good. Together they were very good—better, perhaps, than any couple he'd ever seen in his life. Even Dick was impressed, and whistled through his teeth and cried, "This country capon can dance, eh?" And breathlessly Emily answered, "Dance? He could dance a ring around the moon." And she swung out of his grip and swirled onto the bed and flopped back on it, joyfully clapping her hands.

He took advantage of a pause in the flow of her gossip to say, "Emily, what was in that letter? Why do we have to dance?"

She turned slowly. She said, "You don't know at all, do you? You don't know what Fowler's job is?"

Jason thought, and answered, "No. There were some women in his Caversham Tavern that I didn't trust the looks of much." Emily laughed shortly but cut herself off as he went on. "I suppose from what's happened here that he wrote in the letter that he'd seen me dancing there—I drank a lot of sack one night and danced by myself, and after that Master Fowler gave me my supper, free, every night, just to dance. That was strange, wasn't it?"

"Very," Emily said gravely.

"But I can't understand why he didn't say anything about Coromandel in the letter. That's the only reason he wrote it."

"Look, Jason," Emily said carefully, "Couldn't you forget about Coromandel—for a time, anyway? I don't know what it is or where it is, but—I'll tell you something. Here, people pay to see good dancers. You're the best dancer in London. You can make a lot of money, just dancing. You can make more with the old women afterward."

"How?" Jason said. "I don't understand."

"'Steeth!" she snapped. "You're just a lump of Wiltshire dung, aren't you? And what do you think I am? Shhh, here's Humphrey."

67

A youngish man with a purple doublet, a small ruff, and a small head, had pushed through the crowd and now reached their table. Emily stood up and made a deep, half-mocking curtsy. She said, "My Lord Nailsworth."

The man had small pink eyes, reddish hair and beard, and a freckled skin. He glanced coldly at Jason and said, "Who's this fellow?"

Emily said, "My brother Jason, my lord. He has just returned from a successful voyage to America. His vessel lies at Falmouth now."

"I haven't—" Jason began.

Emily shot him a hard look and went on a little louder, "His backers will receive four hundred per cent return on every guinea they lent him."

Lord Nailsworth's little eyes sharpened, and he said, much more graciously, "A sea captain, eh? Well, we must have a talk one day."

Jason glared at Emily, who met his eyes unwinkingly. He looked away from her as Lord Nailsworth touched her on the arm and began to mutter into her ear.

The woman at the next table was staring at him with undisguised interest. He noticed that she was plump, dark, over forty, and alone—which was strange. She had four rings on her left hand, and a big purse chained to her girdle. She couldn't have helped hearing what Emily said just now. He cursed Emily and looked away from the strange woman.

Dick o' the Ruff elbowed his way to them and sat down. Emily and Lord Nailsworth were giggling and drinking and whispering in each other's ears. Jason sat brooding, as far away from the others as he could get. The woman at the next table was watching and listening.

What *did* he think Emily was? She might be a strumpet, only he didn't know what a strumpet would look like. Old Voy used to talk about them sometimes, but about what they did, not what they looked like. Could a strumpet dance? He wanted to like Emily, but he didn't understand her.

A man stuck his head through a far door and shouted above the heads of the crowd, "Four to one on Lord Openshaw's white."

"Taken, taken!" several voices cried.

Dick o' the Ruff called, "Are they in the ring yet?"

"Aye, just starting, Dick." The man's head disappeared.

"Come along." Dick beckoned Jason.

Jason said, "No, thank you." He did not want to leave Emily alone with Lord Nailsworth.

But Emily frowned at him, and Dick took his arm so firmly as to lift him out of his seat. He followed Dick through the far door and found himself in a low room where the walls were lined with benches. A few men were sitting on the benches, and others were standing behind them. The two fighting cocks were sparring for position. The lamp smoked under the rafters, a haze of tobacco filled the air, and the floor was covered with sand and spilled wine.

The cocks leaped into the air, and the long steel spurs glittered on their heels. Jason stood back against the wall. Voices shouted bets in his ear, hands threw money across him. This was London. He saw long, lean faces, tight at the spilling blood; shaved and powdered faces, slavering with greed; stubbly beggars' faces, wet with sweat; murderers' faces, smiling. He saw greased hair tumbling over white lace collars as the heads jerked up in the frenzy of watching. He heard Dick o' the Ruff shouting odds as the cocks fought, and saw him catching money with one hand and throwing it away with the other.

The fight ended. Lord Openshaw stepped into the ring and kicked his bird disgustedly. "Twenty guineas you've lost me, you—!" The cock lay in the stained sand, kicking feebly, its blood matting the spotted white feathers at its throat. Lord Openshaw wrung its neck, flung it down, and stalked away. A woman at the ringside stooped, stuffed it under her skirt, and winked at her companion.

"Lost six guineas," Dick said. "We'll make it back in the next match. Pen Grave's bird can't lose. Hey, where are you going?"

"I'd rather listen to the music," Jason said. He had heard a fiddle and a drum strike up in the middle of the cockfight, and now their music came quite clear to him at the side of the cockpit.

"Well, leave Emily alone, d'you hear?" Dick said coldly. "She's got her teeth into ten thousand a year."

Jason shouldered through the press and back into the front room. Emily was still at the table with Lord Nailsworth. The plump woman was still there, gazing and listening, her rings flashing. Jason leaned against the wall close to the fiddler.

Emily's face was averted from his as she whispered to the lord. Did the lord love her? It seemed impossible that people could do anything as ordinary as "love" each other in this place. This was a world turned upside down. How could Emily stand being with that lord? He was worse than Ahab Stiles. But Molly was going to marry Ahab. That made Molly a strumpet. Ah, now he knew what a strumpet looked like. Like your sister.

He laughed shortly, and the owner of the tavern brought him a drink. The man said, "Any time you want anything, master, just say the word. Any friend of Dick's a friend of mine." He winked. Jason took the big mug of mulled and spiced ale in his hands and sipped it.

He found that his feet were tapping to the fiddler's time. It would make a good dance.

A drunken woman jumped off a man's lap and staggered about the sanded floor. She waved her arms, her hair falling over her eyes in a brown mass like seaweed, and sang in a faulty voice, " 'Twas he and me and never thee, that went to the lonely haymow, haymow, haymow. 'Twas he and me and—' I can't remember any more." She held the sides of her skirt and swayed violently.

The tune changed to "Meadowsweet," and from her table Emily looked up quickly. Jason shouted eagerly to the fiddler, "You know that?"

"It sounds like it," the little old fiddler said sarcastically, bowing away.

"You're from Shrewford Pennel?"

"Never heard of it."

The drunken woman sat down on the floor. A man came up, bent over, and hauled her to her feet. Holding on to him, she bellowed angrily at the fiddler, "Why don't you play a tune a girl can dance to, you whoreson pimp?"

The fiddler snapped, "Go home and trull in Salop, and you'll be a queen. It is a dancing tune. This gentleman knows it."

"Oh, *he* knows it, does he?" The woman came and leaned against Jason and then fell away, holding on to the front of his silk coat.

Dick o' the Ruff stuck his head round the far door and said, "Mind that coat, you. She's going to be sick."

The woman shouted, "If he knows it, why don't he dance it? Little pretty boy!" She stroked his cheek.

Jason said suddenly, "I'll dance it." A moment of silence had passed across the room as he spoke, and everyone heard him. He flushed furiously and turned to escape, but a lazy voice said, "Oh no, you dance for us now."

Emily was at his side. She smiled sweetly at the speaker and said, "*We'll dance*, Master Levoller, my brother and I together. But our purse is empty." Aside she muttered to Jason, "And I thought you were an innocent farmer's boy."

Jason said, "What do you mean?"

Levoller tossed a golden guinea to the floor at their feet and said, "More if it is good."

Emily said, "Mean? Why, you donkey, if you dance in public *before* Dick makes the arrangements, and the people like you, you can force Dick to give you better terms. But you're not going to steal a march on *me* that way. Come on!" She held out her hands.

Jason took them and said earnestly, "Emily, I wasn't thinking of—"

She interrupted harshly. "Oh, hold your tongue. Dance!"

They pointed their toes. The fiddler said, "One, and two, and—" They began to dance.

It is the spiced ale, he thought—but I am not drunk. It is all the things that I have seen today, or the floating-away feeling of being so tired. But I was only tired when I began, not now. It is the warmth inside here and the blowing sleet outside. I can see faces pressed to the windows as I turn. . . . He knew he was dancing better than he had ever danced. His body swung, and his feet flew. He saw Emily's face shining before him; their fingers met, locked, parted; she swung away. She lifted the sides of her skirt, and her bare calves flashed. In the tavern they had stopped talking, stopped drinking, eating, breathing. Emily's eyes flashed, and her white teeth flashed. She laughed defiantly and met his eyes. "See!" he heard her say. "This is how I live." They left the known dance behind and made up new ones as they went along, never missing, never failing. In his own leaps his head flew along under the black beams. Emily twirled and swirled after him, arms out, skirts flying.

Now they'd end, this great leap and turn—and then together with her, fingers locked, eyes locked, and the sweat running down their faces, into the curve of Emily's breasts, into his eyes, blinding him.

They stood still, facing each other.

A moment of silence; then the applause exploded like a cannon. Jason stepped a pace back from the sudden fierceness of it. It was like anger, like a mountain falling on them, like a sword piercing in through clothes and skin to the pit of the stomach. Levoller's face was pale, and his mouth wide open and bellowing meaningless words. They were all shouting, clapping, throwing clothes and money and hats with both hands, the golden rain of guineas bursting like hail on the stone floor. Jason stood with his chest heaving and his eyes wide. The gold was right; it made a good carpet for their dance; it was good and musical to walk upon. Dick o' the Ruff was sweeping it up quickly into a small sack.

71

Lord Nailsworth was hugging Emily and shaking Jason's hand and gabbling, "Never seen such dancing. Wonderful!" Levoller was shouting in his ear, "More!" Jason shook his head. Dick o' the Ruff said, "Perhaps tomorrow, Master Levoller, if there is enough support."

Levoller recovered some of his posed lassitude. He said, "Support? By'r Lady, I'll empty Whitehall and bring them here."

Lord Nailsworth stood up, clutching Emily's arm. She said to Jason, "Good night. We did that well, didn't we?" She wrapped her cloak around her and went out on Nailsworth's arm. Jason found himself alone in the small clear space by the musicians. He had left his hat —Dick's hat—on the table where they had eaten the stewed eels. He went over to get it.

The woman at the next table was still there, still alone. As he took his hat she said, "Pray let me tell you that you and your sister dance like angels, sir. I have always liked to dance, but my husbands did not approve. I suppose you practice on board your ship?" She had a round weatherbeaten face and round blue eyes set wide apart, and a snub nose and wide mouth.

Jason said, "What ship, mistress?"

"Now don't try to tease me, sir, just because I'm a lonely widow. I know you are a rich sea captain."

Jason's head still whirled with the dance and the applause and the golden money. He liked the woman's face because it reminded him of Mother Bolling's in Shrewford, but he could not think what she was talking about. He said, "I'm not rich, mistress. I wish I was, but I haven't got but a few pennies except what people have just given us for the dancing."

She looked at him closely, and his manner seemed to force belief on her; and at the same moment Jason remembered the foolish lie with which Emily had tried to impress Lord Nailsworth. His shoulders slumped, and the gaiety went out of him. He said aloud, "The damned trull!"

The woman said, "You mean Emily? Well, I never! But you ought not to speak of your sister like that." She shook her head reproachfully and said, "And all that about the ship was not true? Well, I never!" She looked at him with an admiration that was not now mixed with her previous archness, and said, "Won't you sit down, sir, and allow me to toast your health in a bottle of sack? My name is Dempster, Mabel Dempster."

Jason said, "Thank you, Mistress Dempster, but I am very tired. I must be going."

She fumbled in her purse and pulled out two guineas and slipped them into his hand. She said, "There. I didn't give any before because I thought it was not right to throw money at a sea captain. But—"

Jason looked at the gold sprinkling his palm. Then he gave it back to her and said, "I don't want any money. Please give it to someone else. Give it to the musicians."

He went out, leaving Mabel Dempster staring in amazement after him. He ran down the street among the clanging Christmas bells.

✻   ✻   ✻

The bells were silent, and Jason swam out of sleep to the sound of voices. He found he was curled up on the hard floor under the window, with a couple of blankets over him, and there was a harder white light that hurt his eyes, shining down on him from the ceiling. Emily and Dick o' the Ruff were talking, Emily in her bed, Dick sitting on the edge.

Jason got up, yawned, and shook his heavy head. The snow lay thick in the street and on the window ledges, and the sun shone, and people moved about soundlessly in the untainted whiteness.

"You're awake at last, are you?" Dick said. "I want to talk to you."

Jason said, "Can I have a drink of water?"

Emily showed him the jug on the table. He broke the thin ice on the water and drank. The water seared his throat as the hard light had seared his eyes. His tongue felt sticky, and his feet weighed a hundred pounds apiece.

Dick said, "Why did you run away? We could have got another ten guineas if you'd come round the tables with me later."

"I went just after Emily went," Jason said sullenly.

Emily looked rosy and pretty and innocent in the big bed, sitting up with a blanket round her, and over that her cloak. Jason had been asleep in Dick o' the Ruff's bed when she came in late during the night. No one had showed him any other place he could sleep, so he'd climbed angrily in there, muttering, "Let the bastard pull me out and see what happens." But it was Emily who came and whispered for him to get out or Dick would kill him. He'd cursed her for a whore; she'd dragged him out, and down to her room. The sleet had already turned to snow by then. There was snow on her

73

cloak and on her big, sweeping hat. She'd told him to sleep in the corner, and no tricks. He'd shouted that he wouldn't touch her with a dung fork. Someone had knocked angrily on the ceiling below. Then she'd tried to kiss him, and told him she did not love Lord Nailsworth or any of the men, that this was only a steppingstone to something better. She was making a lady out of herself. Couldn't she have dreams too? What in damnation was this Coromandel but a dream? Only, a woman couldn't go out seeking Coromandel. He had refused to be softened and refused to sleep in the bed with her, though she was tearful and drunk; and had lain down on the floor.

Now Emily said, "Dick's arranged about our dancing."

Dick said, "Yes. I talked with Jemmy that owns the Cockpit, till four this morning. You and Emily will dance there twice a night every night except Wednesday and Thursday. Jemmy's going to put out handbills round the town. He'll put up his prices for wine and food, and he'll pay the fiddler and the drummer."

"But he'll make more out of the cocks, too, won't he?" Emily said keenly.

Dick said, "Yes, that's why I'm only going to give him ten per cent of what we make, and nothing to the musicians. You two take half the rest between you, and I keep the other half."

"Half!" Emily said indignantly. "You only take a third of what I get now."

Dick said, "You're just a stupid whore, Emily. This is different. I'll have to have more men. You don't think the Rakes and the Frogs and John Ames's crew are going to stand by idle, do you? I'll have to find another three bullies and keep them in the Cockpit every night. But I'll give you a guinea out of every six that we take from the drunks—between you, that is. Only I've agreed with Jemmy that we won't rob or kill anyone in the tavern or as far as the end of the street either way. And, you"—he turned to Jason—"don't forget to hand over to me a third of anything *you* get privately, same as Emily does. I pay the rent here."

Jason said, "Only women are whores." He looked bitterly at Emily.

Dick laughed shortly and said, "Don't play baby to me. I saw you with Old Popeyes last night. You'll get a hundred out of her unless you're a fool."

Jason said, "Popeyes? Do you mean Mistress Dempster? I wouldn't take any of her money. I thought she looked kind and lonely."

Dick said, "Jesus' bones, I believe he's real. Listen, you do what

74

she wants. Blow the light out, and you'll find she's no worse than a sheep. Swyve her upright, sideways, and endways, and make it ten guineas a crack. She's rich as an earl, married two city merchants who both died. Ever since, she's been spending her time in the taverns. She's picked up dancers and bearleaders and fiddlers and bullies and cockhandlers and poets. I know fifty men who've dug into that old bag of tripes."

"She's lonely," Jason said furiously.

"Christ and the Virgin, what do I care if she's lonely? Do what you're told."

"I won't!" Jason said. "And I'm not going to dance for money."

Dick o' the Ruff got up slowly. He drew back his lips, and his nose came down to meet his jaw. He said, "You are. I say so."

Jason said, "I don't like it, and all the other things you've been talking about. Why, you're no better than a pimp and a robber and a—"

There was a dagger at his throat, the blade glittering like the hard snow-light on the ceiling. Dick said, "How would you like your nose cut off?"

Emily shouted, "Stand still, Jason! He means it. Dick, please go away and let me talk to him."

For a moment longer Jason looked into Dick's hard eyes. He was a rat, and Jason hated him but was afraid to move. Dick would kill him and feel no worms of death, no pity, no shame. Dick put the knife away and swaggered out, saying, "When Dick o' the Ruff speaks, don't argue." Jason glared at the huge white ruff as it disappeared. A rat—vain, ferocious, criminal, but terrifying.

Emily swung her legs out of the bed, put up her hands, and caught Jason's. She said, "Jason, please do what he wants. For one thing, he will really kill you if you don't. And don't you see that this is the only way I can get away, get up from what I am doing now? If people will pay to see us dance, why don't we let them? One day I'll grow old and get like the women you see by the river in the mornings, who hang about the taverns for scraps of food because not even a drunken sailor will pay a penny to lift their skirts. But this way we can make a lot of money quickly. You can go to Coromandel. I can buy a farm and have chickens and pigs and a riding horse."

"After a few weeks like this I might not want to go to Coromandel," Jason said slowly, remembering the terrifying, sick ecstasy of the applause. "And you'll never go to a farm."

She was silent. Jason insisted, "Would you?" There were tears in the corners of her eyes, and he felt the flutterings of love in his stomach. She needed looking after, protecting from Dick and Lord Nailsworth and all the rest of them.

She muttered, "Perhaps not. But what is there better than this? You meet anybody and everybody here. Whatever you want to dream about, it's here, only better. I saw a play at the theater—Will Shakespeare's *A Winter's Tale*—and afterward I felt bigger and better than I am. Perhaps I'll be able to buy a farm one day."

Jason said, "Didn't you say that one of those men in the Cockpit was an India merchant?"

She said, "Yes. Nathan Wigmore—five-handed old bullfrog that lives in Leadenhall Street. But don't go to Coromandel yet, Jason. Stay here and dance with me. It's the only way you'll get the money."

Jason thought of the dancing, and of Emily. Perhaps he would really fall in love with her—and then what would happen to them? He would like to see *A Winter's Tale*. What kind of tale was it, and why did it make Emily feel bigger?

He said, "I'll stay and dance with you for a few weeks, Emily." She jumped up and flung her arms tightly round him. "But I won't do anything of the other. I won't take a penny from Mistress Dempster or any woman."

"Oh, don't be a silly," Emily said. "You wait till some of the court ladies come after you. But don't you dare fall in love with any of them. Promise!"

Jason said, "I don't like to see you going with Lord Nailsworth. I don't like him. And why did you go up to Dick's bedroom last night when you came in?"

She jerked away from him, her heavy golden hair flying out above her shoulders, and snapped, "Oh, go away. Mind your own business. I don't care who you fall in love with."

※　　　※　　　※

He let go of Emily's hands and stood with his own right hand over his heart, bowing slightly, smiling lightly at the applause. After two weeks he had come to listen closely to the texture of it. Usually, like tonight, it was deafening and close-knit. Three evenings ago it had been as loud but not so forceful, and there were holes of silence and half-hearted cheers among it. That night he had turned quickly on his heel and left Emily standing alone. It had been her fault. She danced well, but sometimes she had other things on her mind—how she looked, whether Lord Nailsworth and the rest of the Whitehall crowd were in their places, whether Levoller had brought the Lord Chamberlain. They might yell at her legs and gape at the straining breasts under her dress, but *he* was the dancer of the two of them. They must practice a new step he had worked out.

He left her and walked by habit to the far corner and sat down at a small table there. Mistress Dempster said eagerly, "You were better than ever, Jason. There's cold roast beef tonight. Will that be enough? Do you like cold roast beef?"

Jason said, "Very much." He smiled at her and picked up a slice of beef and ate it. He ate only lightly before the first dancing nowadays, and then took another light meal after the second dancing. He did not want to be with Dick o' the Ruff more than he had to; Emily still went out with Lord Nailsworth as soon as the dancing was finished, ignoring the cold look he fixed on them; and Mabel Dempster liked to give him food and drink. She was a nice woman, and comfortable to be with. She was sitting back now and watching him eat, her hands folded in her wide lap.

She had told him a lot about herself in these two weeks. As Dick said, she had been widowed twice. The second time she had suddenly decided to do what she really wanted to do instead of what her relatives and her husbands' relatives thought she ought to do. She liked taverns, music, food, and drink. She liked being with men —but she did not talk about them much and had never, so far, made any effort to seduce him. She had tried to give him a jeweled dagger, which he had refused. He let her pay for these late suppers, though.

He finished the beef and sat back, stretching luxuriously against the wall. She said suddenly, "I have never met anyone like you, Jason."

Jason said, "You've been lucky." God's blood, he hated himself sometimes.

She said earnestly, "No, no, I've been terribly unlucky. You don't seem to want to order me about, and you don't want to take my money. All the men I've known have wanted one thing or the other. I loved them all, but they never loved me. There must be something wrong with me—but I don't feel wrong inside." She dabbed her eyes, and Jason made a sympathetic noise.

Her hand crept across the table and covered his. She said, "I'm forty-four."

77

Jason said, "I've never thought of it." That was not quite true, because when he first saw her he had wondered why a woman past her youth should sit alone in the Cockpit Tavern. But since then he had not thought of her age.

She said, "How old are you?"

He said, "Twenty."

Her hand closed convulsively over his. He thought she had drunk too much mulled wine—perhaps to bring herself to the point of saying this that he was hearing—"I love you, Jason. The others wanted my money, and you'll laugh at me, but I must tell you I love you." Her big mouth quivered, and her big blue eyes looked fearfully into his.

He turned quickly, feeling torn and affectionate inside at her fear that he would laugh at her. He said, "I think you're the kindest person in the world."

She sat for a while, looking down at the table; then she said heavily, "I'm not a young girl any more. I must go home."

Jason said, "I'll come with you."

She looked up at him with a sudden, almost fearful movement. She said, "Do you want to—really?"

He said, "Of course. Where did you leave your cloak?"

She shivered a little as he wrapped the cloak round her, and then they went out together. He walked slowly along the street in the pitch-dark at her side. He knew where she lived, but he had never been to the house. She held his hand tightly, and neither spoke. She stopped at last, whispered, "This is my house. The servants sleep at the top. They won't come down." She opened the door with a big key from her purse, and he saw a long, low room, lit by a night light on a table, and silver glowing on a shelf against the far wall. The light gleamed dimly in her face.

Jason said, "Well, you're home safe now. Good night."

She stood on the step of her house, staring at him, her mouth working. Suddenly she dropped the key and put her arms round his neck and her wet face into his shoulder. He heard her mumbling, "Jason, Jason," and patted her shoulders and did not know whether to go now, or stay.

She recovered herself in a moment and took his hand. She said, laughing through the end of tears, "Come in for a moment, Jason, and let me show you my house. I'm very proud of it."

Jason said, "Thank you. I'd like to." And he went with her into the house. Now she was hugging his arm so tightly that he had to keep close beside her.

She said, "There!" She lit an oil lamp, and then the room seemed smaller again, and the two of them were in it, and there was a clean stone floor and an arras of light green cloth to one side.

He saw four books lying alone, one above another, on their sides, among the silver on the shelf, and went toward them.

Mabel said, "That's a set of plate the Fishmongers' Company gave my first husband. He was quite an old man."

Jason picked up the first book and opened it. The printing did not cover all of each page, but ended irregularly on the right—some lines short, some long. He wanted to ask what book it was but felt ashamed because he could not read, so said negligently, "This is supposed to be good, isn't it?"

Mabel said, "Oh yes. That is one of Will Shakespeare's plays. My second husband bought it. All the books here are his."

Jason said, "Shakespeare? Is it *A Winter's Tale?*"

Mabel said, "Oh yes. It's beautiful. I've read it a score of times. So sad. Would you like a glass of canary wine, dear?"

Jason said, "No, thank you. Please read to me a little out of *A Winter's Tale*. I like your voice." He did like to hear her speaking. Her voice was pleasant and comfortable, like the rest of her.

She said, "No, Jason, you read to me. I'll get the wine."

"I don't want any wine, please, Mabel. I've had enough." He pushed the book into her hands and smiled at her.

Slowly she went scarlet and at last muttered, "Jason, I—I've always wanted to read, but I can't."

His jaw dropped. He said, "Nor can I!"

They looked at each other for a moment. Jason thought he could never have seen her properly before. She was a handsome woman with fine eyes and thick brown hair. The house smelled clean but lived-in.

He said, "I am a farmer's son. I had no time for schooling."

She said, "My father would not have me taught, because I was a girl. Then I asked both my husbands, and they forbade me. They said, 'What does a woman want with reading?' And when I was free there seemed so many other things I wanted to do."

"Do you really want to learn to read?" Jason asked. They had sat down together on the padded seat of a high-backed bench in front of the empty fireplace. They were holding hands.

79

"Oh yes!" she said. "More than anything! Why, if you can read you can travel without ever leaving your chair. You are as wise as the wisest man who writes the books."

Jason said, "And you have a thousand eyes and a thousand ears. You're everywhere. You're all the people you want to be but aren't. If I could read, perhaps I would not want to go to Coromandel." He said it almost from force of habit. He had not thought of Coromandel for over a week now. The dancing was so important, the applause so fiery in his veins.

She said, "Coromandel? Where's that? There's no need to leave home if you can read, that's what I think. I don't want to go anywhere. I've got a big house here, and all the servants I need. I eat what I like and drink what I like. *Jason*, I'll get a clerk to teach us to read!"

Jason said, "Are there such people?"

"Plenty," she said. "We could have a lesson every morning, at noon, before dinner, and another in the afternoon. The clerk can have dinner with us."

Jason turned and took her in his arms. He kissed her cheek and said, "I can't thank you enough, Mabel. I'm too excited. Can we begin tomorrow?"

She said, "You must not try to thank me. Oh, Jason, I thought you wanted my money, but you don't. Then I thought just now that you only wanted to lie in the bed with me—that was better, because you could have any girl you wanted, couldn't you? But still it wasn't right. Now I really believe you like me. I feel as if I were sixteen again —I feel so foolish, I love you so much. Can you really forget I'm so old?"

Jason thought, and answered, "Yes. But—" Now he ought to tell her that he was not in love with her. This strangely comfortable feeling he had for her couldn't be love. It wasn't at all like what Jane Pennel had done to him. It was more like Mary Bowcher—and it had turned out that he did not love Mary. He might be in love with Emily—only she was a strumpet.

So he ought to tell her, because she was lonely. But, looking into her eyes now, he saw that she was happy. She was not like Mary, after all. She wanted to learn to read. She looked like a merchant's plump and sedate hen, but she lived hungrily at the corner of the table where the actors and the dancers and the wild singers fed.

She had dreams, like him, and yet—she was comfortable, and kind, and enfolding.

He said, "But I must go home." He kissed her gently on the lips.

*　　*　　*

Dick and Emily were talking at the far end of Emily's room. Jason leaned out of the low window. It was late January, and there was a hard frost. The ice on the Thames would be thicker today. Yesterday he had been walking along the bank with Mabel, and they'd seen two children drowned while trying to slide on the ice. He had wanted to run out to them, but they just disappeared while Mabel held him, crying that he mustn't go.

He'd felt miserable after that. But all the same London was a good town when you got to know it. He understood better now what Emily had been trying to tell him about how no one needed to leave London. He looked down at himself. His clothes were not yet luxurious, but they were very different from anything he had owned or worn before. He had talked about buying a long silk coat once, but Dick wouldn't let him. Dick said it was all right to dress well—in fact it was necessary, or people would give you the kind of small money they thought should satisfy a beggar—but it did not do to dress too richly, or people would give you nothing. They'd say to themselves, Why, that dancer's got better clothes than I have; and if they were lords or noblemen they'd resent it; and if they were not, they'd still resent it, because perhaps they'd worked a lifetime in a merchant's business and had never been able to afford or dared to wear such clothes.

Jason said, "I had dinner with Thomas Overpride yesterday. He asked me if we had thought of moving to Vauxhall Gardens in the spring."

Dick sneered. "Where would you dance there, my lord?"

Jason said coldly, "Overpride will build a hut there for selling cakes and ale and whatever people want, and he will build a stage with a shelter over it. Two or three times as many people will be able to watch us as can in the tavern, and we would have more room to dance."

"And how are we going to make them pay to see when they can see without paying?" Dick said.

"Overpride will build a wooden fence round the stage, and—"

"Oh, hold your mouth! Run along to your old bag. It won't pay."

81

"It will! After a year or two it will pay twice as well as the Cock-pit!" Jason noticed that Emily was looking at him with a curious, almost scornful, smile.

She said now, "Mabel Popeyes doesn't care where you dance, does she, as long as she can watch you? Have you told her I'm not your sister?"

Jason said shortly, "Yes. This has nothing to do with her."

Actually Mabel had said that of course he must go on with his dancing. He liked to dance, and she was happy only in helping him do what he liked. Emily was jealous, that was the trouble. What right had she to be jealous? Why did she think she could be nice to him and kiss him, and then go off with Lord Nailsworth and expect him to love her just the same?

He and Mabel had never mentioned marriage, but she had made it plain that anything he liked she would like. Would he want to have younger girls as well? She would expect that, as long as he did not leave her or lose his affection for her.

Emily said, "And when is Popeyes going to put the halter on you?"

Jason said nothing. Dick o' the Ruff laughed.

How would a murderer and pimp like Dick understand what was between him and Mabel? Let him laugh his evil head off, but when they decided to get married, they would.

"You!" Emily said. "Twenty, and a dancer! Wandering about with cow eyes after a woman old enough to be your grandmother."

"She's only forty," Jason snapped.

"She's paying for you to learn to read. That's the only reason, isn't it? When you can read, you'll leave her crying, and she'll go back to her fiddlers and tapsters."

Jason slapped her face hard. Dick o' the Ruff drawled, "Popeyes must bake gunpowder into her cakes. They've turned our capon into a hero. You wouldn't like to do that to me, would you?"

"Don't you dare, Jason!" Emily said quickly and caught Jason's arm as he stepped forward. Her cheek was blazing red where he had hit her. Dick began to laugh, a high whinnying cackle, and, still laughing, went out and down the long stairs.

Jason went to the looking glass and examined his face and collar. Let the whole lot of them stew in hell. The power to read, that was what mattered. He had learned a little, but not much so far. He could spell *cat* and *rat*, but the words in Mabel's Shakespeare play

—it had turned out to be *The Tragedy of King Richard II*—were too long. He could remember them better than he could read them. He had made the clerk read some of it aloud:

> *O, who can hold a fire in his hand*
> *By thinking on the frosty Caucasus?*
> *Or cloy the hungry edge of appetite*
> *By bare imagination of a feast?*
> *Or wallow naked in December snow*
> *By thinking on fantastic summer's heat?*

Well, he could. Master Shakespeare must have been thinking of other people, people who could walk past Stonehenge at dawn without a tremor.

"Jason." Emily's voice was low and trembly. He did not answer her. She was a sullen strumpet and nothing more.

"Jason—did you ask the clerk to read the map of Coromandel for you?"

God's blood, he had been a fool to mention the map to Emily. As a matter of fact he had, as a joke, asked the clerk to read some of the words on it. The clerk had peered at the writing and said, "This here is Latin. *Quae visa, vera; quae non, veriora.* That means—" Then Mabel had broken in laughingly, "It's just a silly old map! You know it's not even true, Jason, don't you? You told me about that wonderful old rogue—Voy, you called him." Jason had kept his finger down on the map and asked the clerk, "What does it say here?" The clerk read: "*Ye City of Pearl.* That is most interesting." But Mabel snatched the map away and said, "I won't have you dreaming of these horrible places. Aren't you comfortable here?" It was a very comfortable house, Mabel's; and the cook was good too. *Ye City of Pearl.* You might call London a City of Gold. . . .

Emily said, "Jason, are you really going to Coromandel someday?"

He said, "Yes." He thought: Someday, yes, I'm going.

He thought again, with sudden harshness: You whoreson liar, you're not going anywhere. You're going to eat Mabel's cakes, and they haven't got any gunpowder in them.

Emily said, "I'll never have pigs or chickens or a horse."

He said, "No, you won't."

She said, "I have always pretended to myself that I wanted a farm with pigs and chickens and a horse, but I don't really. I don't dream about them. I can't see myself there in the country with them. Jason —couldn't, can you take me to Coromandel with you?"

Jason started violently. Coromandel again! With Emily! He blurted, "What do you know of Coromandel? You're a whore!"

She leaned back as if he had hit her, and for a moment he thought he was going to have the barbaric satisfaction of seeing her wailing and crying in anguish. But she recovered herself. Her mouth hardened and, with the old tears still streaking her face, she said, "I wouldn't come with you, anyway, you dirty, selfish—pimp!"

Jason began to say, "I'm sorry." He began to go toward her, to tell her he loved her, or could love her; that if she dreamed of Coromandel she was already his lover; but she turned her back and said coldly, "Run along to Popeyes."

❖   ❖   ❖

In Mabel's house the clerk's voice droned on, low, obsequious. Mabel had a lot of money. The cook and the kitchen maids stepped softly in the kitchen and set their pots down gently on the fire. The faint smell of rich food seeped under the door into the room where they were. The winter sun made long patterns on the floor. Jason's new doublet reflected the light from its stiff folds. Mabel's skirt crinkled like cloth of gold. She had given him a Bible and the play of Will Shakespeare. Now he had four. Her voice was low and musical beside him. *"The cat bit the rat."*

Did he like cinnamon cakes? Did he care for turmeric in his stews? The ceiling is low there, with a beam across—mind your head. We venture outside into excitement, but that is not our home. This is our home. We bring back the memories of the dancing and the music to here, like the flowers we pluck by the river's bank to press between the pages of the new books. The flowers are still there in the books many days later, but they are not the same.

"B-o-o-k, l-o-o-k."

Here she had canary wine in bottles. But who made the wine— where, how, under what sun? Perhaps that was all written in books, as the descriptions of danger and voyaging were. But the book didn't smell of gunpowder, nor the bottle smell of the full vats gurgling in the hold of a ship.

"H-a-t. Aitch, ay, tee—*hat. H*—write it, stroke up, stroke down, across."

"Cathy, please light the fire for us. Jason, you look cold. Come and sit this side, dear, closer to the fire. There."

*　　*　　*

Mabel watched him closely but looked away when she thought he might glance up and catch her doing it. He was very young. She remembered being young as though it were this morning; and then a clock struck twelve and it was afternoon, and she was old; but only a minute had passed between morning and afternoon, and if there had been no clock no one would have known.

She loved him. But she'd loved all her men, including her husbands. She had never done anything without love.

Love wasn't enough. Suppose this wild dream he had, of Coromandel, would not die after she had fed him and wined him and made him comfortable? Then he might run away. He might.

But the clock strikes for him too. He is going to learn that you don't have to travel to discover things. She had learned that through not being allowed to travel, but it was hard to teach the lesson to anyone, harder to a young man, hardest of all to teach it to Jason.

Suppose she could find enough wisdom to divert his passion for movement into some other kind of passion? Suppose she could show him how to translate his dreams into poetry or music? By the good Lord who'd blessed her, she'd be happy then.

He thought she didn't know that he was in love with Emily. He was very young. He thought she really didn't mind it when his eyes wandered over the young women in the Cockpit, just because she said she didn't mind. He was very young. She could bear it, though.

The danger was, how much did Emily love him? What was Emily? A dancer and a loose woman, but perhaps, if you were a young man, and could talk to her alone at night, you'd find something else—foolish matched dreams, even love.

For herself—she looked down at the rings on her plump fingers—she had little to fight with, except money and love. They were more use together than young people sometimes realized.

*　　*　　*

It was getting near time for the second dancing. Jason glanced round the crowded room to find Emily. The first dancing had been the best yet. Mabel, beside him at the table, was ordering a roast duck

85

for afterward. Jemmy, the host, leaned attentively over her with a large skewer in his hand. No one ever laughed openly at Mabel, because she had a lot of money. Now, while Jason was with her, people were extra attentive. Jason was the best dancer in London. They were saying it everywhere, even in Whitehall.

He was, too, and he loved dancing, but just now his belly quaked inside as though he were standing on the edge of a steep and crumbly quarry.

Mabel caressed the gold locket hanging on a gold chain about his neck and said, "It suits you." Jason looked down his nose and saw the dull links falling in their twin streams across the red silk of his doublet to join at the head of the heart-shaped locket. There was nothing inside the locket yet, though. Mabel was going to have a little miniature painting of herself done, and put it in.

He saw Emily, and the queasy feeling became stronger. How could he think of going to Coromandel with her? No, he'd done right. He was doing right. He had followed the map Old Voy sold him, and it had led him here. He had saved some money and would save more. He would not even need money when he and Mabel were married, but it would be good to have some of his own. Emily was a dancing partner, nothing more. Dick o' the Ruff insulted him often but would not quarrel with him, because he made too much of Dick's money. As long as he did not wound Dick's fearful vanity, Dick would be there to protect him against ruffians, judges, justices, and aldermen. Mabel loved him. He—loved Mabel (liar!). She was so kind that it was difficult to imagine anything that could make her turn against him.

But—Coromandel!

He nodded at Emily. She let go of Lord Nailsworth's hand and came to him. He took off his new chain and his doublet and left them with Mabel. He said apologetically, "The chain would fly out while I was dancing, and might hurt Emily."

Mabel said, "Of course. You were wonderful in the first dance, Emily."

"Thank you."

They stepped into the small cleared space at the side of the room. The fiddler tuned up, and the tabor man rattled a ruffle. The people shouted and settled in their places and fell silent.

The tabor man called, "Meadowsweet, meadowsweet, one, and two, and away we go."

After a time Emily shot him a look as she turned, and muttered, "A little faster, Jason. You're dragging the tune."

Her warning smile flared into a bright light in his head; the words knocked around his ears like the message of a heavy drum. He shook his head. What was he doing here, with his map forgotten and tucked away in the sack in Dick o' the Ruff's upper room? Why was he dancing the Harvest Ring with tobacco smoke streaming in a thin layer under the rafters and the tabor banging away in his ear in the little room—a drum within a drum within a drum, and the City of Pearl ten thousand miles away? Why did the young men shine in satin, standing on the chairs and benches, their faces rapt as though they were at a hanging? Why did the lord with the ginger beard ogle Emily's legs? Why did Emily paint and scent and puff out her breasts? Because she was a whore. So was he a whore.

"Slower!" Emily said with sharp anger. "You're spoiling it!"

Faster, he danced—faster, faster. The fiddler chased his racing feet, Emily sweated to catch him, but he left them both behind. The watchers blurred and whirled. He knew steps better than any of these—faster, wilder steps. He was always in the center of the whirling blur, his head in smoke, and the blue-white-red-green-brown flying round him—faces, beams, windows, pots, faces; always Emily's face steady before his eyes while the rest raced round. She was the middle of the world. No, for himself he must be the middle; he was, he was. She stayed there only because he held tight to her hands, leaned back, and whirled her round like a stick.

He let go. Emily flew across the cleared space, cannoned into a table, fell over it, lay on her face among the broken glass, spilled ale running down her legs—kicking, showing all her legs and more than her legs, her big, white, woman's cheeks. The men shouted wildly, crazy with laughing and seeing that. Jason walked over and slapped her sharply on her naked buttocks.

She jumped up and grabbed the nearest thing that came to hand. Her deep eyes burned full and fiery. She threw the baked fish at his head and screamed, "I hate you. I'll never dance with you again." She ran off, sobbing.

But Jason stood with his breathing under full control and wiped pieces of mackerel off his face and shirt. Dick had paid for that shirt, and he would be annoyed, but not annoyed enough. No one was angry enough yet, except perhaps Emily. He went and sat down calmly beside Mabel.

She said anxiously, "Did you *mean* to do that, Jason?" She was worried, although she knew what good dancers they were, and although she could not really like Emily much. She was very kind.

"Yes, I meant to do it," Jason said. He thought of calling for a bottle of wine and drinking it all, but he must be sober or they would forgive him, saying, Jason was only drunk, he didn't mean all those things he did.

He put out his hand suddenly and covered Mabel's plump one beside him. The moment had come. He said, "Mabel, dear, I'm going to Coromandel."

Her fingers curled up and held his tight. She said, "With Emily?"

He said, "No. By myself. I'm sorry, Mabel. I must."

She said, "Dick o' the Ruff won't let you go. You're making too much money for him."

Jason said, "I think he will if I can insult him. I must humble him in front of someone else. Then he will be glad that I've gone."

"He might kill you if you did anything like that."

Jason said in a low voice, "I can kill too." He showed her the knife hidden in the top of his breeches. He got up suddenly and looked straight at her. "Good-by."

"Good-by. Oh, Jason!"

He went out, remembering that her eyes were dry and her voice steady. It had looked for a time as though they might be happy together, and he was sorry. But the sun of Coromandel shone too strongly on the crinkled sea, and comfort and good food and kindness were not for him, nor could he lie to her or to himself a moment longer, saying that he loved her.

At this time of night Dick was often down by the river, getting gossip from the wherrymen. About now he usually came back to the tavern to collect the money from the bully who picked it off the floor.

Jason edged back into a deep doorway and hunched his shoulders. It was a bitter night—black frost on earth, and the stars crackling in the sky, and the cobbles ringing like bells to a footstep. A man went hurrying home under the houses opposite, and he glanced at Jason and rested his hand on his sword until he had passed. His breath hung frozen in puffs behind him.

It was warmer in the doorway, from the drowsy house and the banked fires inside—stock in the pot and the servant girl asleep on the rushes, frowsty in her clothes, dreaming of perfumed silk.

He heard sharper footsteps and glanced out cautiously. It would not matter how many men Dick had with him as long as there was at least one. Four or five might be difficult, because they could prevent him from doing what he had to do; but none would be much worse, because then there would be no one to tell the tale, and Dick could pretend it hadn't happened.

Dick and one. Dick and a woman. Dick and Emily. That wasn't good; it ought to have been one of Dick's fawning cronies to see the humiliation. But this was the time, and there could be no waiting.

Jason peered into the street. The refuse was hard-frozen into lumps and sheets. There were thrown-out slops there, and horse dung, and ordure from the houses. It would do. It might not be too hard all the way through.

He heard Dick's nasal "I—I—I" coming closer.

He stepped out and said, "Dick, I want to talk to you."

"Who—? Oh, it's Jason. I want to talk to *you*. Emily came running to tell me that you made a mess of the dancing and insulted her. She says you were drunk. What do you mean by it?"

Emily was looking at him calmly. She was not angry now. He thought she was going to say something, but she only waited, standing a little to one side of them.

Jason turned to Dick. Now he must begin. He said, "Go and hang yourself. I want my money. I'm leaving, and I want my money—all of it. *I* know you've been cheating me."

Emily sighed. Dick looked at him more closely and said, "Why, you're not drunk."

"God's blood, who said I was?" Jason snarled. "I said, I want my money."

Emily said, "There's no need to make him angry, Jason." But Dick was speaking too, in a forced-friendly voice, saying, "Let's talk sensibly, Jason. Emily's angry with you, but you know I haven't been stealing any of your money. It's not worth my while. I want to keep you happy. Tell me what happened." He caught Jason's arm in a gesture of familiarity. His face was twisted into a white smile. "Let's be reasonable," he said.

"Reasonable!" Jason shouted. He stooped, grabbed up a handful of clotted filth, and rammed it in Dick's face. Then he seized Dick's huge ruff in both hands and tore it off, shouting, "You're a fool, a fop. Look at this ruff! Do you think there's a bully in London doesn't wet

himself laughing, seeing you strut by in this? There, there, there!"
He ripped the heavy starched cotton into shreds as he shouted, and
threw the pieces into Dick's face.

Dick seemed to realize at last that it was he, Dick o' the Ruff,
who was being treated like this. As he whipped out his sword Jason
kicked him in the fork. The sword fell singing in the gutter; Dick
fell to his knees and rolled, gasping and gnashing. Jason kicked him
in the side of the jaw, and he lay still. Jason knelt quickly beside
him, appalled at what he had done.

Emily said, "Don't worry. He's done it to plenty of people. Take
the money out of his coat. Go on! You're going to Master Wigmore?
Tell him I sent you. But I told you you didn't need to make Dick
angry. I'd have made him let you go without that."

Jason stood up. "How? It doesn't matter. I've done it now. I've
got to go."

"How? Because I'm his wife," Emily said quietly. "He loves me. But
I would have gone to Coromandel with you. Not now, Jason, not any
longer. It was only a foolish dream you made me dream. I wouldn't
be happy in Coromandel any more than I would with chickens and
pigs and a riding horse, would I? I'm a dancer and a whore. Run
now, Jason."

Jason began to run, forcing his legs to move his heavy feet. This
was a cruel horse that he was riding. He hadn't meant to do anyone
any harm.

He ran up the stairs in Chain Street, swept together his belongings,
ran down, ran eastward. Half an hour later, when he could run no
more, he pounded on the door of a house that showed a light. This
was somewhere near. He shouted up, "Hey, master! Can you tell
me the way to Master Nathan Wigmore's house in Leadenhall
Street?"

The old couple leaned out of the upper window, wrapped in whatever they'd grabbed up, the candle in the woman's hand, the flame
writhing, leaning flat, towering in a new cold wind. They told him
the way. A church clock down the street sang aloud its old, clear
time.

Chapter Three

He strained his eyes into the west and held to the spar with hands and knees. The sails bellied and slatted below him in the irregular wind. He could not be quite sure yet. He stood up against the mast, swinging in circles, swooping from sky to sea, and looked out under his hand. The rising sun climbed slowly out of the trough of the waves astern.

Ahead the sea stretched to a low dark line that might be the land. From horizon to horizon, covering all that sea, the white horses rode westward toward the doubtful coast. The waves swept up from behind the ship, passed her, and surged on in triumph. Squadrons of flying fishes flew by like the arrows of battle and flashed for a moment in the sunlight before striking the sea.

Jason saw the land harden before his eyes as the ship rose on a great wave. He shouted, "Land ho!" and then: "Coromandel!"

From the deck they answered him and went about their business as if nothing special had happened. But it was Coromandel, after so long. It did not tower out of the sea like the great cape of Africa. It did not rise at dusk, star-spangled among racing waves, like Ceylon. It lay low against the water, and there was a small pink cloud over it. It was Coromandel.

Jason glanced down. Master Drayton and the officers had gone below. They would not see land from the deck for an hour or two, even if the wind steadied. He felt in his breeches pocket and brought out his map. It was stained now and torn round the edges, but he could read the short words on it. He spread it out, holding on to nothing except the spar between his legs.

In London he had learned how to read, but on this voyage he had learned other things too. He knew what a palm tree and a camel looked like. He had learned to keep his beliefs and dreams to himself. When he tried to share them men only laughed at him. The dreams seemed smaller and less valuable when he kept them to himself like this, but it was safer.

He had become quite a favorite of Master Drayton, who was one of the ship's owners and, here on board, represented the other owners, of whom Nathan Wigmore was one. Green, the sailing master, and Silvester, the mate, did not like him. But that was because Master Drayton did, and they did not like Drayton.

And now, with his two eyes, he saw Coromandel. The palm trees of the map would line that low coast ahead. The City of Pearl would swim up as the ship swam forward, climbing up over the mysterious horizon, which always rolled away but yet did not slide the waters with it into disaster. But he could see no mountains. On the map some humps were marked about halfway between sea and sea; but he could not see them. He reminded himself that he had no way of knowing how far inland those mountains stood. Meru was much farther, and he did not expect to see that. He folded the map away. He'd have to go and find out.

He glanced round the circle of sea. He clambered hastily to his feet and peered ahead. Half a mile or more away something dark rolled heavily in the swells. It might be a log—but there was a man on it. He shouted down to the deck, "Deck ahoy! Shipwrecked mariner a point off the larboard bow."

The watch on deck repeated the cry. Master Drayton and the officers climbed up from the cabin and walked forward.

Down there by the log something long and pale glistened in the sun. "He's signaling!" Jason cried excitedly. "No, he's paddling!" Now he saw that the man on the log was using a flat stick as a paddle.

On deck Fremantle limped forward to join the officers. Fremantle was old now and did little work about the vessel, but when he was young the Portuguese had captured him off this coast and then put him in prison. He had escaped, only to spend ten years as a slave of the King of Madura. The owners had taken him on more as a guide and interpreter than as a sailor. On the voyage he had taught everybody a few words of Tamil, which he said was the local language.

From the bows Fremantle examined the log and its rider. Then he shouted up, " 'Tis a fisherman of this coast, Jason."

Green called an order to the helmsman, and the *Phoebe* bore down on the strange craft. The crew lined the lee bulwark, and Jason ran out along the spar. Fremantle cupped his hands and shouted in the native tongue. The man on the log stood up and grasped a rope trailing from the *Phoebe's* bow.

Jason stared down in fascination. The man was slim, dark brown, and shining wet with the sea. He wore no clothes at all. His boat was three rough logs, unplaned and uncut, loosely tied together with cord at bow and stern. A forked stick, the tines pointing backward and fastened by the forward cord, made a kind of prow. The sea ran freely in and out between the logs, and lay several inches deep in the middle of the craft, where there was a pile of fish-netting. Four silver fish lay, bellies up, in the water inside the craft, so the man must have caught them. At least they would keep fresh that way.

Jason muttered to himself, "'Tisn't a boat, 'tis no more than a bundle of waterlogged tree roots." And even from the masthead of the *Phoebe* he could only just see the land.

Fremantle shouted, "Manairuppu?" That was the name of the city of Coromandel toward which they were heading.

The fisherman pointed a little north of their present course. Master Drayton dropped an English knife into the well of the little craft, and the fisherman let go his hold on the rope. The wind strengthened, and in a few moments Jason could hardly pick out the craft and the fisherman in the swell of the sea.

His relief scrambled up to him and shouted, "Shipwrecked mariner, eh? Silvester will give you a scolding for that." Jason slid down the rigging to the deck.

As his feet hit the planking Master Drayton beckoned him and said, "I am going ashore as soon as we have anchored off Manairuppu. Master Silvester will accompany me, with Fremantle to interpret. You and Grant will also come, as my escort."

Drayton was a young fellow of the cavalier sort. He took snuff from a gold box, and even in the stiffest wind he wore a wide hat with flowing feathers. Today he was wearing a blue silk coat, and his boots, as always, seemed several sizes too large for him. They hung from his calves in folds and wrinkles, and the huge golden spurs on them clanked against the deck as he turned away.

Jason said, "Aye, aye, sir," and touched his forehead.

This afternoon his feet would tread the sands of Coromandel. He ran below.

*   *   *

But Jason did not go ashore till the following day. The wind beat in on the open roadstead, and a heavy storm blew up, such as had pursued them for the last thousand miles from Africa. For safety they put out to sea again, and at dusk, when they approached the land once more, two men came out in a log boat and explained through

93

Fremantle that such a ship as the *Phoebe* could not cross the bar of the Coromandel river until high tide, and then only in daylight.

So they crossed the bar at ten o'clock of a burning June day in the year of Our Lord 1628, and dropped anchor in the muddy stream of the Coromandel, opposite the sprawling city of Manairuppu, half a mile from the sea.

At once a bigger boat than those Jason had seen earlier paddled out from the shore, loaded down with the weight of the three naked paddlers and three richly clothed fat men. The sun glowed high in the sky; the paddlers' naked shoulders shone with sweat; and Jason's clothes clung to his dripping body.

The boat bumped the side of the *Phoebe*, and the three fat men clambered awkwardly on board. Green, the sailing master, led them to the poop, where Master Drayton awaited them, his left hand resting on the hilt of his sword and his right foot thrust negligently forward.

Jason watched from a distance, among the crew. The fat men wore white skirts that folded in between their legs, and above those they wore long, heavy coats of pink velvet embroidered with gold thread. Strange marks were painted on their foreheads, and two of them carried palm-leaf fans.

A long, slow confabulation began on the poop. Gradually Jason lost interest and turned his attention to the bank of the river.

The ship lay less than a hundred yards out from a kind of rough stone jetty, which appeared to have been recently constructed. The muddy foreshore of the river sloped up to the jumbled houses of the city, except that a square of waste land lay directly behind the jetty. Half a hundred logs lay along the bank above the high-tide mark, and Jason thought they had been dragged up there for firewood until he saw two naked Indians come out of a house, drag together three of the logs, whip cords around them fore and aft, haul the "boat" to the river, and paddle out to sea in it.

The houses were of all sizes and patterns and colors. There were low hovels, such as men used for pigs in England; and whitewashed houses with thatched roofs and children playing in the square doorways; and, in the distance, a tall, flat-sided tower of dark red stone.

But—he nudged Grant beside him—the women! He muttered, "Have a look at that!" The women wore nothing above the waist, but strutted about with their breasts sticking out ahead of them, as proud of their nakedness as the Whitehall ladies of their finery.

"Grant! Savage!" Master Drayton called them, and they ran aft. The sailing master was showing the deputation over the side and using scant ceremony in the process. When Grant and Jason arrived at the poop Master Drayton said angrily, "Are you ready?"

"Aye, aye, sir."

"I'm going ashore now. But not to see the king. We have to see Don Manoel d'Alvarez, the Portugal agent here." He kicked the deck petulantly and turned to glower at the men in the pink velvet coats. "Those fellows say that the king will not see us until we have talked with the Portugals."

"The Dons have a strong hold on this coast," Silvester, the mate, said.

"*I* was told they had not," Drayton snapped. "Well, we shall go and see the Don."

The sailors lowered the shallop into the water, and they were rowed ashore, At noon Jason jumped onto the jetty and rubbed his bare feet against the hot stones. Rows of strong-smelling fish lay drying in the sun there, and a half-naked girl was staring at him with open interest.

Coromandel!

They crossed the waste land and entered the city. The people gathered together and ran along behind them in scores, shouting cheerfully to one another and trying to finger the English clothes. Sometimes one of the men in pink coats, who was acting as a guide, would shout commandingly, and for a moment the people would fall back, only to engulf the party again a minute later. Dust rose thick in the narrow street, and flies buzzed about Jason's head as he walked, and the sudden blare of unseen horns deafened him. He saw a cow eating from a shopkeeper's stall; and then a troop of brown monkeys jabbering on a housetop caught his eye; and then, above and behind, he saw a fat man in a yellow hat peering down at them from the upper balcony of a domed and pillared palace. Jason waved his hand cheerfully in greeting, and the man moved behind a pillar, but his head and his yellow hat still stuck out.

Jason drew a deep breath. What a place! Anything could be true here! Any dream could come true here! He began to laugh aloud and shout back his few words of Tamil to the people hurrying and jabbering beside him. "Food!" he shouted, and, "Pearls. Which way? No. Yes. Woman. Which road? How much?" The people laughed and shouted back.

Then the guide stopped at a wrought-iron gate in a high wall and called out in a loud voice. There was a long wait, and the crowd drifted away. Now the street was almost empty, except for their own party and an old man standing on his head beside the wrought-iron gate. A shady garden lay beyond the gate, and Jason stared at it longingly. At last a black man came running and opened the gate from the inside. The guide gestured slightly, indicating that the Englishmen should enter. One behind another, they passed through into the garden. The servant clanged the gate shut behind them. Jason glanced back and saw the guide waddling away along the street.

Behind the black man they walked up a wide gravel path among orange trees and banks of scarlet flowers, all wilting and heavy in the coppery heat. Now they could see the blue walls of a house beyond the orchard, and Jason thought: This is familiar; this reminds me of something. Then he remembered—this was very like some of the houses he had seen in the two days the ship had spent at Lisbon, in Portugal, on another wide river.

The Englishmen climbed slowly up a flight of shallow steps and passed through open double doors. The servant held back a tall crimson curtain on the right, and they entered a great hall. It was like a church in there, cool and stony, and the air musty with aromatic wood. The floor was of red and white stone tiles. On one side three tall windows pierced the wall; the other walls were bare. A low dais occupied the farther end of this cathedral nave, and a throne of carved black wood stood on the dais, and a man sat on the throne. Drayton's spurs made an abominable clatter, and he began to walk on tiptoe, trying to quiet them.

A coat of arms, painted on a metal shield six feet high, hung over the throne. The man up there had a round face, spectacles, and a short, pointed beard. His clothes and skullcap were of dull crimson, and his ruff was white, deep, and small. A shaven-headed old priest in black robes stood at his right hand. The priest's gold crucifix shone warmly in the light from the windows.

The magnificence and the silence awed Jason, and he was glad his feet were bare. Drayton's spurs still clinked noisily, for it was impossible to quiet them. Suddenly Jason wished he had big boots like that. He would clump them down and let his scabbard strike loudly on the tiles as he walked, to show the silent man on the black throne that he was not afraid of him. John Silvester, the mate, must have felt the same, for he muttered, "'Tis only a blind Portugoose and a black Popish beetle, Master Drayton. Tell him we are Englishmen."

Drayton recovered his poise and strolled on across the stone acres. Near the throne he stopped. The sailors stopped behind him. No one spoke. Behind the spectacles the small brown eyes of the man on the throne darted from one to another of their faces. A crimson ring glittered on the little finger of his right hand, and Jason saw that the hand was shaking.

Master Drayton said, "In my country, Sir Don, it is the manner of a host to make some welcoming remark to those who visit him—'Steeth, I suppose he doesn't understand English."

The man on the throne said, "The servants of His Most Catholic Majesty are under no obligation to be polite to pirates." He spoke good English—slow, but nearly faultless in accent.

"Pirates, you say?" Silvester broke out indignantly. "The *Phoebe* is a ship of the Company of Merchants of London, and—"

"Be calm, master mate," Drayton muttered. The priest had a long jowl and pale, dull eyes. Drayton continued, "Sir Don, we are not pirates but traders. As a matter of courtesy—no more—we have come here to tell you of our plans. We hope you will help us in a work of trade which will bring great good to all Christendom."

Silvester muttered, "Hope he will help us! Blow his teeth in, I say."

The man on the throne said, "Great good to Christendom! But talking will do no harm. Perhaps you will dismiss your sailors so that we may speak freely. They can wait in the garden."

Drayton said, "Very well. Savage, Grant, Fremantle, leave us. We will be some hours. I have a lot to discuss with His Excellency Sir Don—?"

"Dom Manoel d'Alvarez, milord. My chaplain, Padre Felipe. And may I have the honor of . . . ?"

Jason followed the other two sailors out of the room.

*　　*　　*

The heat in the garden was stifling. Old Fremantle lay asleep under an orange tree. Grant sat with his back to the wall, his head nodding, Jason went to the gate and peered through into the street.

The earlier bustle had subsided, and the city was much quieter. The smells were the same—of filth and animals and dead fish and cooking food—but now he could smell the sea too, a salty tang which underlay all the other smells. Occasionally a woman passed and Jason stared surreptitiously at her breasts, but he was becoming used to that now, and almost woke up Grant when a very young girl who had her nakedness decently covered by a bodice hurried by.

And now a man came slowly down the street, and, though he seemed strong and well, he walked with painful slowness and swept the ground in front of him with a long-handled brush as he came.

This was too strange. Jason looked at Fremantle, then at Grant. They were both asleep. God's blood, it wasn't very long since he had decided it was no use trying to share the wonders that he saw and felt.

He climbed over the gate and dropped lightly into the dusty street. The man who was sweeping the road passed carefully by. Jason walked alongside him and tried to find the words to ask him in Tamil why he swept the ground so carefully before putting his feet down on it. But he did not know the words, and the man took no notice of him, so Jason returned to the gate. There was the old man he had noticed when they first came, still standing on his head against the garden wall.

Jason went close, turned his own head upside down, and saw that the old man's skin was wrinkled and that he had no teeth. From this angle the street looked very strange. The old man's eyes flickered, reminding Jason of a cockerel's just before it died.

Jason said, "Why?"

The old man's eyes flickered again, but he did not answer. Jason sighed and walked away down the street, jingling his money in his breeches.

At a stall he tasted a round yellow sweetmeat and grinned at the stall keeper because it was very good, and held out his money, but the stall keeper would not take any. Five or six children had begun to follow him, and he threw them a penny. They grabbed it and ran away down an alley. He strolled on, breathing deeply of the exotically tainted air. Perhaps this place Manairuppu was the City of Pearl of his map. If so he might find pearl houses, a pearl-paved street. . . . The road to Meru began here.

He turned down a shady side street. Soon it ended in an open square by a muddy stream. Several big trees grew in the square, and high in the sky hundreds of brown and white birds, like hawks, wheeled silently above the city. Jason stopped to watch them as they swooped down in twos and threes and swept up refuse from the ground and rose again, fighting in the air over what they had found.

A huge red stone tower filled the side of the square opposite him. It was the one he had seen in the distance from the ship, but then he had seen only its upper part rising above the houses. It was not square, like an English tower, but had two sides much longer than the others, and the sides sloped sharply in as they rose a hundred and more feet into the air so that it looked like a book stood on its edge, the pages a little open. A black doorway with a stone slab atop gaped in the side facing the square, and people went in and out like beetles. But the carvings in the outer stone! He walked forward. The red stone writhed to life as he approached. Not a square foot of stone was uncarved. The tower crawled with men and girls and animals, none ordinary, all vividly alive, all climbing on one another's backs in fretted tiers, to the blue sky and the circling hawks.

Jason walked slowly under the stone slab of the doorway and into darkness. After many paces in the sudden cold, the yellow light strengthened, the black walls fell back, and he stepped out into a sunbathed courtyard.

A wide cloister, supported by squat stone pillars, surrounded the courtyard. On the far side a heavy building, of the same red stone as the tower, rose in tortured shapes to a stone spire and a final golden spike. Yellow and white flowers lay scattered in the dusty sunlight, and a humpbacked white bull sat at ease in the cloisters, leaning against a pillar and chewing cud.

Wondering, and prepared to believe anything amid these marvels, Jason crossed the courtyard. At the far side he crossed the cloister and entered the building with the spire and spike. He was in a wide, dark tunnel, and for a moment he could hardly see. He paused and sniffed the air—he smelled burning wood, and cow dung, and crushed flowers.

Now he could see. He took another pace and stopped dead. Here too the stone walls crawled with moving, living sculpture. He bent to look.

An elephant. Off the coast of Africa, Fremantle had drawn an elephant for him on the deck of the *Phoebe,* and this was one. But this elephant had four trunks. More monkeys. Bulls being led to market for slaughter—no, Fremantle said the people here did not like to eat any kind of meat. And here was a war, with men fighting, and among them a troop of women with breasts as round as watermelons. That was wrong. They ought to know better *here!* He'd never seen a woman like that, and he'd wager no one else had either. And

—God's blood! God's very bones! Here was the act of a man swyving a woman, and another, and another—hundreds of times, over and over.

He walked on, peering in amazement. Men and women, bulls and cows, monkeys, elephants—and the bodies twisted in so many lascivious ways. It was interesting. He would never have believed there were so many ways of— "Why, that's impossible!" he muttered. He knelt to have a closer look.

He heard a sucked-in gasp of breath near him and turned quickly, flushing to his hair. It was a girl; she'd caught him looking at these. He leaped to his feet and swept off his sailor's woolen hat. He said, "I was just looking at the carvings, mistress. I am—"

She was plump and short and shining brown. Her eyes were black and black-rimmed, the lashes picked out most clearly in black. She had three violet spots painted or tattooed on her cheeks, two on the right and one on the left, and in her right nostril was a tiny gold ornament with a red stone in the center of it. She wore a skirt of blue and silver that was drawn in between her thighs in the universal fashion here, and showed her dimpled knees. Her breasts were hidden, but poorly, by a short silver jacket with flowered designs on it. Her mouth was deep red, deep-lipped, and small. Her hair was oiled-black, drawn back tightly from her forehead, with a white flower stuck in it above her ear. Heavy silver bangles hung on her wrists; and on her ankles were silver anklets in the likeness of snakes; and her feet were long, slim, and bare. The nails of her toes and fingers were painted glossy black.

Jason stared and stared, and his mouth drooped open, and words failed him. Her face was like a heart; the brown column of her neck slid down under the jacket; she was inhumanly beautiful. He had never seen, never dreamed of, such beauty—and he had dreamed much. She had a flute in her hand. Such riches—gold, rubies, silver! She could be nothing but a princess. This was a palace that he had wandered into. She was a princess, and her divine eyes were flashing angrily at him.

He fell on his knees and said humbly, "Forgive me, Princess. There were no gates. No one stopped me." He had spoken in English. He searched frantically in his memory, but no phrase of Fremantle's Tamil suited.

She came slowly to him, her hips swaying and her navel sliding round and round. She stopped above him and said— But what did she say?

He gazed up at her and said, "Jason Savage, Your Royal Highness. Jason Savage, an English sailor. May I go now?"

She spoke again, and pointed to the darker recesses of the building and cocked her head to one side. A queer, muted music began in there. She pointed to the flute, then to herself, and said, "Devadassi." She held out her hand, palm up. Jason took it reverently and pressed it to his lips. She jerked it free and sprang a pace back from him. She was looking at her hand as though he had fouled it with his lips.

Two men in white skirts, with strings slung across their naked chests, walked slowly forward out of the inner gloom where the music was. The princess had begun to laugh silently.

Jason stammered, "I—I am sorry, Your Royal Highness. I did not mean any harm." He turned and fled, rushing down the dark tunnel, past the coupling carvings, across the cloister, across the courtyard, through the red tower, into the square.

There he stopped and took a deep, trembling breath. Her soft laughter still shivered in his ears. At his feet two kites fought over the corpse of a rat. He began to run toward Don Manoel's mansion.

He climbed over the gate and stopped, one foot on the ground and one upon the gate, his hand still grasping an iron curlicue. He stared in astonishment at Grant and Fremantle. Grant was sitting with his back to the wall, his head nodding. Fremantle lay asprawl under the orange tree.

Jason shook his head in disbelief. He'd seen a dead rat, a thousand carvings, an old man standing on his head, and a princess, and still those two slept. He peered back through the wrought-iron tracery. Yes, the man was still there, still upside down.

The shade of the orange tree, which had been two feet from Fremantle's head, was now painting the old sailor's gray hair with false gold. Only an hour had passed. Jason grunted discontentedly. Drayton and Silvester ought to have finished their talking by now. He walked slowly toward the house. He'd go up the steps as far as he dared, and listen to see whether the conference was near an end.

As he walked he began to sing.

> *"Alas, my love, you do me wrong,*
> *To cast me off discourteously,*

And I have lovèd you so long,
    Delighting in your company."

It was a yearning and mysterious tune. He used to sing it with
Molly under the Plain, and for a moment he felt the wind in his face
and felt the turf under his feet and saw Shrewford Ring before his
eyes, and stopped singing.

He began again. He was in Coromandel.

"Greensleeves was all my joy,
    Greensleeves was my delight . . ."

The first thing he must do was learn to speak Tamil properly. Then
gradually he would work his way up until he became rich and powerful. He knew her name already—Princess Devadassi, a beautiful
name. He spoke it two or three times in varying tones of entreaty,
then returned to his singing.

"Greensleeves was my hart of gold,
    And who but my lady Greensleeves?"

He could rescue the king her father from drowning, or from a
runaway horse. He had not seen many horses here, though—a runaway elephant.

With the treasure, by God!—with the treasure he could dress so
magnificently and bring her so many elephant and camel loads of
gifts that the people would line the streets, gaping, to watch him
pass by, and the king would have to treat him like an ambassador
at the least. He wondered how often the princess came to d'Alvarez's
palace here for dinner, and whether they danced afterward. Even if
they didn't, he could make an opportunity to dance for them, and
then—and then!

He stopped. A girl was working in a flowerbed a yard off the path.
She was sitting back on her heels and looking at him, a trowel in
her hand and the earth turned over among the roots of the dark red
flowers in front of her.

Jason thought he must have frightened her. He took off his cap
and said, "I am an English sailor, mistress. Our Master Drayton is
with Don d'Alvarez. He told us to wait out here."

She said, "Dom Manoel is my father. He has been preparing for
this ever since your ship was sighted yesterday. Was that you singing
'Greensleeves'?"

Jason looked round. She was staring a little to the side of him and over his head, but there was no one near her, except him, who could have been singing. "Yes," he said. "Grant and Fremantle are asleep by the gate. But you speak English!"

The girl said, "My father spent six years in England, senhor, in His Majesty's embassy there. My mother and I were with him. I was a child. After that we went to Rome, then back home to Portugal, and then, two years ago, we came out here. You have been in the city."

Jason started and looked more closely at her as she rose to her feet. She was slight and dark-haired and not at all beautiful. Her eyes were strange—wide-set, brown, and fully open under dark, questioning eyebrows. She had an olive skin and long thin hands. She said again, "You have been in the city."

"I didn't mean any harm," Jason muttered. "You saw me climbing over the gate? I have a right to go wherever I want," he finished more bravely.

The girl said, "I didn't see. I can smell the city on you. Why did you go, and your friends slept? Did you want to steal something?"

Stung to anger, Jason said, "I went to see if this was the City of Pearl which is marked on my map." He shut his mouth, cursing himself. It was better to tell lies.

But the girl said, "You've come here because of a map? Is there treasure on it?"

"Yes," Jason said unwillingly.

"Where do you have to go to get to the treasure?"

"I don't know. I can't read all the words on the map yet."

The girl said slowly, "Manairuppu isn't the City of Pearl. But there is a place ten miles down the coast where a few pearl fishermen live. It is only a village, but it might be marked on such a map as the City of Pearl. You came straight here from England?"

"Yes."

She said, "And you can't read! Oh, how wonderful! Let me touch you." She put out her hands. Jason stood still apprehensively. God's blood, this one was really off her noggin, a sort of female Softy. They ought to shut her up.

Her thin fingers passed gently down the sides of his face and over his shoulders. Then she said, "Now stand away over there, please, at least fifty paces from me, down the path."

"But mistress—" Jason said.

"Please!" she said.

He backed away. She was looking tense, as if thinking of something else. At last she raised her hand and said, "Now I can see you. You are a nice-looking young man. Come close again. What is your name?"

"Jason Savage."

She said, "I live in a dungeon. I cannot see anything close to me. I see nothing but a colored blur. I never have. I have a pair of spectacles, and with them I can read if I hold the paper very far away from my eyes. Without the spectacles I can see things a little, but only if they are more than fifty paces from me. You thought I was touched in the head?"

"Oh no," Jason said quickly, lying.

"You did! You are going away?"

"I don't know, mistress."

"Don't go."

A female voice called sharply. Jason looked up and saw a square, stern face glowering at them from a window near the corner of the mansion. The girl called back mildly in the same language, picked up her trowel, and said, "She is telling me to come in at once. My name is Catherine." She smiled blindly in Jason's direction and went toward the house. The older woman's baleful eye fixed Jason until Catherine was safely round the corner.

Jason stared at the blank windows. He wiped the sweat off his forehead with his finger and dashed it to the earth. "Don't go," she'd said. Perhaps he hadn't heard right. Perhaps she *was* dotty. He returned to his friends. This time he sat down with his back to a tree not far from them and closed his eyes. . . .

Devadassi, Princess of Manairuppu—Your Royal Highness, wilt thou accept these little gifts from thine humble servant, Sir Jason Savage, knight, of the county of Wiltshire? Devadassi, your eyes are like stars. But her eyes were tilted ever so slightly upward at the corners. Devadassi!

❋　　❋　　❋

"Wake up, you lousy dogs!"

Silvester was in a bad temper. The three sprang to their feet like wooden toys, barking sleepily, "Aye, aye, sir!"

"Where's that blackamoor who brought us here?" Drayton asked peevishly. "We'll never find our way back to the ship through this stinking warren."

"I think I can, sir," Jason said.

Silvester said, "Lead on, then. You, open the gate, and step lively." The servant unlocked the gate, and they went out. It was late afternoon, and the people of Manairuppu were again about in the streets.

Jason walked a pace ahead of Drayton and Silvester. He knew the road quite well. On his way to the princess's palace he had seen the river and the masts of the *Phoebe* down an alley to the left, and noted their position.

Drayton said, "Do you think the Portugal ship is really coming soon?"

Silvester answered with heat, "I don't know, Master Drayton. But I say it doesn't matter a whip. What if she is? What if she does carry twenty-eight guns to our six? The truth is we've been warned off by a stinking Portugee, told to clear out in three days or we'll be blown out of the water! Everyone knows the Portugals are on their last legs out here. Should we bow down and kiss the Don's arse because a sniveling Pope of Rome divided the world two hundred years ago and gave half to the Spanish and half to the Portugals? 'Twasn't his to give! God's bread and little fishes, our business is to stay on this coast, Master Drayton, and trade wherever we've a mind, and let the Don chew his beard off. When the *Isabella* comes—*if* she comes—we'll fight her. We'll lie up and board her. The Dons don't like steel. The—"

Drayton said, "My good fellow, what would the company say if we got their ship full of holes and had to limp back to England with nothing sold?"

Jason saw that Drayton was being superior and foppish to try to hide the fact that he had no stomach for the risks Silvester hungered for; but he was not deceiving anyone, and he knew it. So he turned on Fremantle and snapped, "Why did you not tell us that the Portugals had such a hold on the Coromandel coast? You must have known."

"I was in the King of Madura's jail most of my time here, master," Fremantle said. "And from what I did hear, Master Silvester is right. The Portugals have never been so strong here as in Goa. They're just pretending. One good push and they'll fall down. I think we ought to do as the mate says."

"No one asked you for your opinion," Drayton snapped. "Down

here? This place stinks worse than Billingsgate at high noon. D'Alvarez would not even tell us where the pearl fisheries are."

"I know," Jason broke in eagerly. "There is one ten miles down the coast. The Don's daughter told me."

"His daughter? Why should she be talking to you?" Silvester asked crossly.

"I don't know, sir."

Drayton said, "Ten miles? We might take the *Phoebe* down there and see."

"Not worth it," Silvester said bluntly. "We need water and fresh vegetables and meat on the hoof, even if it's only goats, and that's all we'll get here. Are we going to wait and fight the *Isabella*, or are we going to run away with our tails between our legs?"

"I have not made up my mind," Drayton said. "I shall discuss the matter with the sailing master tonight. Those places d'Alvarez mentioned, farther up the coast, sound promising."

"Bah!" Silvester said. "He was just holding out a carrot as well as beating us with a stick."

"I shall discuss it all with Master Green," Drayton repeated coldly.

Jason thought: That settles it; we shall sail in a couple of days, and we shall be running away. Green was an old windbag who said he had served with Grenville as a boy, but the crew thought his chief services had been in the Tilbury alehouses.

Drayton said, "But there is one thing we can do. We can send a man down to the pearlers to buy some pearls. Then we will know whether they are of sufficiently good quality for us to try to develop the trade. I shall send you, Jason."

"Him?" Silvester interjected. "He's too scatterbrained. You ought to send one of the officers."

"Perhaps Savage is too intelligent for mere shipmen to be able to appreciate his qualities," Drayton said. "But at all events he can be trusted with the money. Call for the shallop."

They were standing on the jetty, and it was evening. Silvester, seething with rage, cupped his hands and bellowed, almost in Drayton's ear, "*Phoebe* ahoy! Send the shallop! Look lively, you whoreson scum!"

❊   ❊   ❊

It was dark. In the east two low stars shone out under the black clouds to seaward. The river slapped against the ship, and the ocean grumbled on the bar. Scattered lights glowed with faint, steady beams in the city, and somewhere among distant fields an animal howled mournfully. Drayton, Silvester, and Jason stood in the waist of the *Phoebe,* looking toward the invisible jetty. Grant sat in the shallop below, his oars shipped, his face a dim white blur.

Jason's heart beat with a steady, thudding pound inside his chest. Now he was really to slide on a rope over the side of a ship in the middle of a tropical night. Now the Dons really lay in wait for him.

Silvester said, "I haven't seen any native guards on the shore, Master Drayton. If you ask me, the king of this place isn't anxious to help the Portugals any more than he has to. In fact he's probably waiting for us to send envoys to him, but in secret. Why should he help us if we won't help ourselves?"

Drayton ignored the mate and said, "You have the money, Jason?"

Jason tapped his waist, where he wore a money belt under his shirt. The buckled shoes felt awkward on his feet after so many months barefoot at sea, but he had twenty miles to walk.

"Off you go, then," Drayton said.

Jason slid down the rope into the shallop, and Grant rowed him ashore. "Good luck," Grant muttered. "And we'll have a wee drink with the silver that sticks in your ain purse, eh?"

"I'm not going to keep a penny," Jason whispered indignantly.

The shallop slipped quietly back toward the ship. As soon as he could no longer hear the quiet gurgle of the oars Jason slipped across the waste land and entered the streets. It was nearly midnight.

He worked southward through deserted streets and soon came to the square where the princess's great palace stood. Fitful moonbeams scurried over the climbing animals and gave a livid urgency to their movements. A tiny light shone far and deep inside the tunnel-like entrance under the carved tower, and Jason imagined the sentries on guard round *her* chamber, and the king asleep in another part of the palace.

He hurried on, moving always under the loom of the houses. After half an hour there were no more houses. Single palm trees stood up like gallows in the empty land. The sandy track shone white, wavering on southward, and to right and left tall reeds bent in the hot land wind. Spice and pepper and the bittersweet tang of Coromandel fruit scented the wind as it blew on his right cheek, and from his left, struggling up to him against the wind, he heard the steady cannon fire of the surf on the Coromandel coast.

Now he was moving parallel with that shore, but he wanted to walk down the sands until he came to the pearlers. A dim path led off to the left, and he took it. The sound of the sea grew louder, and soon he reached the dunes, crossed them, and headed south along the glistening sand. After two hours of hard going he crept into the lee of a dune, muffled his face against the scurrying grains, and went to sleep.

He awoke at first light and found that he had stopped only two hundred yards short of a thin point of sand, where the beach bent back to form a bay before continuing its arrow line southward. Scores of the familiar logs were drawn up in the cove, where a muddy streamlet meandered out of the reeds into the sea. A dozen dark and naked men were tying the logs together, getting ready to go to sea. A huddle of palm-leaf and palm-thatch hovels crouched on the trampled mud beside the stream. He saw women squatting outside the openings of the hovels, and then one of the women looked up, saw him, and called to the men at the boats. One of the men straightened up, separated himself from the group, and walked slowly forward. Jason went down the sand to meet him.

The man was slight of bone, and built small and square, so that there were big areas of taut skin between the bones, and he had hollow cheeks and a tight belly. He was young, perhaps not much older than Jason. They looked at each other for a time; then the young man pointed to his chest and said, "Simon." Two lockets hung on a thin cord round his neck. He opened one of them and showed Jason the crucifix inside. Astonished, Jason cried, "You are a Christian!"

The young man nodded and smiled and repeated, "Simon, Simon! Ave Maria, pater noster, credo . . ." and then a long gabble in Tamil, ending in the words "Padre Felipe."

Jason said, "You know Padre Felipe?"

The man nodded excitedly and held up the crucifix. All right, Jason thought; Padre Felipe made him a Christian, and his Christian name is Simon. Very interesting, but it was not going to help much, except that the man seemed very willing to be friendly.

In his carefully rehearsed Tamil, Jason said, "Pearls. I want to see pearls."

Simon clapped his hands in pleasure, gently took Jason's arm, and led him to the log boats. The other men smiled shyly, and Jason smiled back at them. Simon whipped the cord round his logs fore and aft, pushed the craft into the shallow water, and beckoned to Jason to get in.

Jason looked at his shoes. He could take them off and leave them here until he returned. It was early. Drayton would not expect him back on the *Phoebe* until the middle of the night. He sat down, took off his shoes, left them well up the sand, and ran into the sea. The sun came up out of the east and sparkled in the drops his feet kicked up. It was a lovely and exciting morning, and he was going out to catch pearls asleep in their oyster beds.

He climbed carefully into the craft and sat down. It began to rock violently and did not settle until a woman—who, he decided, was Simon's wife—slipped in behind him and steadied it. Then Simon bent his rough paddle into the water, and the muscles stood out on his shoulders and forearms, and the boat started moving. They crossed the little cove, cleared the point, and faced the sea.

The water gurgled over Jason's feet, where a big, roped stone lay, and he laughed delightedly. He was not on the sea, but in it. In this craft he was not a sailor but a fish or a seagull, his eyes far below the level of the crested waves. The seas steadily increased in size as the boat increased its distance from the line of sand and the cluster of palm trees that marked the shore. For a moment Jason thought he was going to be seasick and afraid. But—he looked round at the heaving water—what could go wrong? This craft could not over-turn or be swamped. And a volley of flying fish skimmed out of the sea and over the boat, and plopped into the sea on the other side, and Jason laughed again. He had not come to Coromandel to be comfortable.

After three hours Simon and his wife stopped paddling. All round them the other log boats of the little fleet rose and fell in dizzy swoops. The shore had dropped below the horizon. Simon stood up and, with an apologetic murmur, threw three small handfuls of rice into the sea. He stayed there a moment with his palms joined, rock-ing easily to the boat's wild motion. Then he murmured, "Ave Maria, ave Maria!" and sat down.

His wife picked up the roped stone with her feet and, holding it as easily as if her toes were fingers, swung her legs over the stern. Simon caught the other end of the rope in his hands and held it fast. His wife sucked air deep into her lungs. She was a slim, short girl with a deep chest and fine legs. She wore nothing but a net fastened round her waist. The cavity of her chest swelled and swelled, and suddenly she slipped over the stern and slid down into the deep. Her brown body wavered down, glistening and distorted in the moving water, and then began to move along the bottom. Simon gave an occasional stroke with his paddle to keep the craft steady against wind and sea. The water was not very clear, and Jason could not really see what she was doing. Then he leaned far over, put his head under water, and opened his eyes. Ah! the salt stung him, but he could see—a dark spider down there, and wavery tentacles that might be her arms, reaching out and in, out and in, with a rhythm of movement that matched the rhythm of the waves.

When he could hold his breath no more, Jason raised his head, wiped his dripping face, and crouched back in the center of the boat. A long time passed, and he looked at Simon in alarm and pointed down. Simon nodded and smiled.

Long after that the girl's head slowly broke surface, and she hung over the side of the log boat, breathing in slowly, the water running down her flat nose and in a stream off her chin into the inside of the boat. Simon hauled the stone up and into the boat. The woman handed Simon the net from her waist, and Simon emptied it amidships. All round them the other pearlers, men and women, dived and surfaced. Simon took a blunt knife from the string round his waist and began to open the oysters. The shells flew overboard in a stream, but already his wife had taken the stone between her feet and again sunk below the surface. Now Simon paddled the craft, split the oysters, threw the shells overboard, and kept touching the rope that led to the bottom of the sea. There were no pearls in the first catch.

The girl came up again; more shells poured into the boat. Jason got out his knife and began to open oysters.

The work went on steadily. After every four or five dives man and wife changed roles, and Simon dived while his wife stayed in the boat. Every time anyone in the fleet got a pearl he stood up in his boat and shouted, "Pearl!" But when the red sun touched the water, and all around the sea was like wine, and Jason's fingers bled from the sharp edges of the oysters, the whole fleet had found only four pearls.

At last Simon, who was diving, said, "One more." This time he added, smiling at Jason, "For you." He made the sign of the cross, threw another handful of rice into the sea, and went down with the stone. The young wife's face was gray and pinched, and she moved

110

listlessly at her tasks. Jason took the rope from her and let it run through his hands as Simon swept the bottom. Through the hours Jason had gained confidence, and now he knelt up in the shallow well, his feet over one side and his head peering down into the sea on the other.

He heard a hollow booming of wood on wood and glanced up. All day one or another of the pearlers had been standing upright in his craft, taking no part in the fishing but only looking ceaselessly around the low horizon. Now this man was beating his paddle regularly against the side of his boat, and loudly shouting a single word over and over again.

Jason turned to Simon's wife and said, "What?" She scrambled up to him, tugged at the rope, and shrieked the same word in his ear. Jason hauled hard on the rope, thinking to pull Simon to the surface by main force. But the rope came up easily, and Jason fell backward into the sea.

Bitter sea water flooded his mouth and stomach before he managed to control himself. He sank slowly through the water, and all was green and blurry, just the way he had thought it would be when he had tried to be a trout; but his eyes smarted and his chest hurt and he wanted to be sick. He saw the underside of the log boat quite near, and the rope swaying beside it. Now he *was* a fish, and everything looked just as he had imagined. But were a fish's eyes—?

Oh, Mother, I shall drown! He was in great danger; it was foolish to be worrying about whether his imagination had been true; he ought to struggle. He began to kick and push with arms and legs.

When he broke surface he flailed madly with his arms and croaked, "Help!" The log boat rocked ten feet away from him, and the girl's naked back was turned to him, and he heard many loud noises of booming and screams, as all the pearlers shouted and banged their paddles against the logs. A breaking wave forced him under the water once more, but not before he had seen a black triangle, like a sail, cruising slowly past the stern of the boat.

He struggled to get at his knife. He had seen plenty of sharks. As he struggled he sank, and a great white belly swung lazily over him, and the curved rows of teeth shone, and the dark mouth grinned. He slammed his legs together, surfaced, gulped air, and sank in a flurry of foam.

The shark's back glistened in the water as it turned, and he saw one cold eye, getting larger. Then Simon's face swam down in front of his bulging eyes, and he saw a trail of thin bubbles rising from Simon's mouth.

As soon as Simon's hands touched him, Jason's panic exploded. He opened his mouth to yell, grabbed Simon, and held tight with all his strength. The sea rushed down into his belly, and Simon's fingers jabbed like pointed sticks into his eyes. With the last of his consciousness he let go his grip.

The girl was dragging him into the boat by his hair. He fainted again.

He awoke to the sound of retching and moaning. It was himself, lying face down in the bottom of the boat, with his head resting on Simon's feet and the water swirling an inch below his nostrils. Simon sat in the stern and the girl in the bow, both paddling. Jason sat up shakily. Their little boat, with all the fleet, was headed for the setting sun.

After a time he muttered, "Thank you, Simon."

Simon laid down his paddle and searched with his fingers in the strong cloth bag he wore round his neck. He brought out a single large pearl and said, "For you. I said."

Jason asked, "You found this the last time?"

Simon nodded, smiled, and made the sign of the cross. Then he pointed at Jason and spoke again, slowly, in Tamil. Jason understood that it was Jesus, aided by Jason himself, who had found the pearl for Simon.

When they got ashore it was dusk. Jason put on his shoes and tried to tell Simon that he wanted to buy some pearls and then go back to the ship. But Simon took his arm and dragged him persistently toward the huts, saying, "We must eat; then you can go; but rest here now while the women cook." He pointed to the clean sand behind the huts and sat down with a sigh. The women went into the huts, and soon wood smoke began to drift across the sand and tingle in the men's nostrils.

Jason stretched out beside his new friend and waited comfortably. He ought to be buying pearls, but that could wait. He smelled savory fish, and the bare mud, and hot spice, and the burning driftwood. The wind was backing into the southwest. There'd be a land wind every night at this season. He'd seen a shark. He hadn't been very brave, but he'd do better next time. He'd found the City of Pearl. He must dry his wonderful map.

It was a night of stars, and the breeze was soft and warm, and the sea thunderous at his right hand. He walked quickly northward on his return journey, his mind in an active reverie. These pearlers of Coromandel were as strange and deep as anyone else when you began to get to know them. They put red heathen marks on their foreheads, but some of them were Christians. Simon had two lockets, and in one he kept a crucifix and in the other a small stone emblem, red-painted and squatly deformed, but unmistakably a representation of a man's sexual organ. Then there were crosses daubed on the leaf walls of some of the hovels, and among the very crosses crude red and black drawings of picks and trowels and triangles and swastikas. And Simon said "Ave Maria" as he launched a big leaf onto the small waves at the edge of the sea, the leaf loaded with a tiny pile of rice, a few flowers, and a pinch of turmeric.

Doing business with them was not easy, though the language problem had not been as difficult as he had feared. A word or two of Portuguese learned in Lisbon, his small stock of Tamil, the liberal use of pantomime—even English, spoken slowly—and they could understand one another. But buying the big pearl and two smaller ones had been hard. First they had tried to give him the three pearls, and it took a long time to make them understand that he wanted to pay. Then they became nervous and told him they were not allowed to sell their pearls to anyone but the king, and the king's price was very low. So Jason said he would pay them well, and brought out his money to show them he meant what he said. Then they bit the coins as he offered them, and argued among themselves. Finally they agreed to take three guineas for the three pearls, and Jason accepted. They told him he must never say how or where he had got the pearls, or the king would send men down to punish them. They asked if he could come again to buy more pearls. If he would, they would go out more often. As it was, they went pearling only once a week, or even less often, because the king's price was so bad that they had to spend most of their time fishing for food rather than for pearls, and gathering coconuts, and working to raise rice in the little fields beside the marshy stream. They had given him a fiery whitish drink out of a coconut shell, but they were very poor; and the fish had smelled good, but it had not tasted good, and there was not much of it. Already he felt hungry again.

The tower of the king's palace loomed against the stars ahead.

Damnation on his foggy brain! He had meant to ask Simon more about the king and his daughter, and whether there were many princes—but what was the use? Drayton and Green were as frightened as rabbits with a ferret in the warren, and the *Phoebe* would sail tomorrow—today; it was after midnight.

He'd never see the Princess Devadassi or his new friends the pearlers again. He ought to stay here and set up in business for himself when the *Phoebe* sailed. What business? He was only a farmer. No, he was a dancer too. But perhaps they wouldn't like his dancing here.

Now he was passing the palace. His footsteps dragged, and he looked up at the tower and whispered, "Princess, I love you." . . . She smiled at him and spoke in a sweet voice, sweeter than the flute. It was cool where she was, but outside the sun beat at your eyes in blinding waves. A fallen leaf scurried in the dust behind him, and then a big white flash lit the world.

❈   ❈   ❈

He watched an ant crawling, crawling. Dust thickened in his nostrils, and in the back of his head the bones groaned together with a terrible jangling sound. The dust tilted, the light faded—he was in a boat. He could not be; that was dirt in his clutching fingers. A bare foot, its toenails black-painted, moved near his eye. He sat up slowly.

Princess Devadassi was bending over him. He sighed and put his hands to his head. The night had passed, and it was dawn, and cold. The tower of her palace climbed up by fretted, diminishing stages into the gray sky behind her.

He tried to stand up but failed. The princess squatted down opposite him on her heels, her big kohl-rimmed eyes looking seriously into his, but she made no effort to help him up.

He said, "I don't know what happened." There was a big lump, painful to the gentlest touch, on the back of his head.

She said, "Money?"

Jason gasped and plunged his hand into his waistband. He pulled out a few pennies. Everything else had gone. He said, "I have been robbed!" Then in Tamil: "Money—gone. Three pearls—gone."

She nodded calmly. He struggled to his feet and looked helplessly at her. She signed to him to wait, and went into her palace. After some minutes she came back with an earthenware pitcher of water and poured some of it into his hands and over his head. The water freshened him, and he said humbly, "Thank you, Your Royal Highness."

She smiled and made him a little sign, joining her hands together and touching her forehead. She turned and walked back into her palace. Her hips swung lazily, her little jacket shivered, and once again she looked at him, smiling over her shoulder, before she disappeared into her palace tower.

Jason half raised his hand. But the *Phoebe* would sail away, and— He swore aloud and staggered off toward the ship, his knees as unstable as a baby's.

The river shone like a ribbon of pearls, and the *Phoebe* floated like a brown swan on it, her masts and yards blending into the palms on the far bank. He walked to the end of the jetty and hailed her. A few fishermen working at their nets looked curiously at him but did not come near him.

When he reached the deck Drayton, Green, and Silvester were waiting for him on the poop. Drayton said cheerfully, "You're late back, Jason. Still, all's well that ends well. What are the pearls like?"

Jason said, "I went down to the pearlers' village, as you told me—"

Silvester barked keenly, "Where are the pearls, eh?"

Jason said, "And I went out pearling with their fleet. They go to sea in log boats like—"

Silvester said, "You didn't get any pearls! Where's the money?"

Master Drayton said, "Pray be quiet, master mate. Show me the pearls, Jason."

Jason said, "I haven't got any. I was robbed."

The river lapped against the hull; deep in the ship the mast creaked; a sailor working on a rope behind them laughed once.

Master Drayton flushed and stamped his boot so that his gold spurs jangled. "This is no time for joking! We sail on tomorrow's tide."

"I'm not joking," Jason said. "I was robbed. I've got a bump on my head."

Silvester said, "But of course he can be trusted with money, not like ignorant ship officers."

"You're a lying dog, Savage!" Drayton shouted, beside himself with mortification. "You spent it on drink and women. That's why you're late. I can smell the rum on your breath! Liar, thief, liar!" He lashed out with the back of his hand and hit Jason across the face.

Jason gasped. "I'm not a liar." He found his knife in his hands and a mist blurring his eyes.

Silvester said, "Aaah! A mutineer as well as a thief and a liar." Three swords whirred out and faced him, the tips quivering like the tongues of adders at his throat. Silvester said, "Tie him to the mast there. Gunner!"

They tied Jason to the mast, and the gunner flogged him with a rope's end while the crew watched. Then they carried him down to the cramped dark hole of the forepeak and chained him to the iron ring that was screwed into the vessel's stem, and left him.

Two rats crept out of a hole near his knees and sat up on their hind legs to watch him, their eyes like four tiny red coals in the gloom. His comrades' feet pattered along the deck above his head. The water chuckled, the heat grew, and soon sweat bathed him from head to toe and ran in salty channels across the planking. For a time he brooded sullenly on his flogging. They were sailing on to-morrow's tide. And they believed he was a liar. He curled up as best he could, lying on his face because his back smarted, and thought of Devadassi. Soon he smelled the perfume of her, and then he forgot his bitterness.

*　　*　　*

The gunner came down in the evening, unchained him, and gave him a crust of bread. Jason tore off a piece of the crust and put it down beside him for the rats. Then he went to sleep.

He slept well and was still asleep when the gunner came and said gruffly, "On deck, you!" Clambering up the companion, he found it was early morning. A strong land wind rattled through the rigging, and baskets of fruit lay all over the deck, and chickens clucked in crates by the mast, and tethered goats bleated in the bows. The bank seemed close today, and the houses very clean and inviting, and the sun shone on the tower of the princess's palace.

As the gunner led him aft he made up his mind. He had crossed half the world to come to this Coromandel. Voy's map was in its hiding place in his breeches, and he must follow it. Besides, if he stayed in this ship he would go to other places and might find one as wonderful as Coromandel. He might meet another girl as beautiful as the princess, and fall in love with her. He felt an awful pang at the thought of the bliss and the disloyalty lying in wait for him over the horizon.

The gunner took him to the poop and stopped. Silvester shouted, "All hands to the break of the poop!" The crew ran aft.

Drayton said, "Savage, I have decided to punish you no further if you will confess to the crew that you stole the money. They would have shared in the profit."

The smell of the shore was very strong here. If he didn't confess they'd chain him up in the forepeak again, and he'd never get another chance. He said, "All right. I will."

Behind him Fremantle spat in disgust and said, "You dirty little tyke—and I've been telling the lads *you* couldn't have done that."

Silvester said, "Speak up, Savage, so's they can all hear."

Jason took a deep breath. Now that the moment had come it was not easy to say the words. He said, "I beg your grace to forgive me that I drew my knife against you."

Drayton nodded. "Go on."

Jason looked helplessly round at the sailors and said, "I—I—"

"Deck there! Sail ho!" The shout came down strongly from the masthead. Green leaped back and bawled, "Where, what sort?"

"On the horizon, due east! Must be a Europe ship."

Drayton cried, "The *Isabella!* Get to sea at once, Master Green—at once, d'you hear?"

But Green was already shouting, "All hands to set sail! Anchormen to your places! Hurry, hurry!"

Silvester muttered, "Damned lily-livered bag of pox! You, you—hoist the shallop inboard!"

The crew scattered to their duties, and in a moment Jason found himself alone. He went to the mainmast and tapped the small freshwater barrel that was kept roped to it. It was full. He prized out the bung with the point of his knife and watched the water run out across the deck. Then he replaced the bung and kicked it well home, cut the securing ropes with his knife, and went below. He rolled up his belongings, hoisted his heavy sack with its four books onto his shoulder, and returned up the companion. Now the timbers groaned and creaked as the sails tugged at the masts and the masts in their footings strained the bowels of the vessel.

Jason poked his head above deck level and looked around. She had already begun to turn and was now pointed across the stream. A strong ebb tide was making out to sea, and Silvester, the only officer who might retain enough wits to stop him, was busy in the bows.

Jason stepped out, crossed the deck, picked up the barrel, walked to the bulwark, and jumped overboard.

As he hit the water the barrel smashed up under his chest and winded him. He hung on and after a moment found strength to kick with his legs. The poop of the *Phoebe* towered over him, and he saw Drayton and a couple of sailors staring down and shouting, but he could not hear what they were saying.

Then the *Phoebe* drew away and Jason kicked harder, being carried down all the while on the tide, and came at last to land, among some gaping fishermen near the bar at the mouth of the river. He gave them the barrel and walked quickly south toward the pearlers' cove, turning occasionally to watch the *Phoebe* as she struggled over the bar, put down her helm, and ran northeast before the wind.

❋   ❋   ❋

After three weeks here with the pearlers, still, whenever he came in from the fields or the sea, the poverty of their little settlement struck him like a chill. Plenty of people in England were poor. Many children went barefoot in the winter slush; in many houses women shivered at their work because they had neither wood for fires nor candles for light, and only cracked boards or torn paper to keep out the rain; many men worked all day with only a piece of bread and a raw turnip for food. Jason knew families in Pennel who had to make their bread from such ears of corn as they could pick up in the fields after the harvesters had finished.

But the poverty at the pearlers' cove was like a deformation, something that could not be got rid of, something like Flossie Henman's club foot or Softy Turpin's upside-down brain.

He and Simon were sitting outside Simon's hut in the twilight, chewing betel nut. Jason said, "Simon, we must force the king to give us more money for our pearls." By now he spoke bad but ready Tamil.

Simon said, "It is impossible. The king is the king. What can we do?" He shrugged and spat a stream of red juice.

"We *must* do something," Jason said energetically. "Otherwise we will all starve to death. I am so hungry now that I can hardly work. I have a plan. Let us all go out pearling every day this week. At the end of the week we will march to Manairuppu, every man, woman, and child of us, and take the catch to the king. That will show him how much we can get if we fish every day for pearls. We will tell him we can get the same amount every week if he pays us enough so that we can buy food instead of having to grow it or fish for it."

Simon said, "The king will take the pearls at the old price, and there will be no fish drying in the sun here for us to eat, and no rice, either. If we starve, we starve. It is written on our foreheads."

Jason sighed. He had another idea, but this one he must carry out himself, and he did not want to talk about it now, in case he failed. He meant to ask the Princess Devadassi to help them. She had a kind face and would surely see the justice of their case once he explained it to her. But he had better not raise the pearlers' hopes just yet. She might have left Manairuppu on a visit. She might be too frightened of her father the king to intervene in the matter. She might have got married.

He stirred in sudden anxious impatience. He must go to the city at once. But the Portuguese ship had not sailed yet. One of the pearlers had been in Manairuppu yesterday, and reported on his return that the *Isabella* was still lying in the river. He had heard that it was ready to sail, though. As far as the pearler had been able to find out for Jason, there had been no sea fight when the *Phoebe* left. That same evening the *Isabella* came in, but no one had heard gunfire.

Drayton ought to have fought. The example would have shown other people here how they too could get what they wanted by fighting. It didn't always need to be fighting with guns. The pearlers, for instance—in London they would have been a guild years ago. He had seen the power of the London guilds during the week he stayed with Master Wigmore in Leadenhall Street. A guild could force even the king to do what it wanted, as far as concerned its own business. Simon and the rest of them were good, kind people, but they would starve unless they banded together and stood ready to fight. "It is written on our foreheads," they kept saying. God's blood, where could a man go if he believed that?

Well, and why didn't he, Jason, practice what he preached? Why shouldn't he go and court the princess? Probably no one had ever showed determination to marry her. Probably she was only waiting for such a man to come along. That was it—determination and money, that's what got you what you wanted, the same here as in England. He'd never earn enough money by pearling to impress the king. He must find the treasure.

He unfolded his map. The light fell flat now across the sandy point, and a violet haze hung over sea and beach. He said, "When we have got a better price from the king, Simon, I must leave you. I am going to look for treasure with this map." He put his finger on it and said, "This is where we are now. The City of Pearl. I want to ask you about the other places."

Simon looked dubiously at the map, pointed at the mountains, and said, "What are these?"

Jason said, "High hills," but Simon did not understand. Perhaps he has never seen a hill, Jason thought. He made motions in the air and pointed to the sky. Simon touched the two emblems of his locket, joined his hands in the Christian mode of prayer, and pointed to the sky. Jason realized that Simon thought the map was a new kind of Bible.

Jason tried again, asking after horsemen—but Simon talked of mysterious gods who lived in the forests. Jason sighed and put the map away.

Simon said earnestly, "Always keep it. It is a good *puja*. It will bring you good food, a good woman, good pearls."

Simon went into his hut. Jason sat a while longer, staring at the river. Money and will: gold in his hands and a high heart under his shirt. The map had changed its character somehow. In England the map itself had been more important than the treasure. Now he needed the money. He wondered: If someone gave me a hundred thousand pieces of eight, would I throw the map away?

He dropped into a reverie about many matters. When the Portuguese ship left and he came out of hiding, what would be Don d'Alvarez's power to work him evil? Would the Don care about the doings of a single Englishman? The Don's daughter was almost blind, perhaps a little potty. *Would* he throw the map away? He wouldn't need it to search for money. But perhaps he'd need it for something else. But money was the most important thing now.

Later it began to rain. He crawled into the little hut they had built for him, and went to sleep.

✳   ✳   ✳

He awoke, and heard soft voices in the dawn outside. He crawled out, stiff all over, and itching from the bites of the marsh mosquitoes, and stood yawning by the muddy stream. It had been a hot night, full of the noises of water, and now the stream was swollen and the paddies overfull.

He saw seven strangers talking to Simon—rather, one of the strangers, the most richly dressed of them, was speaking, and Simon was crouched on his knees in front of him, listening. The speaker was the man with the pink coat who had guided Drayton's party to the Don's house.

Simon's wife whispered in Jason's ear, "They are the king's men. They have come for you."

Jason turned and dived inside his hut. He began to tear out the palm-leaf wall at the back, but it was stronger than it looked, and before he could make a hole three of the strangers scrambled in and seized him. He hit out at them with his fists, but they held tight, and then more of them came in, and they all made soothing motions, and Simon cried aloud in a frenzy of anxiety, "Do not fight, Jason! They are the king's men."

They pulled him gently into the open. The man in the pink coat said, "Does he understand Tamil?"

Simon said, "Yes, lord, very well, though it is not always easy to understand what *he* says."

The man said, "The king is now ready to receive you. The Portugal ship left Manairuppu yesterday afternoon." He smiled a small, careful smile. "One half-hour later the king bade me bring you to his presence. Do you have all your belongings with you? Good. Do not be afraid, sir. See, we have brought a palanquin for you—with curtains, so that you may be protected from prying eyes."

He showed Jason the palanquin. Jason had seen several of them in the streets of the city. They were like the chairs in which rich men had themselves carried to and fro in London, only in India you lay down instead of sitting up.

Simon said, "It is good, Jason. Think of the king sending such a palanquin for you! You will become a great man. *I* know. I dreamed it after the first time you came to us."

Jason did not answer. He felt trapped and unhappy. Sullenly he got into the palanquin, the bearers picked it up, the man in the pink coat climbed, puffing, onto a potbellied roan horse, and, *jig-jog, jig-jog*, they left the pearlers' cove and splashed away along the muddy path to Manairuppu.

Simon trotted alongside for a time, whispering good-bys and good wishes, until the man in the pink coat said, "Go back, you."

Simon said, "I am going, lord, I am going. You will speak to the king about us, Jason?"

Jason said, "If I can. But I'm not going to be given a robe of honor. I'm going to be killed." Then the leader shouted more angrily, and Simon fell back.

One of the bearers drew the curtains. Jason shouted, "I don't want them drawn. It's hot in here."

The man in the pink coat said politely, "It is better to keep them drawn. Don d'Alvarez has spies everywhere."

121

The curtains stayed drawn. Jason collected himself and began to think. How could he escape? What were they going to do to him? Why the palanquin? He was a rat in a revolving, jolting cage. But why hadn't they killed him there at the pearlers' cove? The dust seeped in through the curtains and made him cough. He became very thirsty; and then the noises of the city grew loud and passed by like waves in a dark sea, swelling up—sharp slap of a word against the curtain, echo from the wall—then all fading behind in the swirl of many voices. *Tap-tap-tap*—an old blind man with a stick. Incense —women; he thought of Devadassi. The *yelp-yiff-yiff* of a dog hit by a stone. Cows; why in the name of God did they have cows in the palace? He felt seasick.

The motion stopped with a final jerk and sway, and the bearers lowered the palanquin to the ground. The man in the pink coat drew back the curtain and said, "Please to get out now." They were in a courtyard like the one beyond the high tower where Devadassi lived, but smaller. Jason said, "Where am I?"

"This is the king's palace."

Then it was part of that same building where he had met the princess. He could not see the great tower, but that was not surprising in this enclosed little courtyard. He said, "I am hungry and thirsty. Can't I eat before I see the king?"

The man in the pink coat said, "It is arranged. You will have a night's rest, too. Your audience is not until tomorrow. Please follow me."

He led into the building through an open stone archway. Almost at once the passage opened into another courtyard, still smaller than the first. Here the usual white bulls rested in the hot shade, and a group of naked-chested soldiers squatted at cards in a corner, their spears standing in a row behind them, and there were three women whispering beside a pillar. At his guide's heels Jason crossed the open space, entered a door on the far side, and climbed two narrow flights of steps.

The man in the pink coat stopped beside a thick yellow curtain blocking a doorway on the left. He said, "This is the apartment where the king houses his most honored guests." He swept back the curtain and called, "Sugriva!"

A small dark man hurried out of an inner room and stood, smiling uncertainly, in front of them. He brought a savory smell of cooking food with him, and Jason's mouth began to water. The guide said,

"This man is your cook, and he has other servants to command. Sugriva, this is your master. Obey him."

Sugriva bent and touched the inside of Jason's calf with his hand. The man in the pink coat moved about the two rooms, pointing out to Jason the richness of the hangings, the thickness of the cushions, the cool northern exposure, the fine view from the pillared veranda. Finally he turned and said, "And to show you the depth of the king's interest in your embassy, I must tell you that your companion tonight will be the most accomplished *devadassi* in the kingdom." He raised his hands two or three times quickly toward his face and slipped out of the room.

Jason stood stock still, trying to work out the full meaning of what he had heard. These people spoke so quickly. But surely he'd heard the words for "embassy"—which he knew because that was how Drayton had translated his purpose here—and "companion" and "tonight" and "Devadassi." Were they sending him on an embassy tonight to the princess? That didn't make sense. Did they think he was an ambassador? That was possible, considering the extraordinary way they were treating him. But if so, whose ambassador was he supposed to be? And who was to be his companion, and what were they going to do together?

He might ask Sugriva. But what would a servant know? Besides, he was hungry. He'd eat first. He called, "Sugriva, I'm hungry."

The servant's voice answered from the veranda, where smoke rose from a clay fireplace built on the open stones. "Food is ready, lord."

When he had eaten he lay down on the mat on the floor and went to sleep.

*   *   *

He awoke to see Sugriva scattering rose petals about the room. All the veranda lay in blue shade, and someone had been sprinkling water on the stones, both inside and outside, to lay the dust and lessen the heat. He felt fresh and jumpy and as strong as a lion, and wished he knew what was going to happen next. But it was exciting, better than dancing, better than pearling. He said, "Sugriva, why are you scattering rose petals on the floor?"

Sugriva said shyly, "She is a very beautiful woman, lord. You are in great honor."

Jason sat up. He said, "Who is? What do you mean?"

Sugriva said, "It will be Parvati, lord. There is only one best."

123

Jason stood up. Parvati was a woman's name. He said, "A woman called Parvati is coming here? What for?"

"For your pleasure, lord. But the king is paying her. I must go to market—with your lordship's permission." He went out.

The curtain swung to behind him, swaying for a moment like a woman's skirt, until it hung still. Jason began to pace up and down the floor.

A whore, the king was sending him! She would be subtle and fierce, dark, debased, acrobatically lustful. He'd have something to tell Grant after this. But he was never going to see Grant again.

He'd better have nothing to do with her. She'd give him the Italian sickness, which so many people in London had. When she arrived he would thank her and send her away.

God's blood, he hadn't lain with a woman for six months now, and seeing so many naked breasts had made him wish he had a pair himself.

What would the princess think if she knew he had lain with a strumpet here in her own capital city?

But how could she ever know if he didn't talk about it? The girl might talk. Damnation take the king and the man in the pink coat!

He hurried out onto the veranda, peered down into the street, listened to the sounds of the people, glanced at the sun. She might come at any moment. A smoky haze hung along the western horizon, and he could see no hills, only the silver curves of the river among fields and trees.

She would wriggle in, already half undressed, with jewels on her bosom and a ruby in her navel. She would wait for him to give some sign of passion. No, she would sway into him, reeking of woman's scent, and fasten hot lips on him. He practiced receiving such an assault. Oh, blood and death, it was going to be impossible to resist her if she came at him like that. She was faceless, beautiful, lascivious, diabolically skilled. She was hotter than the whispered yarns in the forecastle at night, when the sailors talked of bouts in Hispaniola and Barbary and among the blond Swedes. He could feel her liquid lips, her clinging arms.

How could he ever think himself worthy of the princess if he could not control himself before a whore? He had broken the ties of home and family, he had turned aside from comfort and luxury, now he must conquer lust. There was no Coromandel for a stay-at-home, no princess for a lecher.

His eyes fell on the row of large pots on the veranda. Growing in the pots was a fat-leafed, spiky plant with big creamy flowers. He whipped out his knife, cut off several of the leaves, and stuffed them inside his shirt and down the back of his breeches. Aaah! They hurt, and he had to move carefully now and could not sit down. If the girl tried to embrace him he would scream with the pain. He put his finger in the water jug and found it cold. He lifted the jug and emptied the water over his head. Good, good! Now he was shivering, standing, drenched, in a puddle of water on the clean floor.

He imagined a lusty brown woman coming wheedling at him out of her clothes. Good, good! The prickles hurt so much he could think of nothing but how to stand still. And his teeth were chattering.

Behind him the curtain moved with a stiff whisper. He said, "Sugriva?" and turned expectantly. The Princess Devadassi stood just inside the curtain, calm, unsmiling, lovelier than an April cloud on the edge of the Plain. Jason fell on his knees and whispered, "Oh, Princess, thank God you've come, thank God!"

She joined her palms before her face in the universal gesture of greeting, and said, "I am your servant." Her flute hung from a silver cord about her waist.

Jason took her hand and kissed it, and this time she did not jerk it away as she had the first time, in the temple. She said, "The chamberlain told me you understood Tamil now. Is it true?" She spoke very slowly and distinctly.

"Yes, Princess. I have been living with the pearlers down the coast."

"Ah, that is where you have been. Why are you all wet?"

"I—ah—I felt hot," Jason said.

She said, "You should change your clothes."

He said, "I don't have any others."

She laughed and said, "No. Then lie back here. You'll dry out soon. This is the time for music, and then your servant shall bring us wine and food. What shall I play for you?"

Dazed by her smile, Jason sat down limply on the cushions. He jumped up with a yell. She said, "What is the matter, lord?"

Jason said, "I will leave you for a short time now."

She was standing close to him, peering at his chest. She said, "There are yucca needles sticking through your shirt. Are you some kind of yogi? Do you like to have them there?"

Jason mumbled, "Yes. I always wear them. But not now. They were in the pots. I will leave you."

She said, "You have some in those things too." She pointed at his breeches. Jason nodded unhappily. She said, "Take everything off, and I will get the prickles out."

Jason said, "No! I can do it myself. It's quite easy." He backed off toward the inner room, holding his arms out at full length.

She walked after him with a puzzled smile. "How can you get them out yourself? I sat on a prickly flower once, and another girl had to get them all out of me. Let me see."

God's blood! These places had no doors, and the more he kept pushing his hands at her, palms out, the closer she came.

Cursing monotonously, and crimson to the ears, he hauled off his clothes. She was a princess! This was a different continent, that was all. Things you thought mad weren't necessarily so. Custom of the country. Beautiful princess—strange custom. Suppose the strumpet arrived in the middle of this?

She walked round him, pulling the little needles out of his belly and buttocks. Then she pulled them from the shirt and breeches. Then she said, "There! I don't think there are any more."

Jason hauled up his breeches as fast as he could, fastened them, with his back turned to her, and put on his shirt. He thought of what had just happened to him and smiled. The smile widened, his belly contracted, and he began to laugh. He tried to stop it—surely he should not laugh in the face of the princess he loved, who had only been trying to help him after the custom of her country?—but he couldn't help himself. He would never be able to tell anyone, so he had to do all the laughing for them, the people he couldn't tell, as well as for himself. He laughed so hard that it hurt, while the princess squatted on the floor beside the piled cushions, the flute in her hand, and looked at him curiously.

At last she said, "What is the matter? Why do you laugh?"

He sat down carefully; but she had done her work well, and he could sit in comfort. He said, "It was funny. I'm sorry." It was difficult to tell her he had been laughing at himself, not at her.

She shrugged and said, "Shall I play?" She blew a little trill. "Or shall I sing? Or shall I read to you?"

"Can you read?" Jason said, his interest quickening.

She said, pouting, "Of course I can. Oh, I suppose you would not know. We are the only women allowed to learn to read, and there are forty of us, and I am the best."

"Only the king's daughters allowed to read? *Forty?*" Jason gasped.

She said, "I don't know what you mean, king's daughters. We are devadassis, wives of Shiva, and *I*, Parvati, I am the best—at music, with men, at dancing, at everything. That is why the king sent me to you. But I am glad, too. I liked you from the time I first saw you. We don't like everyone we have to lie with, you know."

Jason said, "What is a devadassi? What do you do? You are married?" His mouth felt dry, and his eyes were beginning to tingle. It felt very like the beginning of the laughter just now, but he did not think there was going to be laughter this time.

She ticked off on her fingers. "We dance before the god in the shrine, morning and evening. We sing in the temple. We take men for what they will pay, and give half to the priests for the god. We walk with the king and other important people when they are calling on each other. We are wives of the god. *Our* god is Shiva."

"H-how did you become a—devadassi?" Jason faltered. "D-did you want to?"

"Oh no. Our parents give us to the god when we are babies. I have never seen my mother or father. At the proper age the god marries us. *We* will never become widows!" She tossed her head proudly.

The light dimmed in Jason's eyes, and the sounds of people talking in the street below hushed to a murmur. He leaned toward her, his hands out, not knowing what he was going to do. He had humiliated himself for her, both now and in his dreams. She was a whore! It was like Emily in London, only an irretrievable step farther. He had fallen in love with this girl before he knew what she was.

She said with a touch of irritation, "You're just like the other men, after all. You don't want to hear me read." She crouched on the cushions, and suddenly her arms wound out and coiled about his neck, and her skirt slipped loose, and her eyes glowed large an inch from his.

Jason sprang up and away from her in a single jump to the middle of the floor. He gasped, "Don't touch me!"

She lay back on one elbow and said, "I won't, unless you want me to. The chamberlain has told me who you are and why the king wants to see you. I think I know who robbed you that time I found you outside the temple."

Jason walked away from her, out onto the veranda. He thought of his knife. But what had she done? She had never tried to deceive him. He had deceived himself. What a fool! He must learn to be careful, suspicious, cautious. All this pain came from his own dreams. He'd better not dream any more.

But it was a fact, and no dream, that he loved her. Her manner was nothing like that of the women of her trade in London. This was Coromandel. He had behaved meanly to Emily, who would have come searching for Coromandel with him if he hadn't kept reminding himself that she was a strumpet.

He turned and went close to Parvati and looked at her velvety brown skin to see if there was some sign written there that he might read. She looked sad and beautiful in the calm dusk against the dulled garishness of the curtains. How could he change so violently toward her unless he was a mean-minded scoundrel? *She* hadn't changed. She had to do this to earn her food. Handed over by her own mother as a baby—treated like a stick or a stone, to be picked up, used, and forgotten! God's blood, that was a temple where he had met her, a place of worship—full of vile stone carvings!

Perhaps she'd been waiting all these years for a man to come who would love her for herself. He could be the man. Perhaps she had hoped from the first that he meant to save her. And now he had spoiled it. Her faith and hope were being broken. He saw it in her dark and doubting eyes.

He loved her. He boiled with anger against the men who used her, and against her because she had to allow it. It was no shame to love. But every time he saw her he would see also the ten or twenty or sixty men who had struggled with her in that slimy pit of a temple since he saw her last.

He groaned in physical pain and put out his hands to her, asking her to help him. She took them gently, and he knelt down beside her. He said, "Parvati, I don't mind that you are a—devadassi. I love you. I'll marry you and take you away from it all." There, he had done it and said the words. A flood of relief surged through him, and joy that he had conquered himself. He stroked her hair.

She rested close in his arms. She said, "You don't want to lie with me now?"

He said, "No! I'll marry you tomorrow, Parvati. But I know you haven't been able to help yourself. I love you, and I—will—marry—you."

She sat back, a little away from him, and said, "You do love me, don't you?" She spoke wonderingly and touched his cheek with her glittering black fingernails. "You make me feel sad. Why? But of course you can't marry me. That is impossible. But you are very handsome and nice, aren't you? Do you understand? You are very nice."

*   *   *

It was cool and damp in the earliest morning when Jason awoke and remembered that soon the chamberlain would come for him. In the long night he had forgotten that he was a prisoner here, just as he had forgotten Parvati's trade. Now Sugriva's low voice called him, and a little trilling bird sat on the yuccas in the veranda, and the new-washed light flowed like honey over the stone floor. Painfully recollection came back. He was Jason Savage, ex-sailor, prisoner, ambassador—a strange mixture, and hard to understand. The girl beside him was Parvati, temple dancer, strumpet, princess. That was harder still. But if he thought of her as a princess still, she would be one for him, wouldn't she?

She was asleep still, or perhaps pretending to be. He frowned down at her. If it had not sounded blasphemous, and if it had not hurt him to say it, he would have said that she liked being a devadassi. Certainly she accepted it, but there was something deeper than acceptance too. Lying with her had been like some mad kind of churchgoing. He no longer felt it strange that the temple should be her place of prostitution. More than once she had reminded him, in her small ritual acts and preparations, of the Club getting ready for the Oak and Horn. Parson always complained that *that* was part of a bad old religion.

She awoke slowly as he began to get into his clothes. She glanced at the light and said, "Hurry!" He did not feel like hurrying. Yesterday he had been worrying about the king and the chamberlain and the pearlers. Now he yawned and smiled.

Impossible, she had said, that they should marry. He set his jaw. Impossible was a favorite word here in Coromandel: impossible for the king to pay a better price for the pearls; impossible for Simon to change his trade, even though he was starving. But a man could get anything if he tried hard enough. Nothing was impossible—except, of course, for there to be women with six arms or men with elephant faces.

"Are you ready?" the chamberlain called from the passage. "Parvati, is he preparing himself?"

129

"Yes, lord," she murmured. "You must not be late, lord. This may be very important to you."

"There, I'm ready," he said. "When shall I see you again?"

She said, "When the king—or you—sends for me. But don't come into the temple looking for me, lord. You were very near the shrine that first day, where outcastes are not allowed."

"We're going to get married," he said forcefully. "You will see. You want to marry me? I must know if you want to."

She said, "It is impossible."

He seized her shoulders, pressed them back on the cushions, and kissed her hard. He muttered, "I love you," and slipped out through the curtain. The chamberlain ushered him quickly away along the passage.

Jason forced his mind away from her. He was going to see the king. The king would be sitting on a throne, with a crown on his head. There would be courtiers, rich hangings, and an impressive silence. Drayton had put himself at a disadvantage with Don d'Alvarez because he was worried about his noisy spurs. Now the chamberlain was trying to hurry him, Jason—so he would not be hurried.

He walked steadily with long slow strides, placing his shoes firmly on the stone paving and, as he went, gradually gaining obstinacy. They could do no worse than kill him, and they would not do that unless they were mad for blood, like weasels, which they were not. They could not have brought him here with such politeness, meaning to strangle him. And now he had Parvati to think of and care for. Her salvation, as well as their chance of happiness together, depended on him.

He looked up. A silver curtain blocked the passage, and two guards stood there with spears in their hands, and the chamberlain had got far ahead of him and was waiting impatiently by the curtain, and beckoning him to hurry. He came to the curtain, passed it, saw another in front, with more soldiers. The chamberlain held the curtain aside for him, and he strode through. The curtain fell into place with a dull rustle. The chamberlain dropped heavily to his knees, then to his face, on the floor.

It was a bare, square room with yellow-washed walls and two windows. A low dais covered by a single huge stuffed pink cushion rose from the center of the floor. Jason peered at the man sitting cross-legged on the cushion. He had seen him before. This was the man who had been watching from an upper balcony when the chamberlain was leading them to the Don's house the day the *Phoebe* anchored in the river.

The Chamberlain said, "It is the king! Kneel down, kiss the ground between his feet—there!" He made frantic gestures.

Jason stared at the king. It wasn't right to lie flat on your belly like a caterpillar, even for a king. King Charles didn't expect people to do that. Jason said, "I won't." This king didn't even have a crown, only a small round cap of yellow velvet, embroidered with pink and gold brocade.

The king said, "Please!" and then Jason didn't mind. He knelt and kissed the stone. Under his lips it was smooth, and sunk in a little hollow two inches deep.

He stood up, and the king was smiling with delight and twirling the little cap round and round on the end of his forefinger. He was a man in his early fifties. He was plump, pale brown, and very simply dressed, since he wore nothing but the hat and a white skirt round his waist. His eyes were very small, dark, and twinkling bright, and he had a soft, black, droopy mustache, salted with gray. Jason liked him at once.

The king said, "You are the one who waved to me. I knew you would be. I have done my part, haven't I? We are not fools in Manairuppu, though the Portuguese think so. What is the message from your master—Drayton, was not that his name?" He put his hat back on his head and leaned forward expectantly.

"Drayton?" Jason said. "I have no message from Master Drayton. I jumped overboard."

"We know that. It was most skillfully done. Don d'Alvarez does not know where you went, or where you are now, though his men have been searching for you ever since that day. But let us get to business. I want nothing more than to lessen the power of the Portuguese in my kingdom. I welcome your English help. When we have driven out the Portuguese you will find me a generous friend. But of course we must take the first thing first, and get rid of the Portuguese, eh?" He twirled his cap on his finger and twinkled cunningly. "What is your Don Drayton's proposal?"

Jason's brain raced uncomfortably. He thought he was catching at least one word in three, and the general sense seemed clear—except that it was nonsense. He said, "I jumped overboard because I did not want to forget Parvati."

The king said, "Parvati? The devadassi? What is this? Come, my friend, have I not said that it was well and skillfully done? I assure you that no one can overhear us." He swept his hand round in a large gesture to show the emptiness of the room and the solidness of its walls. "Now we must bare to each other our secret thoughts, mustn't we?"

Jason said warily, "Yes, lord. But I have no message from Master Drayton."

The king put on his hat and turned to the chamberlain. He said, "Is it possible?" He peered at Jason. "Did you not see me on the balcony? Do you think I invite the stares of passing strangers without cause? Very well, you knew by that sign that I wished to make secret touch with your captain. You waved back. Good—so we understood each other. Did not the Don's jackals keep guard on the jetty so that I could not send any message to you while your ship lay in the river? Were you yourself not robbed by those same jackals one night near the temple while carrying a message to me? And then did not Drayton launch you into the river so that he would be safely at sea when the big Portuguese ship came, while you waited in hiding until it had gone?"

Jason said, "No."

A hushed silence descended on the room. A long time later Jason added, "I didn't know it was you on the upper balcony."

The king said impatiently, "Was I not wearing my yellow hat? It is *impossible* for anyone to wear a yellow hat here who is not me."

Jason said, "We did not know."

"That is impossible!" the king said sternly.

"I am not a liar!" Jason said, suddenly shouting. "I tell you I don't know what you are talking about. Drayton ran away because he was afraid to fight the *Isabella*. I jumped overboard because of Parvati."

The king's hands flew up in alarm. When Jason stopped, the king slowly lowered his hands and examined Jason's face and clothes as though he were some new kind of fish just brought up from the black of the sea. Finally—as though Jason had no ears, was indeed a fish— he said to the chamberlain, "Do you think he can be speaking the truth?"

The chamberlain said, "It is possible, Your Majesty. He does not look intelligent. And he is very young."

The king said, "Ah, looks are deceptive. He might be wise and cunning beyond his years. He must be. See, he has almost made *me* believe him, against all reason."

Jason glowered at the two of them and hitched up his belt. The king leaned forward and said wheedlingly, "*Please* tell me the truth."

"I have," Jason answered shortly.

The king leaned back and gave him a long wink. He twirled the cap violently, suddenly jammed it on his head, and said, "Very well. We must follow your lead. But you wish to be treated well, of course? Your position hinted at, rather than published abroad?"

Jason thought: It doesn't matter what I say—yes? no? He said, "Yes."

The king said, "I see! When do you intend to reveal your presence to the Don?"

Jason said, "I don't know."

"You do not fear that he will try to kill you?"

Jason said, "Why should he? I know his daughter. She told me where the pearlers' village was."

"I *see*. Do *you* see, Chamberlain? It is most skillful, is it not?"

The chamberlain said, "Most. The daughter must have known he was with the pearlers, but she didn't tell her father. A woman in the enemy's camp is worth an army outside the ramparts. That was most cleverly thought out, and most quickly arranged. Of course, the daughter is nearly blind and perhaps on that account very willing to think she is loved. But the young man was quick, all the same."

The king nodded. "Quite right. You do see."

Jason thought as quickly as his muddied mind would let him. This was much harder than talking to Softy Turpin, but they had said one true thing. The half-blind girl, Catherine d'Alvarez, must have guessed where he had gone. At the least, it would have been reasonable for her to tell her father about her conversation with Jason when she learned that her father was looking for him. But she couldn't have. That was strange.

The king said, "Very well. I agree. The chamberlain will provide you with the necessary robes and arms to keep up your state. Otherwise it would look strange, wouldn't it?"

Jason nodded. But in the name of God, to what did the king agree?

The king said, "And you will work by yourself against them? You will not need my help?"

Jason nodded again. It was easier than shaking his head or scratching his ear.

The king said, "I *see*. In some ways your plan is better, from my point of view. If it fails, the Portuguese will be no stronger than they are now. But, of course, if it succeeds—?" He looked expectantly at Jason.

Jason said, "Yes."

The king said, "I thought so." He twirled his hat thoughtfully. "Oh, well, we know the Portuguese. Let us try the English. They can't be worse. I had hoped to play you one against the other"—he smiled ingenuously—"but I see you are too clever for me. You must be wise indeed to be selected for such a task at your age."

Jason grunted.

The king rose with a glance of open admiration and said, "Proof against flattery too! Is there anything else you wish me to do for you?"

Jason woke up. That was a plain question which he could understand. He said, "Yes. I want to marry Parvati."

The king put his hat on. His thin eyebrows disappeared under it. He said, "*Impossible!* But you are joking? Ha, ha!"

Jason said stubbornly, "It is not impossible. I am a man, and she is a woman. Neither of us is married—"

But the king interrupted him, his hands fluttering like doves. "Don't act hastily. You shall have Parvati's company the whole time you are here. I can arrange that with the priests, can't I?" The chamberlain nodded. "Yes, I can arrange that. She is a wonderful cook too. I can't do more. It is impossible. You will agree to that?"

Jason hesitated. He didn't know whether he could bear living with her while she was still a devadassi. But he had no choice. He said sullenly, "Very well. But I'm going to marry her before I leave here."

He turned and stalked out of the room. The chamberlain came running after him. "This way, Lord Jason, this way. The king's tailor will attend on you immediately. When you wish, visit the stables and choose any horse—except the king's white stallion, of course. Will five hundred gold mohurs serve you for the moment? We pray for your success. When will you begin?"

"Tomorrow," Jason said wildly, and ran into his apartment and drew the curtain with a gasp of relief.

Parvati was there waiting for him. He ran to her, hugged her, and said, "I thought you might have gone—back to the temple."

She said, "Tell me what happened."

Jason sat down heavily on the cushions. He said, "What happened? I don't know. I didn't understand everything, but what I did understand didn't make sense. The king kept nodding and saying, 'I *see*.'"

He imitated the king and twirled an imaginary cap round on the end of his finger.

Parvati laughed and clapped her hands. Then she grew serious and knelt beside him and said, "Tell me all you said, and all they said, every word."

Slowly Jason recounted all that had happened. When he had finished Parvati said, "It is quite clear."

"Not to me," he said.

She said, "The king was expecting the English to make an agreement with him, by which the Portuguese would be got rid of—or, at any rate, their position here weakened. But by pretending not to be an English ambassador, you can say that you have no power to make any agreement. But the king must help you all the same, because he dislikes the Portuguese so much. As he said, he can't be worse off. He had hoped to be better off, by playing the English and Portuguese against each other. But you were too clever for him."

Jason said, "Then he does really think that I am an envoy of Master Drayton's—an ambassador from King Charles, even?"

She said, "Of course. You are, aren't you?"

He turned on her and shouted, "No, I am not! I'm only here because of you. God's blood, don't tell me you don't believe me either!"

She said, "I believe you, lord." But, looking deep and directly into her slightly tilted eyes, he was sure that she did not believe him. There was something else about her expression that he could not read. Was she hurt that he still felt it necessary to lie to her? Or was she admiring his strength of will in keeping this "secret" from everybody against every temptation?

He gave up. One day he'd convince her. Meanwhile— He said, "What am I to do?"

She said, "Nothing. That is why your plan is so wise. I mean, why it is so lucky that the king and Don d'Alvarez believe you are an English envoy. You should be seen about in the city. Visit the nobles and the important priests. Soon the Don will arrange to talk privately with you. He must. He knows that you will soon learn that the big Portuguese ship with many guns will not come back."

"What?" Jason cried, sitting up with a start. "The *Isabella*'s not coming back? How do you know?"

"The king sent me to lie with the Portuguese inspector-general who came on the ship," she said simply. Jason groaned, but she went on. "He was a big, drunken man with a black beard and a loud voice.

He and the master of the ship were talking late, while I and three other devadassis were there. I suppose they thought none of us could speak Portuguese, but one of the other women can. The *Isabella* is going back to Portugal, and Don d'Alvarez has been told he can expect no further help here. If he can keep his position against the English and Dutch, good. If not, his people can't help him any more, because they don't have the warships any more. Only a small trading ship will come here from Goa, once or twice a year, to collect money and bring goods."

Jason got up slowly. He was an ambassador, was he? A powerful man with a warship—more than one, who knew?—waiting over the horizon to enforce whatever arrangements he made.

Everyone was trying to court his favor. Nothing was simple and straightforward here; nothing was what it seemed. But he was no fool, especially now that he was learning to put aside dreams and concentrate on things that mattered, like money and power.

He'd keep his ears open and his mouth shut, except to nod and say "Yes" sometimes. The people, from the king to Parvati, would read secret meanings in that, and in his silence; and then they'd answer with remarks which once would have seemed meaningless to him, but now would give him a clue as to what they had thought he meant the first time.

He said, "I'm hungry, Parvati. Cook me a rice and lentil stew, but not with fish. I'm tired of fish."

She made a brief obeisance, and he watched her swing easily out onto the veranda.

*　　　*　　　*

Now he was eating in a different place, and many days later. He rolled the wine round on his tongue and sleepily examined his host, Don Manoel d'Alvarez. It was worth being rich, in spite of the trouble and occasional embarrassment it caused—as when he tripped over his scimitar, or used the wrong knife. The Don set out more knives and forks on a table than were necessary. Even the lords didn't do that in England. And today he had dropped a goblet of veined yellow glass, which Father Felipe told him was worth ten pieces of gold.

But, against these annoyances, he knew how to keep cool in the soggy heat; he had a slave to fan him and another to wash him down with a wet cloth. He knew what to drink when he had eaten too much—cold sour milk in a silver bowl. When he was tired Parvati massaged him most skillfully. It was good to be rich, all right, especially after tasting the miserable life of the pearlers. To think that he might still be living with them! He ought to do something soon about trying to help them. The king would have to listen to him.

He stirred uncomfortably and eyed Father Felipe on his left. It was four o'clock of a hot afternoon. The Don was on his right; all three were in high chairs on the shaded veranda facing the orange garden. An hour ago Jason had finished eating a ten-course dinner as the Don's guest. He felt heavy and dull and, because of that, important—also wise; also powerful.

The Don stirred and said, "Milord, I would welcome your honest opinion of this wine. One of my predecessors brought it from Oporto forty years ago."

Father Felipe said, "The wines of Oporto are famous in our country." He knew no English, and when he spoke, which was seldom, he used Tamil.

Jason said, "It is a good wine. It has recovered well from its journey." He was glad he had remembered hearing Drayton say something like that, back in London, before they sailed. He had remembered, too, Silvester's respectful murmur.

Don Manoel said, "Ah—h'm—I see you are an expert, milord."

Jason grunted sleepily. The Don was a nervous little man, really. If Jason hadn't been so full—full and sleepy—he would have laughed at being called "milord" all the time. Another shower of rain was drumming on the stone steps and hissing in the leaves of the orange trees.

The rain fell, wet and warm, two or three times a day now. Then the rain curtains hid the view from his apartment, and water streamed down the gold ornaments and stone carvings of the temple, and the backs of the sacred bulls steamed, and the streets ran black with liquid mud. Every day the smells and the flies got worse, and the burning ghats were busy far into the night. But, whether the rain fell or the sun shone, the sea did not change. God stirred it up far out, where the winds began, and all day and all night great waves rolled slowly in to pound on the bar, so that the city boomed and the bass roar of the breakers and the cymbal drag of the sand lay under every other sound. Whole tree trunks rolled ashore on those waves and lay awash like ruined ships at low tide, and jellyfish with sails and poisoned darts drifted in on the seething tides, and the fishermen went to sea only if they were starving.

The Don cleared his throat, and Jason awoke rather impatiently from his reverie. He liked thinking about the sea.

The Don said, "Milord, there is a matter about which I wish to speak frankly, as man to man—as fellow Christians in a heathen land, I might say."

Jason said, "M'm." Here it came. Parvati had been right.

The Don said, "I will take the liberty of asking you, milord, if you are fully aware of the great dangers to the whole European position in the East which are inherent in your present course."

Jason said nothing.

The Don said, "And dangers to you personally."

Jason said, "You mean you will have me killed next time, instead of only robbed?"

The Don exchanged glances with Father Felipe and said, "I had hoped you would not find out who did that. I apologize for it. We did not know who you were at that time, milord. And I do hope you will understand that it was done to protect our position here. It was my duty. The king has undertaken to sell the pearls only to us. The inspector-general from Goa came here on the *Isabella*, you know, and would make secret inquiries into my conduct. There was also a possibility that you might be carrying a—ah—message."

Jason said, "The *Isabella* will never come back here." The Don and the priest exchanged another quick glance. Jason waited lazily. This was a good game.

The Don said, "Your information is incorrect, milord—though it is possible that a smaller ship may replace the *Isabella* on this duty. Nevertheless, let us assume for a moment that what you suggest is true. What then? If your English ships openly attempt to break into the trade here, His Most Catholic Majesty will certainly order resistance to be made. That resistance might not be made in these seas, you understand. You will remember that His Majesty holds large fleets in Spain and Portugal."

Jason grunted. The Don went on slowly, "But if the intrusion was *not* open—if I could be assured that any arrangement made was purely between myself on the one side, and yourself and Master Drayton on the other, and did not commit either of our countries— then I have authority to make such an arrangement."

"You mean your Catholic Majesty will wink at it. Half a loaf is better than no bread."

Don Manoel started explaining, talking carefully, mentioning figures and percentages, and then qualifying everything he had said. Jason thought: They're on their last legs, all right. The real fool here was the king. This kingdom of Manairuppu, according to Parvati, had made the original agreement with the Portuguese, which gave the latter a foothold in the country, only as the price for Portuguese assistance in a petty war against its neighbors. Parvati thought that original agreement had been a good idea. She said, "Of course it was good. It made Manairuppu more important than the other three kings of Coromandel—Tiruvadi, Ponpalamai, and Krishnapatti." But Jason thought it had been a bad and foolish idea. Even now, if the four kings of Coromandel patched up their quarrels, they could, by acting together, easily throw out the Portuguese, and each of them would be better off than before.

Don Manoel was saying, ". . . and ten per cent of the pearl? I think that is just."

"Not enough," Jason said automatically.

Don Manoel sighed and stroked his beard. He was not a ferocious or even a stately man. He was quite frightened now—weak and frightened and sad; the *Phoebe* somewhere over the horizon, his country visibly losing its power, his wife recently dead, and his daughter Catherine half blind and a little queer.

Don Manoel said, ". . . we should continue to insist that the seaward trade of the other three kingdoms must pass through Manairuppu. You agree?"

"I haven't seen any such trade," Jason said.

The Don shrugged. "There is none, because the three kings object to paying dues to the king here. But it makes *him* happy."

Jason thought: I have come a long way from Shrewford Pennel. I am a farm boy, but I am being asked to rule the affairs of kings. I am already rich. Every day gifts, which Parvati carefully locked away in a heavy box, came from the king. Courtiers gave presents too—never openly, though Jason could see no reason why they were so secretive.

He had decided that deviousness was here a form of disease, and that it afflicted everyone. He had nearly broken a tooth on a cake which turned out to contain a large jewel. And then this morning a tray of sweetmeats had come from the chamberlain, and when he and Parvati had eaten off the top layer there was gold money underneath.

Don Manoel said, "The king's annual tribute to us is very considerable, only we call it a gift. Perhaps you noticed my daughter's necklace?"

That daughter, Catherine, had asked him a hundred questions about his travels. Answering her truthfully, he had noticed increasing respect in the glances that Father Felipe occasionally shot across the table at him. He had thought with some pride that the priest was showing admiration for his bravery or wonder at the extent of his travels. The tone of a later remark of the Don's showed him he was wrong. They didn't believe a word of what he said. They were marveling at his skill in duplicity. The girl believed him, he was sure, though it was difficult to tell by her eyes. They were good eyes, which lit with interest at the right moments, but they were focused so far away that she might have been smiling not at him but at a golden bird strutting on a rafter in the high, far corner of the great hall. He was glad she had not mentioned the map.

Don Manoel said, "You will, at least, think about these things, milord?"

He said, "I can promise nothing."

"Of course not," the Don said with a sigh of relief, as though Jason had already agreed. "Take time to consider. When you have had a little more experience with the wiles of these Eastern monarchs, I am sure you will understand." He coughed. "Milord, now that my poor daughter is no longer with us, may I have the privilege of knowing who you really are?"

Jason glanced up in annoyance. They were calling him a liar again. The Don said hastily, "I have a reason for asking—an important reason, and perhaps not unconnected with our other affairs."

Jason said, "Everything I have told you is the truth."

Don Manoel spoke to Father Felipe. The priest chuckled thinly and rubbed his hands. Don Manoel produced a bluff smile and said, "Come, milord, farm boys are not entrusted with missions of this delicacy. I know England, you must remember. And the tale of your being a common dancer in London! It was magnificent! But you may trust us with the truth."

"Why do you want to know?" Jason asked. Don Manoel was getting more like Parson every moment. Soon he'd *have* to lie, or they would believe he was a liar.

The Don seemed embarrassed. He cleared his throat twice and then said, "What I am going to tell you may seem strange to you, milord. Your English customs are somewhat different in this matter, but among us a father arranges the marriage of his daughter, and, if he is well-to-do, provides her with an ample dowry. The gentleman she married would also expect a high position in his father-in-law's household."

Jason drank some wine quickly. He knew he would do better to keep sober, but he needed a nerve now that only more of this thick red wine could give.

The Don said, "In the case of a daughter who is perhaps not so beautiful as one would hope, or who has had the misfortune to be born with a limp or other defect of body, the dowry would be considerably increased. A father would only wish to feel sure, in such a case, that he was linking his blood with blood of an equivalent rank. We have been hereditary grandees for two hundred and fifty years."

He paused expectantly. Jason grunted and ran his fingernails across the heavy crimson brocade on the seat of the chair, making a satisfactory rasping sound.

The Don said, "*My* son-in-law, for instance, would expect to become my principal lieutenant here. Let us suppose you were that man. Should we reach an agreement on the larger matters already discussed, there would be considerable advantages to you, to me, and to Catherine, if you were her husband and so my relative."

Jason said, "You would force Catherine to marry me?" He tried hazily to picture himself as the blind girl's husband. It was impossible. She was—well, there was nothing particularly wrong with her. She was quite interesting, though sad. But how could he think of her or any other woman with the taste of Parvati's lips sweeter than the wine on his tongue?

Don Manoel became more obviously embarrassed. He said, "I—really, I hesitate to tell the truth lest you should think my poor daughter is— She is *virgo intacta*, I assure you, and not all forward or improper."

Jason thought: No, Mistress Catherine isn't forward. She was the only woman he could imagine who could ask to stroke his face and shoulders on first meeting, and yet not be thought forward or worse. She was different.

Don Manoel said, "It is she, Catherine, my daughter, who has insisted I speak to you."

141

Jason took another gulp of his wine.

The Don said hastily, "I am not against the marriage—not at all, milord. I have just pointed out to you some of the advantages of such an arrangement. But I would never have urged it on my own account because there are also difficulties and disadvantages. You are not Portuguese, and the proposal may strike you as sudden, and therefore put you against it. You are not a Christian—I *do* beg your pardon, milord, you are not a Catholic. Would you be willing to become one?"

Jason said, "No."

"I feared so. Then, my daughter is perhaps a little strange—not insane, you understand, but strange, from her unfortunate affliction. She sees more inside her head than outside, and there have been occasions when people who do not know her well have thought she was—" The Don searched in the air with his hand and said, "Ah, I remember your English word—*soft*. They have called her a softy. No, milord, I would not have suggested this, but I love my daughter, and she has insisted that she has no other chance for happiness, and never will. It is strange, and touching to a father's heart, especially when she has never before shown the smallest interest in men or marriage. But the marriage would be impossible if your rank—forgive me—is not as high as I suspect it to be. Therefore, milord, I ask your favor to tell me your real name and station."

Jason got up and said, "I must go. I have an important appointment." He gathered up his new stiff red hat—one with a short brim, modeled after a blue hat which the chamberlain often wore. He wore Indian clothes mostly now. The big curved scimitar which he kept tripping over had been a gift from the commander of the Manairuppu garrison.

The two Portuguese got up with him, and waited expectantly. Jason went out onto the steps. It had stopped raining, and the garden smelled of earth and oranges. He said, "Thank you for the dinner, Sir Don. I will give your greetings to Simon the pearler next time I see him, Father Felipe."

"He was a good boy," the priest said, "but they slip back where they came from. The work of God goes slowly in Coromandel, like everything else."

Jason said, "Good-by. Please give my respects to Mistress Catherine."

"But—?" the Don said, pleading, coming down two steps into the sun. "Your birth? Your rank?"

Jason said, "I am the bastard son of a tinker and a Salisbury washerwoman. Good day."

He strode off down the path. That should stop the Don's crazy scheming and bring the poor softy girl to her senses. He'd known he'd have to lie to be believed.

*　　*　　*

He slept uneasily in short spells, between hours of lying awake, and full of tension. When he was asleep he dreamed of Parvati's clients, and when he was awake he thought over what he would say to the king. As soon as he returned from the Don's mansion he had asked for an audience, because, somewhere along the slimy lanes, he had made up his mind what he must do.

He had followed the map to Coromandel, thinking that the mere following of such a strange and wonderful thing would be enough. Well, it wasn't. That was a silly, childish idea he'd had before he found it didn't pay to be a simpleton.

Then he'd made up his mind that the map was important because it would lead him to treasure. But what did he want to be rich for? So that he could marry Parvati and be an important man.

Well, he didn't need money to marry Parvati. He needed the thing that the Portuguese called "caste" and the Indians "color." And to be an important man money was useful, but not essential. There was a surer way to become important. That was to become a leader here.

It would not be difficult. The Indians were stupid. They kept saying, "Impossible," to things that weren't impossible at all. He had only to show the king that Manairuppu's true interests lay in making an alliance with the other three kingdoms, and persuade the other kings of the same truth; and then the Portuguese would be driven out, and he, Jason Savage, the man who had thought of the plan and put it into execution, could hardly help becoming great and important. Why, he might be the chief minister of the alliance!

He got up and took a drink of water. Now he didn't want to go back to the mat where Parvati lay. He went out on the balcony and leaned out over the dark city.

But if his plan succeeded, wouldn't he be making it just as difficult for the English as for the Portuguese to get a foothold on this coast?

Perhaps. But the English didn't want such a hold. He'd heard the question being discussed many times on the voyage. They wanted only to trade, as they were trying to do in Surat on the other side of India. If the four kings could combine, trade would be opened up and much increased. Everyone would benefit.

The problem of his caste was more difficult, because of the Indians' mad insistence that a man could not become other than what he was. When they said it was impossible for him to marry Parvati, they meant that he was not of the right caste, and that she was married already, to the idol Shiva. God's blood, he'd show them! He'd play their own game on them and tell them it was "written on his forehead" that he must marry Parvati! Then what would they say, eh? And he'd use his power to force the priests to say that the idol intended to divorce her. What would they say to *that*, eh? Dick Whittington became Lord Mayor of London. Jason Savage could become high caste, chief minister, friend of the king, husband of Parvati—rich, famous, in love.

Near dawn he had a sudden exciting vision of warehouses full of silk and spice, of the ships of all nations riding at anchor in the Coromandel river, of white men and brown men trading on the wide square and himself under a big tent seeing fair play for all. They would have to build more jetties and open up a channel through the sand bar. Why, the provisioning of the ships alone would make the people richer. The great king of Madura, who was much greater than any of these four, and whose dominions lay to the southwest, might be persuaded to use the port. . . .

Parvati called softly, "Why are you awake, lord?"

He went in to her and told her all that he had been thinking, trying to make her see the reality and the wonder, and that all this lay in their hands to achieve. She listened quietly till he had finished, and then said, "It is impossible."

For a moment Jason's vision failed him. Then he shook his head obstinately and said, "You wait and see." He got up and began to dress.

But was Parvati, after all, a mere woman, like Mary Bowcher, who could not understand the truth of dreams? He knew she was not, from the nights they had talked together, holding hands. Stranger thoughts came to her than his imagination could encompass. She whispered of gods and hero-demons, and young men riding the clouds, and these fantastic things were more real to her than his sunset galleons. Yet surely a galleon, or a simple agreement between four kings, was more "possible" than a man who drank up the purple sea.

Sugriva sidled in and whispered, "Lord, there is a man waiting in the passage to see you."

"What kind of man?" Jason asked peevishly.

"A colorless fellow," Sugriva said. "A black man who says he knows your lordship. Shall I send him away?"

"Yes—no, let him wait until I have eaten." Jason smelled food cooking, and he was hungry. Besides, he told himself, the king may send for me at any moment, and I must not face this most vital audience on an empty stomach.

He ate leisurely and soon forgot about the man who was waiting to see him. After his meal he had his daily Tamil lesson with Parvati. This was the hour of the day he liked best, when she squatted down in front of him and said a sentence over and over, and made him repeat it until he got it right. After that she would arrange a host of oddments on the floor and name them one by one, and he would repeat the names after her. Sometimes she would take him into the streets, or go wandering through the palace, pointing and naming.

A continuous, annoying cough kept disturbing him, and he shouted, "Sugriva, stop coughing!"

The servant hurried in from the veranda and said, "It is not I, lord. It is that black man. I will send him away."

Jason said, "Oh. Tell him to come in."

He knew in his heart who it must be. He had known from the beginning, but had hoped he might be wrong. He had done nothing for the pearlers, and he could have if he had tried. He sat back on the cushions and waited for Simon to come in. Parvati left him, and he waited alone.

It felt bad, as though he had done something shameful, to see Simon the pearler edging in through the curtain, bowing at every step, his hands joined in front of him and his face nervous with the expectation of being rebuffed. Why did he have to be so helpless?

Jason sprang to his feet and went to shake Simon's hand. "Simon!" he cried. "How are you? You are looking well." Simon was not looking well, and he had a bad cough.

Simon's drawn face slowly relaxed; then he smiled admiringly as he looked round. "This is what you deserve, Jason," he said. A fit of coughing prevented him from speaking for a moment; then he said

145

between gasps, "You—are a—great man now. And you have Parvati the devadassi actually living with you, they told me!"

"Yes," Jason said shortly. "We must have a long talk sometime, but I am expecting the king to call me at any moment now, so—"

"The king!" Simon said. "It is wonderful!" He stood twisting his bare legs one around the other in the splendid apartment.

Jason asked how the pearling was going. Not good; their luck had deserted them since Jason left them. The weather was bad. Circuitously Simon came to the point. As he forced out the slow words Jason's thoughts raced ahead for answers and justifications.

Simon said, "They told me to come and see you. All our people did. Because it is bad down there. It is always bad at this time of year. This year it is worse. We remembered you were going to speak to the king. We know that we said it was impossible, but we are foolish people of low color. We thought perhaps you might have spoken to the king. We wondered—"

Jason said earnestly, "Simon, I have." Oh, damnation on all of them! He had not forgotten. He would help them when he reached power. Why did they make him feel such a scoundrel?

Simon's face lit up as Jason went on, speaking slowly, picking his words, tasting bitter anger against them as he told his lies. "I think soon I shall be able to persuade the king to do what I suggest. You understand that this matter cannot be hurried."

"Yes," Simon said. "We understand. Only, we are very hungry. Panailal's woman died in the boat three days ago."

Jason's hand fidgeted with the hilt of his jeweled scimitar. He said, "I am doing my best, Simon. You must trust me." He found that his voice trembled.

Simon cried, "We do, Lord Jason. How can we not trust you? You are our star."

From the passage the chamberlain's voice called, "The king will see Lord Jason now."

Jason said, "I have to go. Good-by, Simon. Go back to the cove and wait. You will hear from me." He hurried out, the look of awed happiness on Simon's face imprinted on his mind.

❋   ❋   ❋

During the long night Jason had rehearsed what he was going to say. Now he hated himself for what he had said to Simon, and as soon as he began to speak to the king he knew that his words carried

146

the force of that bitterness in them, and he saw that the king and the chamberlain were listening to him with a close, almost nervous attention.

First he recounted what he knew of the powers and privileges of the Portuguese—the tribute paid to them, their monopoly of the pearl buying, their share of all the kingdom's seaward trade, their position above the king's law. Then he said, "And what do they give you in return for this?"

The king said, "Why, they prevent the kings of Tiruvadi, Krishnapatti, and Ponpalamai from having any seaward trade at all." He rubbed his hands cheerfully.

Jason paused a moment before he spoke again. This was the crux of his whole case. He said, "But my lord, that is of no advantage to you! Suppose now that you made an alliance with the three kings. Would you then need the help of the Portuguese?"

The chamberlain began to say something, but the king shushed him with a peremptory wave. The king's little eyes were gleaming like jewels, and he had taken off his hat and now held it expectantly poised on the tip of his forefinger.

Jason expounded further. Let an agreement be made among the four kingdoms to forget their old enmities. Let them form an alliance. Let the Portuguese and all other foreigners be told that they could trade as they wished but would be granted no other privileges. Let the other three kings help in enlarging the port of Manairuppu, for it would also be their port. Let the king of Manairuppu pass to them some of the extra money the port would make. Let the goods of the four kingdoms flow freely to the outside world, at whatever price they would fetch. Let the goods of the outside world flow freely in, at whatever cost the four kingdoms could afford.

Jason finished and stood, breathing deeply, in front of the cushion-throne. The king said slowly, "And what about your people—the English?"

Jason said, "The same for us. Some Englishmen will say that I am a traitor for suggesting this, but it's not true. After a few years everyone will be better off, including the English."

The king said, "Then you are not an envoy of Master Drayton? Oh, I see, I *see*." He clapped his hat on his head and stood up. He said, "Never have I met such guile combined with so much youthfulness! Lord Jason, you are worthy of the highest honors and will receive them. With you at our right hand we cannot help but prevail." He rubbed his hands together. "Excellent, excellent! And the English! Ha ha!" He sat back and roared with laughter, his belly wobbling like a brown syllabub.

When he recovered he said, "And you shall be my ambassador to the three kings, eh? No one else could make them believe. Let me see." The cap twirled, the only point of movement in the room. "Let me see. You shall have my seal. The Brahmins of the temple shall write a letter. Now"—he bit his lower lip—"the timing. I have it. The Dussehra Puja! Let the three kings send their armies to arrive here on the second or third day of the Puja."

"Why should they send their armies?" Jason said.

"Oh, to show Don Manoel that we four kings are indeed in agreement. To provide a sufficient force to overawe Don Manoel's guards. Something like that," the king said with a wink. "That ought to be enough to convince those black-faced monkeys. What else should we think about?"

Jason said, "I must know what you are willing to offer. I must be able to show them how much better off they will be under this plan than they are now. Each king should be allowed to have an officer of his court here in the port, for instance, to satisfy him that your taxes are not being charged on his goods."

"Certainly." The king waved his cap.

Jason thought hard. Parvati's "Impossible!" had prepared him for long arguments. He had expected to spend a month making the king see reason, but the king was agreeing to everything, and before he himself had had time to work out the small details. He said, "I can't think of anything else now. But there will be other things, of course."

"Certainly," said the king with another large wink. "Lord Jason, I shall leave it entirely to you. Promise them anything—anything within reason, that is; otherwise they will become suspicious. But who am I to teach *you*?"

Jason thought: Now for it. He said, "If I can succeed in persuading the three kings to join with you in this alliance, will you help me to marry Parvati?"

The king peered at him in surprise, seemed to think for a few moments, and then answered, "I will do what I can. It is the priests who decide, you know, not I. But I can promise to do my best."

Jason said, "May I take Parvati with me on the embassy?"

The king looked at the chamberlain, then back at Jason, and shook his head admiringly. He said, "It is unnatural, your skill—and that innocent face! Certainly, take Parvati, and several of her sisters as well, if you wish. There will be many important courtiers and advisers to be persuaded. Bend your neck, my son."

Jason bowed his head, and the king placed a heavy gold chain round his neck, saying, "That is for you, a mark of my respect. When you are ready to go on your embassy, come to me for my seal ring. Oh, ha ha ha ha!"

As Jason left the room the king was laughing, and the laughter rang in his ears all the way back to his apartment.

There was something damnably strange about the king's manner today. "Black-faced monkeys," he had called the three kings; but in the same breath he had cheerfully agreed to give them whatever they asked for. Well, perhaps it wasn't necessary for allies to respect one another. But still . . .

God's blood, what did it matter? They were all mad as hatters in this place at the best of times. What mattered was that he, Jason, had done what he set out to do. He had made the impossible easy. During the Dussehra the alliance would be cemented, and the next day Parvati would be his wife!

He rushed through the curtain, seized Parvati by the waist, and danced her round the room. "I've done it!" he shouted. "The king has agreed. We're going on an embassy to Ponpalamai, Tiruvadi, and Krishnapatti!"

Parvati said, "But he couldn't have agreed."

Jason cried, "He has, I tell you! He has! And if I succeed in forming the alliance he is going to make the priests let you go so that you can marry me!"

She said, as once before, "Tell me everything that he said, and you said, and the chamberlain said—every word."

He told her. When he finished she looked at him for a long time in silence and then began to cry, sitting beside him, holding to his hand and letting the tears spoil her painted, lovely eyes.

*   *   *

Jason rode on with a high heart and made the little gray stallion canter through the mud in the path, so that clots of mud flew up behind and the stallion's hoofs came with a *plock* out of the earth at every pace. Ponpalamai gleamed in the sun ahead, and sixty miles of road lay behind, and Parvati cantered at his side. The servants tittuped along several yards back, on small country ponies, leading and driving the pack horses that carried the stores and spare clothes. Every day the rain fell, and they had forded wide rivers and waded for miles through flooded fields, and so they were all covered from head to foot in black mud.

The hair tingled on the back of Jason's neck as he gazed at the city on its hill, just as it had when from the masthead of the *Phoebe* he had spied the low land of Coromandel—but now there was something else as well as discovery. In Ponpalamai he was looking for what he knew as much as for what was strange. He belonged here now; he had a place here as clearly as he had had a place on the farm in Pennel or in the starboard watch of the *Phoebe*. But his place in India was more important than either of those, and he knew all about India, as he knew all about farming and dancing and London and seamanship. He saw a dome and a spire and a spike dominating the city—and knew that was a temple, and knew there would be devadassis and an idol and Brahmins. The people pressed out of the city and passed on either side of his horse, and he looked down and knew them—beggars, fakirs, soldiers, farmers, merchants. He had met all these in Manairuppu, and a king. He had conquered there. He would conquer here.

This was the first of the three kingdoms of his embassy. The success of the whole embassy depended on how this king received him and his proposals, because from here the word would go ahead to Krishnapatti and Tiruvadi. Krishnapatti would not keep out of an alliance already shared by Manairuppu and Ponpalamai. And Tiruvadi would follow that lead.

Jason smiled at Parvati and asked, "Tired?" She answered, "No," and drew her sari more closely across her face. They had entered the outskirts of the town, and the crowds were staring at her.

Jason began to sing. "*Greensleeves was all my joy, . . .*" And Parvati said, "Go slowly, lord. Look." Jason glanced up and saw a line of color and steel stretching across the street ahead of them.

Parvati said, "The escort, come to do you honor. Very slowly, lord. It is the custom. Also, this may be our last chance to talk together before you face the king."

Her eyes smiled at him, but the pink and silver sari hid her mouth and lower face. She said, "You are ready to withstand all their wiles?"

"I am ready," Jason said, "though I have nothing to hide. Parvati, this is the third or fourth time you have spoken to me like this, as though in warning. What is in your mind? If you know something that I do not, you must tell me. Why did you cry that first time, when I came back from the king and told you of the plan? You have never answered me."

She laid her hand gently on his left arm. Their horses walked at a snail's pace down the narrow street, and the line of soldiers loomed minutely nearer. She said, "Because I love you, Jason. They are Vishnu-*bhaktas* here. We are Shiva-*bhaktas*. This is the town of the *yoni*, as Manairuppu is the town of the *lingam*. That is why we have a saying: 'In Manairuppu women lose their secrets, in Ponpalamai men lose their strength.' See!" She nodded at the great temple ahead. Jason looked more closely at it and saw that he had been mistaken in his first, distant impression. On top of the spire, instead of a spike, there was a golden trident. He saw then, with a sudden chill, that the men watching from the doorways wore the same mark of a trident painted on their foreheads, the curved sides in white, the straight center cut in red. He did not know everything, after all. Perhaps he knew nothing.

Parvati said, "They have strong wine here. And they are of the Right-Hand faction."

Jason said impatiently, "Vishnu-bhakta, Shiva-bhakta, Right Hand, Left Hand, Brahmin, Pariah! How many more ways do you divide yourselves?"

She said, "Portuguese, English, Popish, Christian, Wiltshire, London, lords and strumpets—what else have you not told me about?"

Jason said, "That's all different. Anyway, I have nothing to hide."

Parvati dropped her eyes and muttered, "That is why, if I did have any suspicion, I would not tell you. If you fail, our king will have you executed."

"That fat little man!" Jason exclaimed. The king was a nice enough figure of fun, twirling his little cap around on his finger.

Parvati said, "Yes. He is not a cruel man, but he may have to. He might have promised—the priests, perhaps—"

Jason stopped his horse and pretended to adjust his stirrup. He said, "But how will it help me not to tell me what I ought to know? Quick. We must get on."

"Oh, my lord, there is gossip, talk, rumors. I don't tell you of them, because then you might doubt. You have no doubt, so no one can help believing you. Hold your horse steady until the salutes are over."

A band of musicians began playing; six men rushed forward, throwing firecrackers; and a small brass cannon exploded with a roar. Jason swore aloud and struggled for control of his horse. The captain of the escort trotted forward to greet him. The houses were white and blue; the captain wore a violet coat and a steel cap, and his rearing, neighing horse was red; the sky was low and dark violet; and new rain began to fall, slanting like spears across the heavy green of the trees in the market place beyond.

The captain said, "From the King, the Great King, the Keeper of the Vulture, the Sower of the Lake, Lord of Ponpalamai, to the Lord Ambassador of Manairuppu, greeting!"

Jason's stallion calmed down as Jason patted his neck. Jason took a deep breath and said, "Take me to the king, your master."

The escort took station before and behind. Jason huddled into his cloak and looked straight ahead. Parvati fell back among the servants.

The stallion moved quickly under him, the rippling power of its thews held now in check. He had a jeweled scabbard and a pearl-encrusted scimitar. The furniture of his stallion glittered with onyx and amethyst. He commanded men, gold filled his purse, and behind him in the rain rode the most beautiful woman on earth, and she loved him. Power was a physical thing he could master and ride, as he rode this stallion. His power would grow, because he was Jason Savage. With it he would dredge the river, build the roads, make men wise in the council of the port. He would be lord of the pearlers, master of the king's wealth, friend of the foreign shipmasters. He looked back and sought Parvati's eyes, because none of it would matter without her. Or would it? Her eyes would tell him. But she was too far behind for him to interpret any message she had for him, and a steel helmet came between them. Jason turned again and rode on toward the palace of the king of Ponpalamai.

❀   ❀   ❀

Was he winning? Had he made the king understand? Perhaps. He had a rope of diamonds greater than the meridian of the earthquator round his obsidian, and he hadn't asked for it. All given freely with much admiration—most wonderful place in the world, Ponponpattavadi. But he *must* be winning. The king sat at his left and pressed his knee from time to time. Kings did not do that for nothing —nor rubies spill out from an alabaster box; and hadn't he always wanted a grain of mustard seed? He'd got it now, or perhaps it was pepper, as they said. And there were rubies in silver jugs, not spilling —sparkling, swaying, swirling on the floor. Aha, they'd nearly made a booby out of him that time. It was not rubies, nor wine, but the dancing girls, red skirts shimmering and the muscles in their thighs springing tight. The wine was in a cup in his hand. The thing to do was pour the red wine into their ruby navels, just the right size.

He winked at Parvati, reclining on the king's other side. Parvati was the only woman here, not counting the dancers, and there was something wrong with that. Not respectable, not polite, she said, for other women. *Impossible* for them to come, she said. She meant the king's duck-bottomed wives. If it wasn't respectable for them, it wasn't respectable for Parvati. He caught hold of the king's shoulder and opened his mouth to complain about the disrespectable spectacle they'd invited Parvati to attend. Parvati leaned across and popped a pink sweetmeat into his mouth, so he could not speak. The sweetmeat had silver paper on the bottom. When he'd eaten it, he'd complain.

Parvati shook her head slightly. God's blood, did she think he couldn't take a hint? Living as a strumpet in the temple had blunted her outlook. But no more, no more, for—*Alas, my love, you do me wrong, To cast me off discourteously,* and she was his Lady Greensleeves. She was wearing a short-sleeved green bodice because he'd asked her to.

"You sing like a nightingale," the king said. Jason nodded. He had not meant to sing aloud, but if he had, and the king liked it, so much the better.

The dancing, though! What a dance! Such as no man on earth had ever seen, probably. He counted happily. Eighty. Two for each girl. He began muttering under his breath. "Forty girls!" he cried. "Wonderful!" He wrung the king's hand in congratulation.

How could anyone keep his senses in this squealing uproar? They all looked drugged. They stared at him out of large, dull eyes. They'd feel better if they stepped outside for some fresh air, even if it was raining.

The king said, "How do you like our wine, Lord Jason?"

"Wonderful, wonderful! It travels well." There was a girl shrieking behind the violet curtain at the king's back, all hidden, only her toes showing under the curtain. The king had a hairy chest and a barrel of a stomach and fat breasts. He showered gold coins on the dancers, at the feet of the shrieking singer, in Jason's palm. The drummers drummed, the fluters fluted, the girls' navels went round, and—jerk—round.

The king said, "Your king doubtless has better music in Manairuppu than this miserable offering of mine?"

"What, what? They can't make so much noise in Manairuppu, that's why it's better."

The king said, "You speak Tamil with extreme excellence, Lord Jason."

"Oh yes, learned it from the pearl fishermen. Do you know them? Wonderful people, great friends of mine. And Parvati."

Parvati was reaching for another sweet, the long silken line of her arm sweeping down into the curve of her chest. Aha, let the nautch girls twist their navels, let their skirts shake. He was safe from any damned Ponpalamai yoni. He loved Parvati. He began to cry.

The king said, "Wine! Wine for Lord Jason the ambassador!"

Jason cheered up and said, "Gallons! I love it. No one could get drunk on this. Horsepiss, really. You want to get drunk, you try English ale. It's the best. You know, to get drunk on this stuff is IM-*possible*. Ha ha!"

The king said, "So young a man, a stranger and a foreigner—so delicate a mission?"

"No need to wonder. I thought of it. Look. What do the Portuguese *do* . . . ?" Then it got hard to explain, but he came out swimming strongly at the far end. The king would understand now.

The king said, "You must excuse me from believing you, Lord Jason. On the other hand, it would be worth much gold to me to learn the inwardness of this matter—say, five thousand gold pieces. Five thousand."

"I understood the first time. Do you think I'm drunk? Are you calling me a liar?" He rose to his feet and swayed grandly over the king. He saw swords and spear points waving under his nose. He said, "I'll knock your head off."

The king's eyes were cold and dark. He had a thick neck and cold, greasy eyelids. He was a cold, greedy bastard, not like the little fat Manairuppu king. *He* wasn't cruel. He was a funny man with a funny hat.

The king said, "Pray be seated, my lord. No insult was intended, I assure you. Can you tell me a little more about . . . ?"

154

He'd tell them. They were such fools that they couldn't see their own left hand if it was held up in front of their noses.

"Ah, look at that girl in the middle!" The statues were real, after all. Round as a wheel! Phew, what would Grant say to this? Molly would giggle. Emily—Emily would be shocked, because she was what she was.

The king was talking to Parvati. He'd better watch this dance. It was a very difficult one. He was a dancer, and he knew. He'd fix his eye on one part of her—the navel, obviously. But there was a small bright light in the back of his head too, which he had to look at, so he was looking two ways at once.

All the same, the dance was important. He muttered to himself, "The Oak and Horn!" It was nothing like, but this was another dance that had been going on a long time, and if he could understand it, get it silhouetted in front of the little bright light in his head, he'd get rid of that small, cold feeling of being lost. He'd be an Indian.

An Indian! And he'd already been a Roman and a trout and an Englishman and a sailor and a seagull, and one of the men who had built the Henge. But this was the closest and the biggest.

He strained to catch the slightest sound from the dancers' bare feet, but there was none. They stood facing him, their knees bent and their feet flat-placed on the stone floor. The stone wall behind them was carved in trident designs; every man in the room wore the red and white trident on his forehead; and the hangings behind him were violent black and yellow, the trident pattern printed on them.

But the yoni was not at the center of the dance. The dance was something to do with birds, or perhaps God.

Yes, it was the yoni. If you continued that motion the dancer in the middle was making you were a woman with a man. But, controlled, held down to a single flick of a single muscle, there was no woman and no man in it. You couldn't lust after nothing, so the power that made the movement was not lust.

God's blood, he could hardly see a thing. Instead of seeing, he felt. In his head and in his belly the dancers danced now. Say it slowly, what you feel: The holiest, wisest man in the world grew out of lust, four legs in a bed, a lingam and a yoni. Good. But this dance was not the beginning of life. It was the end of creation. They made little movements, but he was thinking of the sky, of mountains, of God. Therefore the movements of the dance were lustful, but the dance itself was not.

The light shivered, and his head began to ache. All gone. He got to his feet. "Late," he muttered. The king gave him gracious permission to retire. Jason looked at Parvati. He wanted her to come with him now. He would tell her about Stonehenge, and she'd break through the curtain between him and the dance. If she did that he'd understand everything—Vishnu-bhaktas, Right-Hand factions, and all.

But Parvati glanced away with a smile for the courtiers on her left, and Jason wobbled out of the room.

*   *   *

He took a gulp of water, put down the jug, and heard a mysterious groan.

Ah, it was himself making that mournful sound. He drank again. Outside the dawn was coming, lifting the golden trident of the temple out of the night; and a few lamps burned in the city. His head opened and shut like a fist. He wiped the back of his hand across his mouth, shuddered, and lay down carefully on the mat.

After a while he said, "Parvati, did they drug me?" She didn't answer.

Just like a woman to be snoring asleep when you needed her. He said, "Wake up. I want to know, was it a drug, or only that wine? God's blood, it tasted like old sour cream. Do we have any coconut milk here?" She didn't answer.

He said, "Where are you?"

He brought the little oil lamp in from the inner room and held it up in his hand.

She was not there where he had been lying. He went through all three rooms of their quarters in the king's palace, searching for her. His head was the middle of a jumpy ball of light, much too bright, and no one in the world loved him enough to stay with him when he was ill.

He whispered, "Parvati? Where are you?"

She wasn't anywhere. He sat down on the stone floor, holding the water jug in one hand and the little lamp in the other.

She might have fainted somewhere. She might have lost her way in these long red passages. She was drugged, as he had been. She was in danger! Where had he seen her last? God's blood, no one was going to harm her. He'd kill them.

156

He wrapped his clothes all round him anyhow, snatched up his sword, and ran into the passage.

The flame bent back in the open bowl of the lamp, and his shadow hurried along, broken at the knees, just behind him, and the cold warnings of day lay in wait at the narrow window slits as he rushed by them. The passages were damp underfoot and smelled of rain and night and the sleeping animals in the stables below.

He saw a soldier leaning against the wall and ran silently up to him, boiling with rage, and shouted, "Where's Parvati? What have you done with her?"

The soldier had been asleep on his feet—an old soldier. He awoke with a yell, and his pike fell clattering to the floor. He clutched at Jason's face, screaming, "Mercy! I am a poor man!"

Jason shouted, "Mercy? Where's Parvati? Tell me or I'll run you through."

The passage was full of galloping soldiers and shouting, and swords clashed against his, and half-naked men jumped up and down around him, and everyone yelled. The sentry's eyes bulged, and his red mouth bawled, "Help, help! That's him!"

Jason shouted, "Where is she? What have you done with her?" His sword flashed and clashed, and his head was ready to split.

A captain ran up from a mile down the passage, waving his sword and shouting, "Don't hurt him! That's the ambassador of Manairuppu."

Jason lowered his sword. This was the same man who had commanded the guard of honor on their arrival in Ponpalamai. Jason grabbed his arm and grated through clenched teeth, "Where is Parvati? Let her free this minute, or, by God, I'll—"

"Please, Jason, be quiet. I am well." She was there at his side, cool, smooth, gentle of eye.

Where had she come from? He looked round in an aching daze. There was a curtained doorway beside him, where the sentry had been, and now he saw two more soldiers peering through from an inner curtain and— He said, "That's the king's room! Was he hurting you?"

One of the soldiers laughed suddenly. Jason glared round at him, and he fell silent.

Parvati took his hand and said, "Let us go back to our room. It is morning."

They went side by side along the passage to their own place. The soldiers behind them began to laugh, louder and louder.

In their quarters Jason said, "I awoke, and you weren't here. I was afraid. Oh, Parvati, you didn't go to the king! No, you didn't!"

She stood in front of him, and she was the same princess he had met the first time in the temple. He turned away, his shoulders hunched in his misery. She said, "I wanted to go."

He said, "How can you say that? Don't you love me?"

She said, "You know I do. But you don't understand. I am married to Shiva. Shiva touched this king, so that he needed to worship him, through me. It was a great victory, for this king is a Vishnu-bhakta, as I told you. I don't know why you are so sad, Jason. I *love* you."

Jason lay down on the mat and closed his eyes. "Go away."

But she would not leave him. She whispered in his ear, "We have almost won. Oh, you were so drunk, and because it was you, and drunk, they could not help believing you."

Was he hurting you? he'd said. No wonder the soldiers laughed. But, O Savior of Men, he could only go on loving her.

She whispered, "There may be more trials in store for us, but I think the king more than half believes."

She loved him, but . . . It was impossible, but . . . They had almost won, but . . .

Her hands stroked his forehead, and he fell asleep.

＊　　　＊　　　＊

"Up! You, up! And you. Come along!"

Through harsh, stony abuse Jason crawled up from sleep. It was midmorning, only four or five hours since he had found Parvati. This time she was here, shrugging slowly into her daytime skirt, and with her back to the men in the room. There were five soldiers here, and the same captain.

"What is this?" Jason asked.

The captain snarled, "You'll find out soon enough. Hurry! Get dressed." He jabbed the point of his sword toward Jason's stomach. "Hurry, dog from Manairuppu!"

Jason backed away. Again the chill of not understanding, of being lost in another world, tightened his chest. He tried to remember where he had put his knife. Parvati said, "Do not fight them, Jason. This is no mistake."

The soldiers dragged them into the passage and hurried them

along. Jason looked at their frowning, scowling masks and could not bring himself to believe that this was really happening. These people had fed him wine and played him music. Their nautch girls had danced for him. But now they were rushing him down the passage, down, down, spirally stone-stepping down, with Parvati behind him, into the belly of the Ponpalamai hill, and their hands hurt on his arm, and it was real. Now it was dark between the fitful tapers, and weeds dripped where the stones met, and he saw men with matted hair clinging like apes to the bars of cells on either side.

The soldiers pushed him into a stone dungeon, and Parvati followed. Two torches flared in brackets on the walls, and a charcoal brazier glowed in the center of the floor, and iron pincers and toothed wheels and whips and saws lay on a table, and dirty red splotches streaked the gutter running out under the door.

The soldiers held him face to face with Parvati. The captain said, "The truth, now! Why were you sent here? Who are you? What does the king of Manairuppu really mean to do? Quick, speak!"

"I have told your king the whole truth," Jason said. "Have you gone mad? Or is it your king's order to treat us like this?"

"Never you mind that," the captain snapped. "Take the woman. You—watch!" He lifted a branding iron off the brazier and raised it to Parvati's right cheek. The velvet bloom of her skin glowed in the red light. He said, "Speak, woman."

The captain glared from Parvati to Jason. Jason's eyes started out, and he shouted, "Let her go! How can I tell you anything when I have nothing to tell?"

The captain snarled, "Liar! Tell the truth!" He brought the red-hot iron closer to Parvati's cheek. Parvati looked steadily at Jason and said, "My lord has told you all the truth."

The captain jabbed the brand against her cheek. Her skin sizzled, and a puff of blue-gray smoke rose to the roof.

Jason fought madly against the men and the chains holding him, mouthing threats and the name of God. Her cheek was a tangle of ugly welts and torn skin. Still she looked at him, still her eyes were on his as her knees sagged. Suddenly her head dropped and she hung limp against her chains.

Heavy drops of sweat stood out all over the captain's forehead and upper lip. Jason bit his tongue until he had control over himself. Then he said, "I shall remember you."

The captain said, "The dead remember nothing. Tell me the truth.

Are you a magician, come to put an evil spell on His Majesty? What trickery is afoot in Manairuppu?"

Jason said, "I have told the truth."

The captain glanced at the wall above Jason's head. Jason remembered seeing a small grating up there as he came in, but now, when he tried to turn, a soldier hit him on the jaw, and the captain said, "His hand—here!"

They seized his left hand and strapped it to the table. The captain took a pair of rusty pincers and with them caught hold of the fingernail of the little finger on Jason's right hand. He said, "One at a time, until you tell the truth," and the sweat dripped off him in a dirty stream onto the table, and his face was gray.

Jason looked at the pincers. That was a terrible thing to do, even to think about, to pull a man's nail out with that. "Aaah!" He tried to pull his hand back, but it was over, and the first nail was gone. The agony wrenched his jaw and shoulder and wrist, down to that little finger and the blood pouring from it. Parvati had come to her senses and was smiling at him lopsidedly. Yes, smiling she was, though her right cheek could not move. He gaped at her in the awe of his love and admiration.

The captain dashed his hand across his forehead, wiped his palms on his coat, and took hold of the nail of Jason's other little finger.

The king of Ponpalamai entered with his chamberlain and two officers. To the captain he cried, "What are you doing? Are you mad? Chamberlain, release the lord ambassador and the Lady Parvati at once."

The officers unchained them, and Jason sprang forward and put his arm round Parvati's shoulder. The king said to the captain, "Word has just reached me of this thing that you were doing. I can still hardly believe it, though I have seen it with my own eyes. Speak, before you lose your head."

The captain said, as though repeating a lesson, "This morning we found the man, with sword drawn, outside your apartment. I thought what I should do. I decided that he might be an impostor, conspiring with the woman to take your life. I have been finding out."

"You had no authority to do such a thing," the king snarled. "For this you shall die—tomorrow at noon." He turned his back. The chamberlain and the soldiers seized the captain and began to chain him.

Jason said, "Let's go back and get some salve for these wounds. Oh, my dear, it must hurt!"

"Not yet," Parvati said. She turned to the king, bent her head, and joined her palms. She said, "Do you see my cheek, Majesty?"

The king muttered, "Yes. Oh, it is terrible, terrible! He shall suffer for it tomorrow, with pincers in his entrails before he dies."

Parvati said, "Your Majesty, we will be gone by then. But it is our right to see his punishment, is it not?"

The king hemmed and cleared his throat, and a new burst of sweat raised pimples on the captain's forehead. The king said, "There are certain formalities and prayers which must be done before an execution, certain—"

"It is our right," Parvati said.

"Parvati," Jason muttered, "can't we leave it? I don't want to see him executed—though he has deserved it."

"No," she said, "we cannot leave it. The king of Ponpalamai must realize that when he gambles against the king of Manairuppu he gambles for life, not for a few cowrie shells—or even for a woman's cheek and a man's fingernail."

The king said, "But I knew nothing of this, I promise you."

Parvati said, "In Manairuppu it is the custom to speak the truth, Your Majesty, as my Lord Jason has been speaking truth, and only truth, to you. We are waiting."

The king looked unhappily at her, then suddenly gave a signal. The captain screamed, "You promised!" But the big soldier behind him leaned forward and garroted him. The king turned away. Parvati watched until the captain died, and Jason, awed and afraid, watched Parvati.

It was Parvati who led him back to their rooms in the upper part of the palace, her left hand in his right.

When they were there— "We have won," she whispered exultantly.

Jason muttered, "Yes, but did we have to kill the captain? I see now that he was only doing what the king ordered him to. The king is the man who ought to suffer for what he has done to us."

Parvati said, "My lord, of course we had to insist that the captain die, or the king would have known that we were not really angry. Then he would know that we were pleased at having come through the test successfully. Besides, the captain had to try to beat us, which means that he had to lose—so he had to die. It is just."

Slowly Jason forgot the captain's strangling face. He looked at his little finger and at Parvati's cheek. He had won, but every such victory left him a little more unsure of himself. Only Parvati knew, only Parvati mattered.

*　　　*　　　*

"It is just," Parvati repeated to herself for the twentieth time. She edged the mare to the side of the road, where there was less mud, and hitched up her sari so that it left only her eyes and forehead showing. A young village girl was waiting beside the path there, and she did not want anyone, least of all such a young and pretty girl, to see the ruin of her cheek. Besides, the heavy green ointment smeared over it made it look almost worse than it was, if that were possible.

And her poor lover, with his aching hand! He had been brave once it was done, but he had looked very frightened for a moment just before, when he realized they were really going to do it. Was it possible that he had not known all along what was going to happen? Well, he said he had not guessed. He loved her, so perhaps he was speaking the truth. On the other hand, perhaps he was not. Why should he? She was a woman and not supposed to understand too much of men's affairs. And yet—and yet—sometimes it was impossible to believe that he was anything but what he seemed to be—an innocent, red-faced child. Those were the times when she felt that she had to warn him against dangers and perils and treachery—as if he didn't know, really! He must have laughed at her in secret often enough. But he loved her.

She cheered up and let the sari fall, so that the soft air could play on her face. No one but her lover could see now. She had done most noble work for the god, her husband, in Ponpalamai. The Brahmins would be pleased with her, and her god would shine the light of his eyes upon her when she went to wash his feet on her return to Manairuppu. This was one of the times when the body and the mysteries inside, which only the Brahmins were wise enough to understand, came together, and then you felt that your own god loved you, and the great God, which they called Being, held you in His care, and every part of creation danced most gently in its allotted place, including a scarred temple prostitute.

Was it, after all, a noble thing to be a devadassi? It was he, her English lover here, who had put that doubt into her mind—not quite for the first time, but with a new strength, so that she found herself questioning what she had always found perfectly clear, and wondering where she had before only marveled. She wished he would not speak like that. She loved him—but there, he believed that men and women could show love only by lying together, which was a silly idea. She had tried every way to tell him she loved him as she loved no earthly man, no living thing—well, her god lived, of course, but not in the same way—and her lover did not understand. The language of flowers, and of the fingers, and of the food she placed before him, and the words she chose when calling him in the evening—he did not understand. She might as well have been speaking to a—to a Vishnu-bhakta! She spat vigorously.

He was so stupid, and so clever; so wise, and so foolish. As Shiva was her witness, if he cared only for lying with her, if that was love, why was he in such a fret? She had gone to him whenever he wanted her, and would continue to do so.

There must be some other reason, which he kept hidden from her, for all his talk of marriage. He knew that was impossible. Yet he kept talking about it so. What could it be?

But a child, now! That too he had spoken of. Her belly quickened, and she held tight to the reins and dropped her eyelids so that he could not see her eyes. The Brahmins saw to it that none of them had any children. One of the girls, a long time ago, ran away because she wanted to keep the one she was going to have. Treachery, faithlessness, blasphemy—adultery, really; it was a terrible thing to have done. Yet that girl had her baby now, and no one knew where she had gone or what had become of her. Parvati bit her lip. She must not think of it. This was another of the ideas that his talk kept in her mind, where it had no business to be. She was *not* as other women. They would be widows. They would crouch, shriveled and unwanted, by dead fires, while *she* basked forever in the love of her husband. He would love her then, toothless and scarred and old, as fiercely as he loved her now.

But was Jason innocent or wise? That was the question. What should she say to him, how much leave him to guess? He was going to be a great man, and then he'd marry. But it was unbelievable that he wasn't married already, at his age. He *never* told her the truth, even about things where he must know that she must know he was lying. She looked at him admiringly and said, "My lord, I love you."

❊   ❊   ❊

The embassy was over, and he had won. The four kings would be allied. His own king had given him an estate of a hundred acres along the river. Jason paced nervously up and down the room, toward the big wall mirror and then away from it. But— Why was he nervous? Why didn't he want to see Don Manoel, whom he was expecting at this very moment?

He didn't know what people were thinking any more. At least he wasn't sure. He strode toward the mirror, frowning at himself. That was a rich man in the mirror. But he didn't like his face. It reminded him of a pouting Stevens girl in Pennel, who was always wanting something she couldn't have, and her face showed it. She didn't want things like Coromandel, or the wings of a plover, or love beyond the act of love, but things like a new pair of shoes or some other girl's kerchief.

He said, "Any sign of the Don yet?"

Sugriva, leaning over the balustrade to look down into the street, said, "No, lord."

Jason resumed his pacing. The Portuguese had no sense of time. Why was the Don coming, anyway? Twice Jason had refused urgent invitations to visit the mansion. Wasn't that a plain enough hint that he did not want to discuss any private agreement, nor yet the negotiations between the four kings—which were secret—and still less the idea of marriage to Mistress Catherine?

Still, Don Manoel was coming, because he'd swallowed his pride and begged to be allowed to visit Jason in the palace apartment. And Jason had reluctantly agreed. And now the Don was late.

What had he been thinking about? Ah yes, that face of his in the mirror. What *was* the matter? Dreams had been good in their time, but what he had now was real. He could hardly count the jewels the three kings had given him on his embassy. His finger had healed. He was fat and well. He had become a partner of Vishnuprodhan the merchant, and all he had to do was say an occasional word to the king or the chamberlain, and then Vishnuprodhan gave him big bags of money. It must be a very good business.

Every soul in Manairuppu knew him as a rich and powerful man and knew that it was he who had given Parvati her golden bangles and golden anklets. Then why did this unease sit like a rat on his shoulders?

"The Don is in the courtyard," Sugriva said. "There is a woman with him."

"What? Let me see." Jason ran and leaned over. He looked down on the top of the Don's wide, feathered hat and some of the white ruff just showing under one side of it. Beside the Don he saw a small dark head covered by a square of blue cloth.

"He has brought his daughter with him," Jason muttered. "Why should he do that?"

Parvati said, "I shall watch from behind the curtain. I want to see the girl more closely. From a little distance I have seen her in the city, and I thought she was beautiful. She is nearly blind, too?"

"Beautiful?" Jason said. He laughed. "You're not a man, or you wouldn't say that."

Parvati said, "Is beauty only on the skin, like the bloom on a peach? Or only in the shape, like the curve of a mango?" She moved slightly, turning the scabs on her cheek toward him.

He said, "Oh, my dearest—" But she walked through the curtain into the inner room.

Sugriva announced Don Manoel and Senhorita Catherine d'Alvarez. The Don waddled in, looking shortsightedly from side to side until he saw Jason in the cool gloom. His left hand rested heavily on the hilt of his sword, and with his right he led his daughter slowly across the floor.

Jason bowed and said curtly, "What do you want to speak to me about?"

Don Manoel said, "Are we alone, milord?"

Jason said, "I have told you that I am not a lord."

The Don said with sudden bitterness, "I am allowed to pretend to myself that you are a nobleman, I presume? I would like to be assured that no one can overhear us."

"Sugriva is outside, and he does not understand English," Jason said.

"And behind the curtain?" the Don said. He gestured with his hand at the inner curtain, but behind the spectacles the sad brown eyes turned meaningly to meet Jason's. That phrase "behind the curtain" meant "in the women's quarters." The Don's expression, in words and eyes, therefore asked: Do you have a woman through there?

Jason said, "Behind the curtain is my affair." He felt a flush of embarrassment rising to color his neck and face. But of course he was being silly. The girl Catherine could not see any expression on

165

his face—she was too blind. She was looking at him—through him, almost—with her intent, un-shy look.

Jason said, "Please come quickly to the point of your visit, Sir Don. My affairs keep me busy."

"I know, I know," the Don said, and his little beard wagged in an old man's sneer. "You are rich and famous and have much on your mind. Well, if you insist on having your black mistress listen to my daughter's shame, I can't prevent you. I have come to make you a formal offer of marriage on her behalf—fifty thousand pieces of eight."

He flung his hat on the floor and glared at Jason. Stuttering now under the stress of his emotion, he said, "Any other f-father would p-put his daughter away rather than s-sink to this. But she's helpless! L-look at her. She made me do it."

Jason stood speechless, while realization of the strength of the old man's love for his daughter crept like a painful light into his mind. And then another, brighter, still more hurtful light came—the girl loved him. No, that was impossible. That word again! But it *was* impossible. They had met only twice. It could not be love. She had a crazy passion for him, as girls sometimes did. She wanted to be looked after, and thought he could be bribed to do it.

Don Manoel snarled, "Answer me, boy! Fifty thousand pieces of eight—yes or no? A grandee's daughter, and no questions about your birth or faith. Why do you look at her like that? She's not mad. She has only decided that she must marry you or live miserable the rest of her life. Also, that you must marry her, or *you* will live miserable the rest of *your* life! That's not madness, is it? You think it is? So do I. Yes or no?"

Jason said, "I cannot marry Mistress Catherine. I am going to marry Parvati as soon as—soon."

The Portuguese girl sighed, a long, half-smiling sigh. "I knew it. Oh, Jason, you are of one perfect piece all through."

Jason said, "I beg— What?"

She was dotty. She had a pointed nose, and the big eyes were like velvet pieces cut out of her face. Her skin was luminous, as though there were a fine layer of olive oil somewhere deep under the surface. She was thin-shouldered and small-boned, and today dressed all in black and pale blue.

The Don sighed too when Jason spoke of Parvati, but his was a sigh of unhappy triumph.

He said, "You heard what Milord Jason said, Catherine? I told you he was in love with a devadassi, didn't I? And he has been honest enough to say so. He is a good young man—but now you see you must give up this folly."

Catherine said, "I always believed it, Father. But you would not believe that he meant to marry her. It makes a great difference, because"—suddenly she dropped into Tamil—"because *she* knows it is impossible that he should marry her, even if he does not know."

Jason started and glanced at the curtain. Parvati would certainly be listening behind there. So when he spoke again he too used Tamil. He said, "Parvati has told me it will be difficult. But with the king's help we shall be married. Mistress Catherine does not know me, so she cannot know that she will be happy with me, or I with her."

The girl sighed again, and with the same contentment. Her eyes crinkled pleasantly, and she said, "How long did it take you to decide to follow your map?"

He muttered, "No time, but—"

She said, "You are my map."

He said doggedly, "But the map is not important to me any more. I had forgotten all about it until you spoke. And—I don't love you. I love Parvati."

She said, "Parvati can come to you whenever you wish, for as long as you wish. It will not be for long."

Jason stared at the girl with his mouth dropping, dumfounded at the arrogant self-confidence of her words. Don Manoel raised his fists and cried, "No! You are without shame, Catherine! What have I done to deserve this?"

The sweat began to trickle down Jason's back under his brocaded coat. He said, "I am sorry. It is impossible."

"There!" the Don said. "Thank God!" He wrung Jason's hand. "I do not know whether you are an earl or a farmer, milord—but you are a kind man. Go out on the veranda, Catherine. I want to talk alone with Milord Jason."

Catherine walked slowly toward the light. The inner curtains rustled as she passed them. Jason cried, "No, Sir Don! I don't want to talk with you. Please go at once."

The Don said, "It is important, milord. I *must* make clear to you the dangers that threaten all of us—I repeat, all of us. I do not think you realize . . ."

Jason saw that Catherine was standing by the curtain. It opened a crack, and Catherine raised a big eyeglass on a holder to her eye. Catherine and Parvati were looking at each other through the gap in the curtain. Don Manoel's voice hurried on in persistent, anxious pleading, but Jason heard only the rustle of feminine whispers from the curtain.

He shouted, "Please go away, both of you!"

The Don said stiffly, "Very well, milord. Do not blame me for the tragedies that may fall on all of us alike, if what I suspect is true." Then his anger broke down under his anxiety, and he said, "Please let me talk to you. I must, I must. You can't know—"

Jason seized him by the shoulders and pushed him toward the outer curtain, shouting, "I don't want to hear. Go away, damn you!"

He ran back for the girl, but when he reached her she put out her hand, laid it in his, and followed him quietly to the curtain, and so out into the passage.

For the space of a breath he was alone. Then Sugriva hurried in from the passage and Parvati from the inner room. Sugriva said, "Lord, there is a fellow waiting in the forecourt to see you. It is the same black man who was here before."

Parvati said, "That girl is the one you must marry, Jason. She is your half that is lost, that you are always looking for in the mirror, that you used to look for in your map. What she suggests is good and possible. Nothing else is."

Jason cried, "God's blood, you are mad! Women are mad. To think that I put yucca in my shirt for you!"

He ran out along the passage, down the steps, turned left into the stables. "A horse, quick—any horse!" he bawled.

"Yes, Lord Jason! Coming this minute!"

The stable boys ran about like ants while he stood raging with jealousy and disquiet in the heavy light. Simon was waiting for him in the forecourt, but he could not bear to see Simon now. Simon would have some moaning complaint about food and pearls and damned starving babies. Why didn't they go to a merchant like Vishnuprodhan? If they had any sense, any will power, they wouldn't be in trouble.

He swung into the saddle and raced through back streets toward the sea. The people scattered like rabbits in his path, saying to one another, "That is the foreigner, Lord Jason—a mighty man, a great man."

As soon as he reached the sandy beach Jason slowed to a canter.

The clouds were dark purple today, the sun hidden far above them, and the sea at his left hand a waste of violet dotted with white. The waves rode in like squadrons of cavalry, and the spray blew in torn sheets across the salt-white sand. The piles of driftwood that were really boats lay in clusters above the high-tide mark, but even in this weather some of the fishermen were preparing for sea.

Jason reined in and watched as two men came down, tied their boat together, and hauled it to the edge of the surf. He called out, "Surely you aren't going fishing in this?"

They glanced up, cried, "We're hungry," and launched the craft into the broken water. They paddled out toward the curved violet vaults of the waves. The strength of the sea caught them, the bow pointed to the sky, then leaned over backward, and the boat capsized, hurling them into the foam. They scrambled aboard and tried again. Three times they tried; each time the sea dashed them back. The fourth time the wave was smaller, and the bow of their craft hung for a second like a finger, trembling, pointing in entreaty at the dark clouds, then dropped down, and they were over. Then the waves hid the boat, so that the men seemed to be sitting in the water, and soon he could no longer see them.

He turned his horse's head south, momentarily feeling small and ashamed. But there was nothing he could do for these pearlers and fishermen—yet. Let them wait a little, until after the Dussehra, and then they'd know the value of having Jason Savage for their friend.

But in truth, whatever advantage he wrought for them would soon go for nothing. They were shiftless people and drank too much and took no thought for the future. They must have had good years in the past. What had they done with the money they'd got then? He knew the answer. They'd spent it in feasting and marrying off their children and getting into debt on account of their silly superstitions.

Marry Catherine d'Alvarez, who thought she would soon drive Parvati from his thoughts! He shook his head angrily. He thought he disliked Mistress Catherine very much now. He had been a fool to feel sorry for her. Perhaps it was foolish to feel sorry for anyone.

He trotted on along the shore, watching the straight miles of sea and the ranks of white foam. When would it begin to rain again? Or were the rains over at last? This might be the last stormcloud before the calm, sunny days which they told him would come at Dussehra.

"Lord! Lord Jason!"

He looked round. Simon was running at the horse's quarter. His deep chest heaved, and his breath came in gasps. The sand was heavy here, and wet with spray. Jason saw Simon's footprints trailing back beside the horse's hoofmarks toward the distant tower of Manairuppu Temple.

God's blood, Simon had an insolence to follow him out here when he wanted to be alone! He snapped, "Simon, why have you followed me?"

Simon joined his hands in supplication and said, "Lord, I am sorry. They told me in the city that you had gone, and the one behind your curtain sent down a message that you did not want to see anyone, but—"

Jason said, "I've told you that I can't help you until I am in a stronger position myself. I'm doing the best I can."

"Yes, yes, lord," Simon said. "We know that. We only pray that you will soon have success. One of our old men is eating earth."

Jason felt very tired. He had seen earth-eaters in Tiruvadi and asked Parvati why they did it. She told him, "Because they are hungry." They knew that they would die from it, but they did it. And after a time no one could help them. No one could do anything but watch them die. He had seen a man die from it. He had seen no greater agony of death.

"Eating earth," he repeated mechanically. But what could he do?

Simon said, "But I did not come to tell you this, Lord Jason. A great ship sailed into our cove yesterday."

Jason cried, "What ship? Was it the English ship—mine, the *Phoebe?*"

"No." Simon shook his head. "It was like it, the man said who saw your ship, but not the same. It was bigger, bigger even than the Portuguese ship."

Jason said, "What nationality was it, then?"

Simon shrugged. "We do not know. But they sent a little boat ashore and asked the way to Manairuppu, and how far. We told them. They spoke only a word or two of Tamil, and no other language we could understand. Then the little boat went back to the big ship, which stayed in our cove until it was dark. After dark it sailed away, straight out to sea. We saw it in the starlight. But before it left, the little boat rowed ashore just behind the point, and one man got out of it, and the rest rowed the little boat back to the ship.

Then the big ship sailed away. The man walked toward Manairuppu."

Jason said, "Were the men on the ship dark, like Don Manoel and Padre Felipe? Or fair?"

"Fair, fairer than you. Like bleached grass was their hair," Simon said.

Jason let the reins rest on the horse's neck. The strangers were unlikely to be Spaniards or Portuguese. They might be English; but he had not heard of any other English ship that was making the voyage to these waters. One might have come, though. The Dutch— they were seafaring people. He'd seen a Dutch ship in the Narrow Seas, and most of its crew were fair-haired. But if the Dutch or any-one else wanted to go to the city of Manairuppu, why didn't they all go there in the ship? Instead of that, the mysterious vessel was some-where out to sea, and only the one man ashore, and he gone by this secret means in the dark of last night toward the city.

Simon said, "Another thing, lord—they asked about pearls."

The spray rattled against Jason's stiff coat. He was worried, and the now familiar feeling of uncertainty was growing. He said, "I must get back to the city now."

Simon shuffled his feet. "I too, lord, to my house."

Jason said, "Good-by. Don't think I have forgotten you."

Simon ran south along the sand, and Jason watched him. *Don't think I have forgotten you!* That was exactly what he had done.

But this ship, and the strange man who went toward Manairuppu in the dark?

He turned his horse's head and galloped north. As soon as he reached the palace he told Parvati what Simon had said. Then he said, "I want you to find out for me who the man is. The priests in the temple will know. They hear everything. They knew where I was, didn't they? Run down to the temple now and ask them. I must know where he is hiding."

Parvati said, "I will go, lord."

She went out. Jason sat on the cushions and stared at the evil-colored sky. The wind rose steadily and droned about the city. Par-vati came back late in the afternoon.

He asked eagerly, "Well?"

She said, "The priests say no white man has come into the town."

"They're lying!" Jason cried angrily. "He must be here. Simon said so."

Parvati said, "The priests say no such man has come."

Jason said, "I must go and tell the king."

Parvati said, "Of what use to tell the king? If the priests say no man has come, he must believe them."

Jason cried, "Nonsense! He has come, and he must still be somewhere in the kingdom. It may be the Dutch, knowing the weakness of the Portuguese, and trying to force in here in their place. That would upset all my plans. The Dutch may be preparing to attack the city! They are no better than pirates. I must tell the king."

He hurried out. At the royal curtain he whispered to the chamberlain that he must see the king at once, and privately. The chamberlain muttered, "He is alone now. I will tell him."

In a moment the chamberlain returned, and Jason entered the presence. Quickly he made his obeisance and rose to his feet and said, "Your Majesty . . ." He told the king what Simon had seen.

The king glanced at the chamberlain with a frown and squeaked agitatedly, "Why has no word of this man's coming reached me?"

The chamberlain said, "Majesty, it is possible that the pearlers are mistaken. They drink much palm toddy sometimes—don't they, Lord Jason?"

"Sometimes," Jason said, "but Simon—"

The king interrupted with a wave of his hat. "Chamberlain, cause thorough inquiries to be made. Have the pearler Simon brought here and questioned. Ask the Brahmins to investigate. We shall find out the truth, Jason. Have no fear." He put on his hat and frowned ferociously.

The chamberlain bowed to the floor, and the interview was over. Jason walked slowly back, worrying, the palms of his hands wet, and his head aching with the thunderous heaviness of the air.

*　　*　　*

All the next day he paced up and down his room, waiting for the king's summons. Every time he turned at the west end he saw himself in the mirror, until, in the late afternoon, he suddenly whipped out his scimitar and jabbed the hilt against the glass and shattered it. Parvati's flute wailed on. The thin, pure notes had no tune in them, started nowhere, wandered far, arrived nowhere. He cried, "Be quiet, Parvati!" The fluting stopped.

Sugriva hurried in. "Lord, the Portuguese woman is here."

Jason snapped, "Who? Send them away." But the curtain opened, and Mistress Catherine d'Alvarez walked slowly forward, with Sugriva fluttering like a hen at her side.

Jason said, "I have nothing to say to you. Please go home."

Parvati opened the inner curtain and stood watching, one hand raised to the curtain, and her hip curved. The blind girl knew she was there and smiled at her. Parvati smiled back and made *namusti* with her hands.

Jason snapped, "Go home! I will not marry you."

Catherine said, "It is not about that. My father has had a heart attack because of something we have found out. I have come to tell you. A foreigner, a European, has come secretly to Manairuppu."

Jason started and said, "How did you know?"

She said patiently, "My father has spies. This stranger is probably Swedish or Dutch. He is hidden here."

Jason turned on Parvati and said, "I told you! The priests are shielding him. But why?" Parvati did not answer.

Catherine said, "It is not only the priests. The man is hidden here, I said. Here, in the palace."

Jason cried urgently, "That's impossible! The king would have to know!" But of course the king need not know. It was a big palace. Someone could be betraying him. But who, and why?

Catherine said, "Parvati knows where the stranger is, but she must do what she is told. She is the wife of Shiva."

Jason shouted, "It's a lie! She would not deceive me. You are trying to turn me against her! You only waste your time in trying, because I don't love you and I won't marry you, whatever happens."

Catherine said, "Very well. I have told you. I can do no more about that. But I can tell you why you must marry me."

She put her hand on Jason's arm. The grip of her thin fingers strengthened. She said, "You know I can't see well. Because of that I can hear and feel better than most people. Do you know why you are unhappy? Because you've forgotten your map. Do you know what Vishnuprodhan's business is? He's a moneylender—a bad, cruel one. Do you know who's more in debt to him than anyone else? Simon and the pearlers."

Her voice fell on his eardrums in cool, trembling waves, and her fingers tightened and relaxed in time with each break of phrase. He struggled against her, and against believing what she said, but there was no escape.

173

"The king here is hugging himself because he is about to outwit the other three kings *and you*. Parvati loves you, but she must do what she must—what is written on her forehead. There is only one thing you can do. Ride now to the three kings and tell them not to do whatever was arranged. I don't know what it is. Give all your money to the pearlers so that they can buy themselves free of Vishnuprodhan and start again. Then marry me, and we will go together to find the treasure on your map. Isn't that the only way for him to be happy, Parvati? Isn't it?" She insisted now, and her voice was firm.

Parvati's huge eyes shimmered under a curtain of tears. She gazed at the Portuguese girl and whispered, "Yes. I love him, though. I do."

"I know." Catherine moved slowly—she always moved slowly and with grace—and kissed Parvati's cheek.

Jason tightened his lips in bitter anger and said, "You are out of your minds, both of you. Now go."

Catherine said, "Here are precious stones worth fifty thousand pieces of eight—for my dowry. Take them and pay off all the pearlers' debts to Vishnuprodhan with them." She pressed a heavy leather bag into his hands.

Jason's temper broke. He shouted, "Very well! I will marry you for fifty thousand pieces of eight. After that I will never see you or speak to you again! Is that what you want?"

The girl said calmly, "Yes. Now I have bought my map. One day you will tell me how much you paid for yours. Don't forget to send that money at once to the moneylender. Make him sign a receipt, and then you send it to Simon by a safe hand."

Sugriva sidled in and said, "Lord—the lord chamberlain wishes to speak with you. He has the black man with him."

Jason said, "Oh, God's blood, who? Simon? I suppose they'd better come in."

The chamberlain entered, and, at his heels, Simon. Simon kept his eyes fixed on his bare feet. The chamberlain looked curiously at Catherine and said, "It is a private matter, Lord Jason."

Jason snapped, "You may speak. The Portuguese also have heard about the stranger."

The chamberlain said smoothly, "That is odd, because we have proved there is no such person. Not only have the priests and the city guards and the watchmen denied that any foreigner has come here, but this fellow has admitted lying to you. You, speak!"

Simon muttered, "It was a lie, Lord Jason. We saw no foreigner. No ship came to our cove." He kept his eyes on the floor, and his black toes wriggled in an agony of discomfort.

Jason said, "But why should you lie to me?"

Simon muttered, "We wanted you to get into trouble here, so you would come back to us—live with us again."

Jason said, "You ran all the way down the sand after me just to tell me a lie?"

An even lower mutter: "Yes."

Jason gazed in stunned, cold astonishment at the pearler. Suddenly he remembered the dungeon at Ponpalamai and ran his thumb over the smooth nail-less tip of his little finger. He said, "They tortured you!"

"No," Simon answered in a very small voice; his bare skin bore no marks of lash or iron.

Jason grabbed the cross on Simon's necklace and held it up in front of his face, so close that Simon had to squint to see it. He said, "Do you swear on this cross that what you told me was a lie?"

Simon's dark eyes turned beseechingly from side to side; the tip of his red tongue rolled round his lips. He whispered, "Yes."

Jason said, "Swear it, then. Take hold of the cross and swear it."

Beside him Parvati moved slightly. She stood against the curtain with the flat golden sunlight on her, her head up, her arms bent and each finger separately bent, her knees slightly bent and her feet flat and turned outward, her jacket fallen apart and her breasts exposed in perfect rounds, all turned to stone.

Simon's eyes were fixed helplessly on Parvati. Blindly he groped for the cross, took it in his hand, and said, "I swear it."

He blundered out of the room. Parvati's fingers relaxed, her arms drooped slowly to her sides, her thighs came together.

Jason said, "And that mad Catherine wanted me to pay off their debts!"

*   *   *

After another day or two all work stopped, the temple conches wailed at midnight, and the people's eyes shone wild as tigers'. This was Dussehra. Processions were born, like rivers, in little streams and quiet places. They grew larger, moved faster, filled the streets from house to house, shouted and babbled, surged into other torrents, tossed to and fro, fought, roared aloud, died down. Behind them, like the dead rats and bleached twigs stranded by a flood, they left blood in the streets and corpses on the dungheaps.

Hurrying back to the palace in the middle of an afternoon, from an errand in the city, Jason and Parvati came upon one of these riots. They waited in the shelter of a side street for the fighting to move on. Jason glanced at the sun and said with nervous anger, "I shall be late for the king's council. Damnation take the fools! *Why* do they fight?"

Parvati asked a woman standing on tiptoe beside her. The woman said, "A man of the Right-Hand faction was beating a drum and carrying an antelope skin on his shoulder. And his companion was waving a red flag the while."

Parvati said, "Insolence!"

Jason cried, "Why shouldn't he?"

Parvati said, "Here in Manairuppu all those things are the privilege of the Left-Hand faction. In Ponpalamai, where the king is of the Right Hand, that evil sect claims the privilege."

Jason said, "But what is the difference between them?"

Parvati said, "I have told you: there is no difference, except that they are not the same. A man is born into a faction, according to his caste and his father's trade."

Jason thought he would scream. But the sense of helplessness and ignorance overcame his anger, and he said, "Please find a way to the palace. This is a very important council. We're going to make the final arrangements for the reception of the three kings tomorrow."

In the street ahead two thousand people milled and screamed together. Heavy clubs whirled down, men bit and stabbed, monkeys jabbered on the rooftops. The king's cavalrymen rode into the fight with no show of impartiality, for the king was of the Left Hand.

Parvati said, "We can go round by the back of the temple." She turned away, and Jason hurried at her side, down lanes and across private courtyards, until they reached the palace. In the apartment he quickly washed himself, arranged his clothes, and shouted for his best sword. As Sugriva fastened the yellow silk sash round his waist he steadied himself. There was no need to get excited. He had won, and tomorrow would seal his triumph. He was excited now only because the fervor of the people had infected him. But the goddess Durga was not his goddess, and he had no cause to be so nervous.

He took both Parvati's hands and said, "In a week, my darling, we will be married." He kissed her longingly and strode slowly through the palace to the king's council chamber.

The king, the chamberlain, and the general commanding the Manairuppu garrison were already there. Jason made his obeisance and began to apologize for coming late. The king silenced him with a wave and said, "Lord Jason, the time has come for us to complete those last little details which matter so much." He chuckled and slapped his thigh.

Jason murmured, "Yes, Your Majesty. Nothing should be spared to do the three kings honor."

The king and the others laughed delightedly. The king shook his head and said, "I could never really believe that you would so befuddle those apes of Ponpalamai, Krishnapatti, and Tiruvadi—but now I know how it was done. Well, it is certain that you succeeded. They are on their way now, and will arrive at the open space by the jetty at about noon tomorrow. Many of their soldiers will be drunk, for they are black-faced scoundrels and we have sent out—how much?"

"Two hundred jars of toddy, in total," the chamberlain said, consulting a scrap of thin paper.

"They will be goats for the slaughter," the king said, twirling his cap. "And all due to you, Jason!"

Jason's knees began to tremble. The king's navel swung round and round in a slow, numbing circle. Jason stuttered, "Wh-what do you mean, s-sire? What slaughter?"

The king burst into a high, cackling laugh, and a tear rolled down either cheek. "Wonderful!" he cried. "It would deceive anybody." He turned to the general. "You are ready?"

The general said, "Not yet, Majesty, but we will be by nightfall. The soldiers will be hidden as you ordered, all round the square."

The king said, "Good, good! Now, Jason, the signal to attack will be the firing of the first gun from the foreigner's ship."

"What ship? What foreigner? What guns?" Jason cried.

"Ah, that is a little surprise for *you*." The king looked at Jason with a cheerful smile. "While you were away on your embassy I arranged for outside help in this affair. Now, now, don't be alarmed. I fear you will not be in quite as strong a position in Manairuppu as you had hoped, because the Hollanders' ship is very powerful—but I assure you that you will continue to sit high in my council. In fact, I have so high an opinion of your skill that you shall carry out all negotiations with the Hollanders on my behalf. I hereby appoint you to be my deputy chamberlain. Give him a seal later, will you? The Holland captain will open fire with his big guns as soon as he is in position, which will be an hour after noon. The tide serves—"

Jason cried, "Your Majesty, what are you saying? What—" But the general interrupted. "I am not happy about the three kings themselves. Their personal guards will be with them, and—"

"I will deal with them," the king said. "Poison."

"Their tasters?"

"A tasteless poison."

Now the rising, choking horror could not be stayed. Jason sprang forward, shouting so that the sentences met in his mouth and for a moment could not be understood. He cried, "Lord, you must not— I swear before God—knew nothing—mad, mad—the Dutch!"

The king's frown changed to a look of bewilderment. Jason tightened his fists and forced himself to speak more slowly. He said, "What is the sense in this? You will only change the Portuguese for the Dutch! What is the sense in making enemies of the three kingdoms when they and you together, but only together, can stand against any foreigners? The Dutch! They will be worse than the Portuguese, because they are strong, while the Portuguese are weak. I have seen them in the Narrow Seas, and I know! In a week or a month you will be worse off than you were before."

The king said, genuinely puzzled, "But Lord Jason, the three kings will be utterly cast down."

"What does that matter?" Jason cried passionately. "How will that help you?"

"It won't," the king said. He was looking at Jason as though Jason were a favorite horse that had broken a leg—a look of sorrow, disbelief, and pity.

"But if you keep to the agreement you made," Jason said, "you and they will be allies, friends—"

"But my son, that is *impossible*," the king said, and put on his little yellow hat with finality. "Of course it's impossible. They are Vishnu-bhaktas, I am a Shiva-bhakta. They are of the Right Hand, I am of the Left. They are Vaisyas and Sudras, I am a Kshatriya. They knew it was impossible for us to be allies, and as for friends —bah! But Shiva inhabited you, and the dulcet honesty of your talk deprived them of their reason, so that, by greed, they cast them-

178

selves down. Greed is the downfall of all such rascals," he finished sententiously.

Jason shouted, "I won't allow this! *I* will be the murderer of all these people!"

The king said, suddenly small and fat and cold, "*You* won't allow? Who are you? A bleached outcaste, helpless. The Hollander has many more guns than your Master Drayton's ship. But I understand your disappointment, Jason." He stepped down from the cushion and put his bare arm round Jason's shoulders. "I will not hold my anger, nor must you. It is natural for a real man to be furious when he is overreached. *I* felt the same when you outmaneuvered us at the beginning, by refusing to admit that you were an English envoy. You prevented me from playing the English against the Portuguese—so I had to turn to the Dutch. But *I* didn't show my anger, did I?" He patted Jason placatingly. "As an Englishman you are defeated, my son. As a man, you are the apple of my eye. There, now let us be friends again."

Jason turned and walked out. The passages were endless, and the stone steps too steep for his strength. His shoes echoed in the hollowness of the palace, the rope of pearls thud-thudded against his chest, his scimitar clinked mockingly.

Outside the apartment his dragging feet came to a halt. He still had money. The king and the general and the chamberlain would be intent on the preparations for their murderous treachery. He still had Parvati, and it was nearly dark. He pulled himself together.

He drew the curtain aside, closed it behind him, and called, "Sugriva!"

"Lord?"

He said quickly, "You and the other servants may go now to enjoy the processions and make your worship. You need not return until tomorrow evening."

His hands were steady and his legs strong. His brain raced—jewels in that box, money in that, two hours. He'd have to leave some of the gold. Better have two horses, go south, pick up Simon and his wife as servants, then head west, get into Madura territory.

Sugriva said, "Thank you, lord."

Jason said, "Hurry."

When Sugriva had gone he called, "Parvati!"

She came out quietly from the inner room. While he had been

179

in the council chamber she had changed her clothes. Now she was wearing exactly what she had worn the day he first saw her in the inner passage of the temple. He said, "Our king is going to murder the three kings and massacre their soldiers when they come here tomorrow."

"I know," she said.

He looked disbelievingly at her face, but she was quite calm and very sad. He said, "You—*knew?*"

She said, "Yes. Until the Portuguese girl came the second time, I thought you knew. I could not believe you did not know. The king and the chamberlain insisted that you knew, but that you were too cunning to say so, even to yourself, in case you gave the secret away in your sleep. They admire you greatly for it. So did I. But when the Portuguese girl came I saw that she understood you as I never have—never can. Then I believed that you really were innocent. I admired you more. I could not love you any more. But it was too late to do anything except what she suggested, and that you would not do."

Jason's knees began to shiver again, and his belly was empty, and the noises of the Dussehra clamored in his ear. He whispered, "But why didn't *you* tell me, why didn't *you* warn me?"

She said, "The Brahmins told me that the god did not wish me to. He is my husband. I must obey him. If it is on their foreheads, the three kings will die tomorrow."

The words *will die tomorrow* rang like a frenzied bell in Jason's ears. He seized her arms. Too late to worry about the past now. He had understood nothing. He had been everyone's fool. But Parvati loved him. He cried, "Quick! We must get away. Start packing the money! Leave out a thousand gold pieces. I shall need that for bribes to get horses. We can be near the borders of Madura by the second night if we ride hard. Don't bring any extra clothes. We'll buy some more when we are safe."

Parvati stood still, upright, smoothly curved and large-eyed, in the middle of the floor. Again she had become one of the stone statues in the temple. Jason cried, "Hurry, my darling. You're all I have left now."

She said, "I cannot leave here. It is impossible. I am married to the god."

Jason muttered the word aloud, but for his own ears. "Impossible.

Impossible." He had been hearing that word much and using it often. He groped for the true meaning of it. Parvati had turned into a Hindu statue. "Impossible" meant different things to different people. Mary Bowcher, Jane Pennel, Mabel Dempster—to them Coromandel had been impossible. But not to him. So he had left them in their places and gone toward—a dream. But to him it was impossible for a ship to go under water, for a man to fly, for a voice to be heard from London to Manairuppu. To Parvati all these, and more, were possible. They had happened in the past—not as fables, but as truth —and they could happen again. Those impossibilities, and all miracles, were in the minds of the gods and in the eyes of the stone statues. To Parvati the impossible was what the will declared could not happen—such as a Right-Hand king making common cause with a Left-Hand king, or a faithful devadassi being unfaithful.

He thought he understood, while Parvati stood so still there, her fingers curved and her eyes steady—but he could not agree. He was English. His mind raced free to far limits, and came then to a towering wall, which he called the impossible. Parvati was Indian, and around her, like pillars in a temple, stood isolated obstacles that could not be removed because they held up the firmament—but beyond those pillars there was no horizon at all.

For a passionate, lyrical moment he understood, as he had understood Stonehenge. He soared with her, and the ecstasy of physical love fired him as he explored a spiritual world that he had never even dreamed of.

Then came the word, like a drumbeat, speaking itself—"Impossible. Impossible." And it was he who spoke it.

He said, "Good-by. I will never love anyone again."

The stone melted. Her tears washed his cheek, and she was not Indian or English, white or brown, saint or harlot. She cried, "I love you. Oh, Jason, I love you."

*　　*　　*

She was gone, and the ecstasy gone, and the moment of understanding when, for the first and only time, he had truly been with her. Now he was alone and heard scornful voices: Softy! Booby! He must be weak in the head—believes all he's told!

What could he do? What if he took his riches and ran away in this night on a strong horse? No one would catch him. He would begin

181

again, already rich, in Madura or Golconda. He would work hard, and in a few years he would be powerful again, again a leader of people.

All his life he would hear them laughing in Manairuppu, and hear the Dutch gun booming in the river at noon, though he were forty miles away when it fired. The gun was the signal of their victory; in the throat of the cannon they laughed at him.

It would be wonderful if, by spending all those golden coins, by emptying every ironbound box, he could prevent the gun from firing. Money was good, but revenge was better, and the power to do to them what they had done to him. Then he could live, because now he knew the answer—to let people laugh, but to make sure that he laughed last, though silently. He could do it, because he had the power to make men and women believe. How wonderful it would be to ride through the world, knowing that there was no laughter behind him, but bitter rue that he had passed that way with his gray eyes and honest tongue. Let the women cry and hang their long hair over their faces.

I did love her. I did love the others too. I shall not love again. Ah yes, but this time it's true, because I am not able to love. There is a sound of laughing in the place where I used to love.

Out, you whoreson pimp! She's gone. The fires of Dussehra shake the temple tower, and palm trees stoop their heads among the stars of Coromandel. The passionate sea moans on the bar. Soldiers march in this dark along the streets, among the processions. The men of Tiruvadi and Ponpalamai and Krishnapatti march to the place where the laughter is to be. The Holland ship rocks on the ocean, the mouths of her guns spread wide, ready to shout with laughter at the touch of the portfire.

He knew what he was going to do. There would be no watch on him, because he had been defeated.

He took as much money as he could carry and left the palace by the main gate. The guards there saluted him respectfully.

*   *   *

A thousand lights burned in the streets, the smoky yellow flames flickering and bowing in every shop and house and courtyard. He walked unhurriedly among the people, waited with patience for the processions to pass, and at last came to the open place where the jetty was—where tomorrow the king would massacre his friends.

A voice challenged him. "Halt! Who are you?" It was a soldier, one of a pair standing in the dark doorway of a house.

He answered, "It is I, Jason Savage, deputy chamberlain. Take me to your captain."

The soldiers walked beside him distrustfully and with swords drawn, until they reached the house on the northeast corner of the open place. The river flowed black and silent in the starlight beyond the outer wall of the courtyard of that house.

Jason had seen this captain once or twice on duty in the palace. Jason said, "The king has ordered me to spend the night here. My task is to row out to the Dutch ship with a message from the king. Is there a boat ready?"

"We can make one, Lord Jason," the captain said cheerfully.

Jason said, "Please have it roped up now and see that a paddle is beside it. Put it just above the high-tide mark."

"It shall be done."

"And awaken me in good time." He took the captain a little aside and said, "These orders are from *the king*. No one else is to know I am here—even though they use the king's name. No one at all. You understand?"

The captain smiled, his strong teeth gleaming. He said, "I understand, Lord Jason. I will awaken you in good time—I myself."

Jason lay down in the corner. It had been easy, as he knew it would be. Among so many layers of intrigue, there was one that would suit any story. There was a boarded window beside him, through which he could probably escape if the king came to seize him. But the king was unlikely to come, and the captain would not give him up to anyone else—not, at least, without a lot of hesitation and argument.

The house was full of soldiers. When he raised himself on one elbow he could see the rows of bare feet in the inner room, and later he heard snoring. He thought of all the other houses round the square, all full of hidden soldiers. What words should he use to make the three kings realize the truth? They might all have been poisoned by then.

At dawn he dozed off, and then the captain was shaking him and it was well into the morning. The dark soldiers filled the room now, and their faces shone with suppressed excitement, and their sword blades and spear points glittered in the streaks of light spreading from the cracks in the closed door and boarded windows. He put his eye to the doorjamb. A fierce sun hung in the sky, lazy white clouds rolled in from the sea, and a breeze stirred the dust in the square. A group of coolies were putting up a gaudy awning on the opposite side of the square.

The captain offered him food. He washed as best he could and ate hungrily. Before he had finished, a man stuck his head round the door and called, "Captain! The ship has been sighted."

The captain said, "Wait! Where are the armies of the kings?"

"Each of them is an hour's march from our gates, and on the move." The captain shut the door behind the messenger and smiled and rubbed his hands.

Time passed. A little boat put out into the river. An old woman hobbled about the square, picking up scraps. The coolies finished putting up the awning and went away. The river made low slapping sounds as the tide hurried in and met the flow of fresh water, stopped it, and banked it in its channel. A small body of Manairuppu cavalry trotted into the square and took position behind the awning, with the river to their left.

The captain said, "Now we're ready."

Jason took careful stock. There was the open square, bounded on three sides by houses and on the fourth—the north—by the river. He was in the house at the northeast corner, and it was full of Manairuppu soldiers. Clearly all the other houses fronting the square also contained soldiers, but the only sign of Manairuppu strength actually visible was the small body of cavalry on the west side, behind the awning. A street led into the square in the center of each of the three sides, and down one or more of those would come the armies of Tiruvadi, Krishnapatti, and Ponpalamai. The four kings would meet under the awning.

The Dutch ship would float in on the tide, with the wind behind her, until she was opposite the square. There would be a signal, and the ship would open fire with her cannon into the packed mass in the square. Yes, that was certainly it, because the Manairuppu cavalry and the awning were close against the west side—so the ship could fire across their front, without harming them. The ship would fire for a time and achieve the greater part of the massacre. Then the soldiers hidden in the houses would rush out and complete the work.

Jason decided to change his plan. He had meant to escape in the boat after he had somehow warned the three kings of treachery—

but he could make better use of it than that. He had told the captain that he was going out to the Dutch ship in it. God's blood, he would! He *would* pretend he was a messenger from the king. If he spoke with enough assurance he could prevent or delay the Dutchmen from opening fire. There were risks, but the king had almost certainly not told the Dutchmen of his existence, and it was a better plan than any other he could think of.

He settled down to await his time.

Music wailed in the hidden streets, and the army of Tiruvadi surged in a mob onto the square, halted, took up a tight formation, shouted twice, and fell silent. They wore coats of every color—or no coat—and some had spears and some swords and one or two long firelocks. They were about a thousand strong.

The army of Ponpalamai marched in from the south, and among them were many horsemen. The army of Krishnapatti flooded in from the west.

A soldier ran down the stairs from the upper room and muttered, "The four kings have come on elephants and are now under the awning."

Jason craned his neck but could see nothing, not even the elephants, for the mass of horses and men and standards filling the square.

The messenger ran down again from the upper room and said, "The ship is crossing the bar!"

Jason said, "Now I must get ready."

He left the house by the back door, slipped across the courtyard, and crouched on his heels at the top of the muddy slope leading down to the river. The boat lay ready, and the paddle lay beside it. He peered carefully round the corner of the wall. Some Manairuppu soldiers were leading goats and buffaloes into the square; twenty bands had begun to play, and some of the mass—that part which, by its position, could see down the river—had turned to stare toward the sea.

The great Dutch ship, her hull black and her sails red, rose to meet the tide rip on the bar. Her bow dipped, and the water curved out from it in a heavy blue wave, and white lace wrinkled along the ship's black sides behind it. She rode over the shallow water of the bar, settled, and came on in silence.

Jason launched his boat and began to paddle toward the ship. Once he glanced over his shoulder. Confusion was spreading in the square. Perhaps the kings were already shouting, "Treachery!" But the music would drown those shouts, and the temple horns were blowing and the priests shouting incantations and the swords falling on the sacrificial animals. He paddled with sudden desperation.

The bow of the ship loomed over him. He stopped paddling and shouted, "Don't fire. I have a message from the king."

Ah, he had spoken in Tamil. They would not understand. He shouted again in English. Three heads sprang up over the bow, two blond and one dark—the chamberlain! The chamberlain's mouth dropped open, and his hat fell off. His arms waved; he was yelling something; the blond heads disappeared. The sails roared down with a clatter and a rush.

Jason swung the boat round with two fierce strokes of the paddle and headed upriver, racing on the tide to beat the ship.

After half a minute's frantic paddling he stood up, waving his paddle in the air, and began to shout and scream his warning to the packed armies in the square. "The houses around you are full of soldiers," he shrieked. "Look to your arms! Treachery! Close up to fight!" The black bulk of the Dutch ship towered behind him; the anchor thundered into the river. In the square the noise rose to a full-throated universal scream, and all the men and animals struggled together in mad confusion.

The Dutch ship fired its guns. The blast hurled Jason to his knees. For a moment he struggled to prevent the craft from rolling over. When he looked up he saw that long avenues had opened up across the square—avenues paved with torn, prostrate figures. A man on one leg was hopping toward the river. The ship fired again and again and again. The houses burst open, and Manairuppu soldiers poured into the square, and swords rose and fell like twinkling fireflies.

A fountain of water jumped out of the river in front of him, and a cannonball whistled viciously over his head. He turned quickly. The Dutchmen were trying to bring the bow chaser to bear on him, but could not depress it sufficiently. The chamberlain was dancing up and down and waving his fists.

Jason paddled furiously toward the bank. The farther he went, the greater would be his danger, because the bow chaser would soon be able to bear—but he could not stay where he was, or they'd bring out the firelocks and shoot him with those.

The first four shots missed him. Ten seconds more and he'd be on the bank. The fifth shot hit the stern of the log boat. The boat flew to pieces, the logs kicked out of the water, catapulting him high in the air. Among logs and rope and flying paddle he fell back into the river.

He struggled quickly through waist-deep water to the bank. A cannonball showered him with mud, and he broke into a gasping run. He glanced back once. The ship's longboat, full of Dutch soldiers in armor, was rowing toward the shore, directly behind him. He ran now along the riverbank, past the square, toward the sea. They could not see him from the square because the bank sloped down sharply to the river.

What was the use of running? Why didn't he take his sword—he had it in his hand—and go and kill the king? The king would be guarded. The Dutch longboat reached the bank. The chamberlain shrieked and yelled. Four horsemen broke loose from the king's bodyguard and began to force their way to the riverbank, where they could run him down. Jason reached the end of the square, ran behind the house where he had spent the night, and plunged into the alleys of the city.

After a moment he untied his cummerbund as he ran, and threw it away. Then the pink sash for the sword, then the sword itself and its encrusted scabbard—he threw them away. Exultant crowds shrieked in the streets. The four horsemen followed him, but he could move faster than they among the press of the people.

Six more cavalrymen rode out of a side alley in front of him. His pursuers, signaling over the heads of the crowd, made the new arrivals understand that they were to let no one pass them. Jason hurried on, untying the strings of his moneybag. When he reached the line of horses across the street he threw gold and pearls, diamonds, pieces of eight, rubies, and gold mohurs into the dirt at their feet. The crowd saw and dived for the money. The soldiers saw and rode their horses together, flung themselves down, and joined the mad, fighting mob on their knees. Jason slipped through among them.

He ran into a courtyard and saw a fat woman cooking at her fire. He tore off the rest of his clothes, grabbed hot ash from the fire and dust from the earth, and rubbed them over his dripping body. He pulled at his hair and ran filthy fingers through it and down his face. The fat woman screamed and screamed beside him. He shouted, "Quiet!" climbed over the back wall, picked up one of the hundred sticks and staves lying in the street, and slowed his pace.

Now, stark naked, smeared with ash from head to foot, his hair matted in front of his face, the long stick in his right hand, he strode south. He shouted angry gibberish as he went, which might have been the challenges and exhortations and holy texts of a fakir, but was not, for it was English blasphemy and cursing against God. People who saw him coming stepped hurriedly out of his way with a prayer and a joining of the hands. He was holy of the holiest, drunk with holiness, because he owned nothing in the world beyond a stick. Wild and filthy, he strode past the soldiers and out of the booming city.

*　　*　　*

The pearling fleet was preparing for sea. Jason stood among the men on the sand, clean again, and wearing a loincloth Simon had given him when he arrived in the middle of the night. The pearlers had been celebrating the Dussehra then, and had paused only momentarily to greet him and help him to a hut, before returning to their jugs of toddy. He had slept, but now, in the early morning, by the scattered wood ash and the broken jugs and the man lying stretched face down on the dry mud above the creek, he knew they had kept it up all night. Simon's eyes were bloodshot, and the women looked worn and disheveled.

Simon stood in his log boat, his wife patiently holding the boat steady with the paddle, and said, "Are you sure you will not come to sea with us, Jason? You will bring us luck."

"No," Jason said shortly. "I must get ready to move on. At any moment the king may send men to find me."

Simon said, "Do not fear. You are born to be a great man. It is in your eyes. What has happened—" He stretched out his arms. "It has happened. Give us a blessing, please, if you cannot come with us."

Jason hesitated—but, damnation, what did he care? He raised his hand and murmured, "Abracadabra, ding dong bell, pussy's in the well." Simon made the sign of the cross, kissed both lingam and crucifix charms. His wife began to paddle, and the boat gathered way.

Jason watched with sullen hostility as the little craft rippled out into the turquoise sea. Simon had been responsible for his present troubles, by lying about the Dutchman. Everyone had lied to him, but, by God, he had tried to help Simon and his miserable pearlers, and this was how they repaid him. He turned back and walked up

188

the beach toward the huts. The drunkard had roused himself and staggered into his hut to sleep it off. Two old women and a crippled man squatted in a group under the largest palm tree, but the mud bank was deserted, and there Jason sat down and put his chin in his hands and thought.

The king knew now that he had tried to prevent the massacre by the river yesterday. The king was a contradictory little man and might not be very angry, since the massacre had succeeded. But it was not safe to assume that. The king also knew that the pearlers were Jason's friends. But he would be busy now. And he would think, perhaps, that Jason was trapped in the kingdom by his own actions, and that there was therefore no reason for haste in catching him. Certainly there would be no shelter in the three neighboring kingdoms, because he had been the treacherous envoy who had beguiled them into destroying themselves. Then there were the Dutch for the king to deal with, and some enemy soldiers would be hiding in the city and would have to be ferreted out; and there were six more days of the Dussehra.

He was probably safe here for a day or two yet. Then he must go. He needed money and a good horse. With them he could leave the kingdom, cross Ponpalamai, and reach Madura. He needed a sword and a dagger. He needed clothes. Above all he needed money, at once. Well, he could get that easily enough. He knew the ways of Coromandel now. Some of the people who looked poor were in fact rich. Women carried their wealth about on them in the form of gold bangles and ornaments.

One of the old women under the palm called, "A stranger is coming."

Jason stood up, his heart beating painfully. But, peering through the reeds, he saw that it was only one person coming down the path. It was a woman. She walked slowly with a big square bundle on her head, one arm uplifted to hold the bundle, and the other swinging wearily at her side. She wore nothing above the waist. Her breasts were small and high, and her belly flat; her cotton skirt swung with the movement of her hips. Jason started forward. It was a red skirt with yellow and black designs. Parvati had sometimes worn a skirt of that color and pattern.

The high sun hid the woman's face in the shadow of the bundle. For a moment he could not be sure. Then he saw. It was Catherine d'Alvarez.

He stared at her naked torso as she came close. He had seen a thousand Indian women like that since he landed in Coromandel—but this was the Portuguese grandee's daughter, who wore high-necked dresses and long sleeves.

He relaxed with a frown. She was not really pretty, and he disliked her. She came to a stop near him. Her dark eyes glistened for a moment, seeking his own; then slowly she leaned forward and fell face down in the mud. The bundle burst open and scattered its contents around her. Jason stared down in disbelief at a necklace, his Wiltshire poaching knife, a blanket, Voy's shoulder sack, her wooden spectacle case, his books. Among the books his map fluttered in the small wind.

The old woman said, "Aren't you going to help her? Is she an enemy?"

Jason started, hurried to the stream, filled a pan with water, held her sitting upright, and dashed the water in her face. After a moment she shook her head and opened her eyes and said, "They murdered my father and the housekeeper and Padre Felipe."

Jason gasped. "Murdered them! But—"

She said, "You murdered them, Jason. My father warned you. I warned you." She burst into a torrent of weeping. "Thank God I could not see. But I heard. They chopped them with axes and swords in the big hall, and Padre Felipe in the orange garden."

Jason said tensely, "It wasn't my fault. How was I to know they would attack you? I risked my life to stop the massacre by the river."

"No, you didn't," she said. "You only cared about turning the tables on the king. You weren't thinking about saving anyone's life." She stood up and leaned heavily on him for a moment. "Where is my bundle?"

"Here. At your feet."

"Everything that we need is here. Parvati gave me this skirt and dyed me. Parvati got your books and the map and the rest from the palace. *She* risked her life. Let go now."

She stood away from him and turned her head slowly round and whispered, "The sun is shining. I can smell mud and seaweed. They have been drinking toddy, and now there is food cooking—fish."

The slim column of her neck fitted gracefully into her shoulders. The sheen of the sun touched the curve of her breasts. The long muscles of her belly ran down on either side of her navel. Jason looked away, flushing.

She said, "I want to sleep. How can I sleep? What I see is more than I can see, more than I saw. Jason, never, never forget what you have done." She spoke at him firmly and without anger. She said, "I know you could not help it, because you are you. But this was really not you. This happened because you had let yourself become selfish. You were thinking only of how *you* could be rich and powerful and—"

"Shut your mouth!" Jason yelled. He hit her on the side of the head with his open hand. He was trembling violently. She stumbled and fell to her knees and stayed there on all fours, her head hanging and her hair trailing in the mud.

Cursing monotonously, Jason picked her up in his arms and carried her to his hut. Her body was warm and her face calm. She was already asleep. He laid her down and knelt beside her head, glowering bitterly at her dark eyelids.

She was helpless. She must have some money hidden away somewhere. She was in love with him, for all her abuse. By God, she spoke to him like a mother, or like Molly, telling him what he had done, what he must do. But by God, she was a slender figure of a woman, lying there in his hut. He was standing in a trance when the old woman shuffled in and said, "Let her sleep now. She's a pretty one, isn't she, but thin. Why is she so thin?"

*　　　*　　　*

Early in the evening the pearlers returned. Simon waved excitedly from the leading boat, and leaped out as soon as the craft reached the shallows, and ran up with his right hand tight shut and his mouth split in a wide smile. He cried, "Look!"

He held his clenched fist under Jason's nose, then slowly opened it. Six big pearls lay on his palm. "It is not to be believed!" he shouted. "There has never been such a catch! These will buy us food for weeks! Months! Even at the king's price! And this in the Dussehra! Because of your blessing! Ave Maria, ave Maria!"

He danced up and down the beach, singing and yelling. Jason smiled with his lips and thought: There's my money. It'll be easy. Then he told Simon of Catherine's arrival, and they went together to the hut to see whether she had waked up.

She was sitting outside the hut, and the two old women were squatting in front of her, staring at her but not speaking. She stood up as they approached and said, "Take me to the sea, please, Jason. Isn't there a sandy point across the cove?"

Jason said, "Yes, but why don't you rest here?"

She said, "I want to bathe myself. And to talk." Her sleep had freshened her, and the mark on her cheek where he had hit her did not show. She held out her hand. Jason stared at it. God's blood, he must guide her. He took her hand, not gently, and led her round the edge of the cove and across the dunes at the neck of the point.

She said, "Now I can hear the sea close, the real sea. Is there anyone watching?" He glanced up and down in the twilight and said, "No." She took off her skirt and walked slowly toward the sighing waves. Jason sat on the dry sand and watched her. She knelt in the sea, washed out the skirt, rinsed it two and three times, carried it out, and spread it on the sand. Then she sat in the shallows and splashed water on her body and face, came out, put on her skirt, and at last walked slowly up the beach to him. It was almost dark. He held his breath and hoped that she would not see him.

But why did he want her to stand there, ten feet from him, the skirt clinging to her thighs and the blue hint of evening on breast and cheek? He could have her whenever he wanted to. He could keep his dislike for her. She was his slave, or she would not be here. She would not have stood naked so carelessly before him.

She said, "Why do you look at me? You know I love you."

He started. How did she know he was there, and gazing? He must remember to find where her money was. She sat down near him and said, "I have washed most of it away—what I saw. It happened, and I remember it all, but it is cleaner now. I am glad you hit me, because I don't think I could have slept otherwise."

Jason said, "Don't talk about it. I lost my temper."

She said, "What shall we do?"

He said, "We?"

She said, "You are engaged to marry me."

He began to answer with anger, but she moved her arms in a small gesture of embrace—not to him, but to the sea and the indigo sky and the whispering dunes—and the pectoral muscle stood out for an instant, pulling up her breast, and he thought: I will have her now.

He put out his hand. She caught it and pressed it to her mouth. She said, "You must take me, Jason, because you need a guide as much as I do. I think I can lead you to where you want to be. We can go together, leading each other. I felt it the moment I heard you singing 'Greensleeves.'"

He whispered quietly in her ear for a moment, talking of their first meeting in the orange garden. God's blood, the poor soft thing really was in love—helpless, hopeless, melted with love. He could not wait a moment longer.

He put his left arm round her, eased her back to the sand, and brought up his right hand. He whispered, "I love you, dearest, I love you." His chest hurt, and he thought: I could, by God, I could—but this time I shall laugh last.

Her mouth softened under his. She said, "I will not lie with you, to make love, until you love me, dearest."

He muttered, "I do, I do! Oh, darling!"

She said, "You don't. I love you, that is all. Even when we are married I will not lie with you until you love me." Gently she put his hand away and sat up.

He said exasperatedly, "How in damnation are you going to know? I've told you, and you won't believe me."

She said, "I'll know."

He tried again, assaulting her slight body with kisses and hard arms. She did not turn stiff against him, and she did not struggle. She even kissed him, but he could not lie with her.

He shouted, "What do you want to marry me for, then?"

She said, "I've told you. Because I love you. To lead you. To be led. Take me back now, dear."

Jason shouted, "I'm not going to marry you."

She said quietly—but he heard the laughter in her voice—"You must. You have taken my dowry, and spent it. Oh Jason, I—"

He bawled, "I haven't spent it! It was stolen or lost. God's blood, you know I didn't mean it when I took it, and I said I'd never see you or speak to you after the marriage."

She said, "Jason, you must take me with you, because you need me. You will never be happy without me, nor I without you."

He bawled, "And lead you by the hand at a snail's pace with the king's cavalry galloping at our heels? I've got enough to do to look after myself."

She said, "Take me back to the hut now, dear." She held out her hand. Jason walked away, leaving her there. After a moment he ran back, grabbed her hand, and dragged her to the huts.

God's blood, he had wanted her for a minute back there, but that was only because she was a woman and had had the obscenity to prance around undressed in front of him. He hated her. Let her laugh now, or smile, or so much as speak, and he'd strangle her. But she did not.

Only, just at the edge of the muddy stream, she stood on tiptoe and kissed his neck under the ear and whispered, "Darling Jason, do hurry and love me."

He shrugged her off and wondered how soon Simon would be safely asleep.

*   *   *

Black as the Windline at new moon; past midnight—the drunken hogs of pearlers snoring beside their black sluts; the Portuguese girl deep asleep beside him; a wind rising in the palms. He took out Voy's sack and put in it his knife and the handfuls of cold rice, wrapped in leaves, which he had taken from his bowl at supper. He backed out of the hut on hands and knees.

He crept into Simon's hut. Simon always kept his pearls in a small box in a hole in the earth under the strewn palm leaves where he slept. Jason listened for the couple's breathing. They slept heavily on opposite sides of the hut. They were childless. Gently he pushed Simon over and moved the leaves. He dug in silence with his fingers, for the earth was dry and friable. In a moment he came to the box, opened it, took out the pearls, and put it back in the hole. God's blood!—they'd said it was due to his blessing that they'd found them in the first place.

He edged out of the hut and waited a moment beside the door. It had been easy, but his breath came fast and his hands were not steady. Now he was himself again. He put the pearls in Voy's sack.

West was his way, west and south. He'd move fast till he came to the first jungle, then lie up till daylight, then go boldly out and buy a horse. Pearls, a steady hand, a gentle tongue, a sharp knife. He glanced at the sky, but clouds hid the Pole Star. The surf rolled like slow, heavy drums on the Coromandel shore, and the palms creaked and bowed under the wind.

He turned away from the sea, threaded between the huts, and walked down to wade the stream. He trod on a sharp stone and sat down with a gasp of pain. He found the stone and angrily flung it away. His foot hurt, and he smelled blood on his fingers. He washed his foot in the stream and wondered whether he should bind it with a leaf. But he had no time. He must get on.

Feet ran up behind him—a soft *thump-thump* in the mud. He jumped up and turned. The rough handle of his knife grated in his palm. Simon's voice called, "Jason? Don't go yet, Jason. I have something to give you. He is here, senhorita."

A second shape appeared, and Catherine said, "Come back, Jason. Simon does not know what you have done. We can put them back before he finds out." She spoke in English.

Jason said, "I'm going now with what I've got."

The three of them stood close in the blackness by the gurgling stream, the whites of their eyes like a grouping of tiny lamps. Simon looked from Jason to Catherine as they spoke tensely in the foreign language.

Catherine said, "I found you had gone. I guessed and woke Simon. You must not go."

Jason said, "You stupid whore!" and turned to run. She flung herself at him and bore him down. Simon shouted distractedly and knelt to separate them. He seized Jason's knife wrist and cried, "Jason, no, no, lord! You don't need a knife!"

Jason wrenched his arm free and struck. The knife sank against resistance. Jason drew back his arm to strike again. Catherine still hung silently around his waist. Lamps ran down the slope, and the pearlers threw themselves on him, and he heard their shouts. "Who is it? A robber! Bring him to the huts!"

Catherine stood up slowly and said, "It is Lord Jason."

One of the men knelt quickly with a little lamp in his hand. He said, "Simon is hurt."

From the back of the group a high, keening wail began. Simon's wife ran forward and threw herself on Simon's body. Jason said, "I killed him." The woman glanced up at him but seemed to see nothing. Her eyes were blank.

Simon sat up and groaned. "I'm hurt—in the side."

Jason said, "I did it."

One of the pearlers said, "It was an accident, Lord Jason. You were his friend."

Jason said, "I meant to kill him. I stole his pearls."

Simon said, "That is *impossible*, Jason. I was going to give them to you." Wide-eyed, filthy children sobbed and clung together on the edge of the crowd.

Jason began to cry. The tears streamed down his face, and he could not close his eyes to check them. Catherine took his hand and said, "Lead me to our hut."

Lead her? He could not see. But he had to dry his eyes and master himself, and all for the sake of this girl. He took her hand and led her to the hut. He lay down and stared at the intertwined leaves of the roof. Slowly, softly, she began to talk. She was not speaking English or Tamil, so he did not know what she said.

He had failed this time. His heart slowly hardened as the tears dried on his cheeks. He would not fail again.

❀   ❀   ❀

In the morning she said, "Give me the pearls. Simon can't afford to give them away."

They were still in his sack. She wasn't so blind she could not have felt in a sack sometime during the night, but she had to make him give them to her. Why should he, damnation take her? But he was helpless here now, and did not know what to do. Simon would recover. He hated them all.

Sullenly he handed over the pearls, and she went out of the hut. In a few minutes she returned and said, "Take me to the sea again, Jason. To the same place, please."

He got up and led her round the beach. On the far slope of the dunes, where the sea wind struck, she sat down. She said, "Go and bathe yourself in the water. Wash all over."

He walked slowly into the sea until the waves broke against his chest. Then he had to fight to keep his footing. For half an hour he fought strenuously against the waves, jumping into them, and trying to beat them down with his fists.

When he went back to her he felt that his strength and confidence had returned. He said shortly, "I'm going to leave this place now."

She said, "You don't have any money."

"I'll get some."

"Then what will you do?"

"It's none of your business." Why should he tell her? Then he changed his mind. He said spitefully, "I'm going to beg and steal, and borrow and not pay back. I'm going to laugh last."

She said, "At the last you will not laugh. No, we must follow your map until we find the treasure."

He laughed sourly. "Don't be a fool."

She said, "If you don't promise to follow the map I won't give you any money."

Startled, he looked at her and blurted, "You haven't got any money."

She said, "I have—several small diamonds. Parvati sewed them into the skirt."

He said, "You had them when you came! What have you done with them? Where are they?"

She put her hand into the fold-over of her skirt and drew out his map. She unfolded it and said, "We must follow this, Jason."

He said, "I tell you it's no good. A trickster called Voy, Speranza Voy, sold it to me in England for forty shillings. How did he know I only had forty-six shillings, three pennies, and two farthings?"

"Because you're you," she said calmly. "What can you lose by following the map? You've got to go somewhere, haven't you? Why not go where the map points?"

"I can't read it," he snarled. "And some of it's in Latin."

"I can read it," she said. "That's why I brought my spectacles. I'll translate the Latin for you, but not before we are near the treasure. Until then you don't need to know what it means."

He said, "I'm not going anywhere with you. What good's a blind woman who won't lie with me?"

She said, "You're going to cook for yourself? Mend your own clothes? You're hoping to have more than a loincloth one day, aren't you? And if you don't take me I won't give you any money."

He looked at her with the purest hate. Blind, thin, weak, half naked, female, and helpless—and she was forcing him to do what he did not want to do.

He relaxed. What was a promise? Something which, if you kept, they laughed at you.

He said, "All right, I'll take you with me."

But he'd better pretend to be angry still, or she would smell a rat. In a surly voice he added, "But remember, I'm not going to treat you as my wife. You're going to be my slave. Do what I tell you. Don't argue. Don't speak unless I speak to you. Otherwise I'll leave you."

She stood up and said with no hint of irony, "Yes, Jason. I am your slave already." She held out her hand.

On the way back to the huts she said, "There's no need to stain your skin. I've heard of albinos, and Padre Felipe said that the farther north you go the paler the people are."

Jason grunted.

She said, "I asked Simon's wife to cook something for us. It will be ready now." She turned into their hut and came out a few moments later to join him.

When they had eaten she said, "Now we must go."

He said, "Where are the diamonds? I'd better look after them."

"I have them safe," she said.

The loathing of her welled up like bile in his throat. By the blood of Jesus, she'd lie dead in a ditch before they'd gone far. She lifted the bundle to her head, and Jason hitched on his sack. Simon came, leaning heavily on his wife's shoulder, and said, "Good-by, Lord Jason. May the gods travel with you. You have been our friend."

Jason turned and led toward the stream. From behind him Catherine called quietly, "Jason." He swore violently, went back, and gave her his hand. They crossed the stream.

Suddenly he felt the full weight of departing. The sea rolled in behind him, and the enormous unknown shape of India rolled away in front. Somewhere there might be a Castle of the Holy Men and a twin-peaked mountain Meru and galloping men with fur hats—but the City of Pearl was a city of bitterness, and he shook the dust of it from his feet.

God's blood! The map was a fraud, and he had an accursed limpet of a blind Portuguese whorelet fastened to the end of his arm. He walked faster—faster, faster, until he was nearly running.

She never said a word, nor stumbled nor dragged. He slowed to a proper pace and shouted aloud in the passion of his hatred, "Our Savior's wounds, what have I done?"

Chapter Four

She rose to her feet and stretched out her hand, Jason took it, and she squeezed his fingers and let go. She said, "I can see that it's an open road."

Jason said, "Gee up!" and beat the little donkey on the rump with the flat of his hand. They set off again after their rest, walking side by side down the wide road. She thought: This is March 1629, and we keep moving north, but each day is hotter than the last.

Nearly six months, and uncounted hundreds of miles, lay between them and Jason's City of Pearl. So many things had passed since they left the shores of Coromandel, all passed in a slow blur before her eyes, from the heavy green of the south to the harsh brown and paler green here, from the sticky embrace of Manairuppu's damp heat to the fiery touch of this sun. In the south a crowd had been a shimmer of black skin and colored cloth; here it was a dotting of brown on white. The food had changed, and the taste of water, and the smell of the air at night.

Jason had changed. When he wounded Simon she had hoped for a moment that he would come to his senses. But he hardened his heart, and the moment passed. He was determined to laugh last; so he had lied and deceived and stolen his way northward. The donkey he had stolen, months back. The fine clothes in the saddlebags were stolen. The pistol—stolen. Surely soon she must find a means to stop him. People had hurt him, though, both here and in England, and he meant to get his own back. It would not be easy to show him that his happiness did not lie in revenge. He was such a good, clever thief. People trusted him.

Jason said, "That's Jarod, on the left—the place Mansur was so frightened of. We've passed the danger now, and nothing's happened. I knew it wouldn't."

The ground rose gently on either hand. She looked to the left but could see only the shapes of the trees. Hidden in there was the earth fortress where black dwarfs hid, and sometimes sallied out with poisoned darts to attack travelers on the road. Mansur had been very nervous of it.

She thought about Mansur. They'd met him in the serai at Sagthali the day before yesterday. He was a thin and fearful-seeming man and had an old, old servant. It was Mansur who gathered the travelers going past Jarod and warned them of the danger from the dwarfs along that road. The people laughed at his nervousness, but twenty or so agreed to go in a band with him at least as far as Madhya. Jason thought he was a craven old fool, but she was not so sure. She could not see people's faces well enough to try to read character in them. She judged by voice, and though Mansur often whinnied from anxiety she did not think he was a cowardly man, nor perhaps as old as he pretended.

And she remembered a strange incident when they had first met him in the serai. He had come up and explained his fear of the dwarfs and then said to Jason, "Are not you the brother of Ali, who is my friend?" Jason answered that he was not, that he had never heard of Ali. Mansur apologized, with much stammering, for his silly mistake.

But why should Mansur make such a mistake in the first place? She and Jason had learned enough Urdu in their time on the road to be able to talk easily enough in it, but no one could have thought it was their native language. Ali was a Mohammedan name; and Jason did not look like a Mohammedan, nor did she wear *burqa*, or veil, as a Mohammedan woman should. It was strange.

The trees passed by like giant, slowly marching soldiers. Her sandals sank into the dust. The road was good, and the life on the road was good; but neither could last forever. She must bring Jason back to his map. She must keep his heart tender and vulnerable to laughter and to love.

Jason said, "Mansur's got money, or something valuable, in his saddlebags. The old servant gave it away; he was looking after them so carefully in Sagthali."

He paused, and she felt his defiance. He wanted her to say something, to tell him he must not rob and steal. But she said nothing, holding herself in check. He went on, "It won't be difficult to get Mansur alone somehow, and then—why, I'll only have to show my teeth and he'll hand over. A chance will come soon."

He spoke so brutally that she could no longer prevent herself from crying out, "Don't do it, Jason!" She knew that her warning would only goad him on, because he thought he hated her, but she had to speak. The sound of his voice touched the chords of her heart, as it had the first day she heard it, and every day since then. She tried to keep herself a little aloof from him so that she would be able to think dispassionately and do what was best; but every time he came close enough so that he touched her, she felt the pain of love blurring her judgment.

Jason said, "I'll do it, when I get a chance."

She said, "How do you know he's not armed? That he doesn't have friends among us—secret friends, perhaps? What a man seems to be isn't always the same as what he really is. You've robbed people you thought were rich, and they turned out to be poor, and—"

"And I found the pistol in the scrip of a starveling," Jason said. "Now mind your own business. You eat, don't you? You're wearing stolen sandals, aren't you? Well, hold your tongue."

I'll hold my tongue, she thought—better than you know. In the convoy there was a retired dancer who had somehow taken a fancy to Catherine, and showed her her jewels. They were magnificent, and Catherine had examined them with delight, her glass to her eye, behind the purdah curtain thrown across a stall of the serai in Sagthali. She had wanted to tell Jason—but she had held her tongue.

She walked on in silence. In the beginning she had often wanted to cry, but not now. This sadness lay too deep for tears.

She saw a cloud of dust in the distance and stepped out of the center of the road. The horseman passed in a flash and a reek of sweat and dust curling up to grate in her teeth. Jason said, "That man was wearing a fur hat, like the men on the map."

She stopped and looked helplessly back down the road. "What did he look like?" she cried.

Jason said, "He had slanted eyes and a droopy mustache, and a bow and a quiver of arrows across his shoulders. What does it matter?"

She said, "The map, Jason! Oh, I wish I could have seen him! We must try to find out where he comes from, and then we will know where to go to." She turned reluctantly. The horseman was only a cloud of dust again. But perhaps this was the sign. Perhaps this would lead to something that would rebuild Jason's faith in the map.

She said, "Do you think Mansur Khan will know?"

Jason said, "I'll ask him." She heard the sudden thoughtfulness in his tone and bit her lip. He was thinking that perhaps this would give him the chance he was looking for—to rob Mansur.

She wondered if he had any idea how much she loved him. Did her blindness still fill him with anger, that he had to look after her? No, because now his hand went out instinctively to help her when she needed help. It was no longer a matter for thought and so for anger. Perhaps, on lonely nights in the jungle, he even thought she was beautiful. He had never tried to make love to her. That she understood—he would laugh last. Perhaps he would. In those warm and scented twilights her affection grew almost too much for her, and she longed to touch him and whisper her love—but she had, with pain, held herself to her promise. He did not love her. When he did— ah, when he did, she would not even need the act of love. A touch of his hand would be enough.

Poor Jason! Once he became sure that she loved him he went more often to the strumpets, and told her where he was going. Several times he had brought a woman to their roadside camp. She went away as long as the woman was there, but otherwise she said nothing, did nothing, and thought she showed nothing. He paid the women with her money.

There was nothing amusing in that, yet she found herself bending her head to hide a smile—not because of the women, but because they had made her think of money, and that, in turn, of Jason's fury at her cunning in hiding what money they had. He could never find it. She had been cunning, all right—she nodded her head—but she had needed to be. A score of times, she knew, Jason had been on the point of leaving her in the dark, pushing her into a river, hitting her on the head—but always she had found something to say that made him change his mind, however unwillingly, and stay at her side. She could cook, and he couldn't. She could sew, and he couldn't. She had a knowledge of healing herbs, and he had none. She knew where she had hidden the few small diamonds remaining to them, and he didn't. She could read—but so could he, because she had taught him, and now the four books were dog-eared with their daily studying.

But where was he going?

The world was a monstrous big place. She kept talking to him about the map, and studying it with the glass held to her eyes, and because of the map they were headed north rather than east or west. But he did not believe in the map. It was not to the mountain

Meru that *he* was going, try as she might to make him. Was she right to try to make him believe the map once more? It was surely a fake and would not lead to any treasure.

She was sure she was right. The map had originally been an inspiration to discovery, a source of wonder. Along the road he had lost that inspiration and come to think of the map merely as a guide to riches. That brought in the cold light of common sense; in that light he had descended the next easy step and disbelieved altogether in the map. But she wanted him to believe in it again, so that, through the quality of belief rather than through any merit of the map, he could rediscover the inspiration and the power to marvel and wonder.

He was, instead, a common thief. He didn't intend to remain one for long. He meant to become a great thief. She thought that many of these mean exploits were a kind of practice to him, and an instruction in the gradual hardening of the heart. Back on the frontiers of Tiruvadi one chilly morning, months ago, he had taken a man's blanket at knife point and later found two silver rupees sewed into a corner of the blanket. All night he had tossed and turned beside her, sleepless because of one dirty blanket and two silver rupees! He slept soundly now after deeds much more cruel than that.

This road led only to the execution block, or to a rajah's courtyard, there to be trampled under elephants as a petty criminal. Yet she was sure he had a very different picture of his goal. Narrowly she examined her mind to remember words that would give her a clue. It was during the reading lessons that he talked most freely and revealingly. What had he asked her to write down, so that he might see it in black letters on the paper? *Jason has a pistol! Jason has fine clothes. Sagthali is a great city.* (And he'd said dreamily, "Greater cities lie ahead—Bhowani, Jhansi, Lashkar, Agra.")

He'd practiced writing more than reading, and once asked, "How long would it take to write a history of my travels? It doesn't matter. Can you play the flute?"

The word pictures fell into place. Perhaps she was wrong, but she did not think so. Jason saw himself in a big, quiet room, writing with a quill pen until it was evening. Then he'd play old tunes on the flute until she brought him his food. There would be other servants and other women, but she had to be there, to kneel in front of him while he ate, and take the silver dishes away when he finished, and so pay with humility for her impertinence in loving him. But where was the money to come from? By robbery—not petty thieving, but something bigger. Twice now he had said, out of his thoughts, "It's only the small people who get caught and punished."

She smelled water in the dust, and the road sloped gently down. She saw the gleam of a river ahead and big boats moored to the near bank. Jason said, "A ferry. Mansur hasn't crossed yet." He urged the donkey up the plank, and the ferrymen poled off. Catherine heard Mansur ask fussily, "Where is the stage, fellow? How far on?"

The ferryman answered, "You won't reach Madhya tonight. Most people sleep in the banyan grove. It is about a mile from here and quite a way into the jungle. There is a big banyan in the center of it. You can't mistake the way in, because there's a path—just past a bijasal that has been split and killed by lightning."

"Are you sure we will be safe there?" Mansur asked anxiously.

The ferryman said, "Safe enough. Keep a watch, of course. And don't leave the grove when you're looking for firewood. There's an evil spirit lives a little farther in—a woman who died in childbirth. But she won't harm you as long as you keep to the grove."

"Do you hear that, everybody?" Mansur squeaked. "Don't move a foot outside the grove!"

Then they disembarked and joined the rest of the travelers waiting on the far bank, and, all together now, hurried westward. It was a dry country, spread with a carpet of desiccated teak leaves, and the light was pale yellow on her eyes. As soon as she saw the loom of the dark grove she knew that Jason would never find a better place than this to rob Mansur Khan. There were scattered bushes among the big trees, and a little stream, and dense scrub all around. He would do it tonight and then slip away with her and the donkey before the camp awoke.

She had never before tried to turn him from any particular act of stealing. This time she must. She was frightened but did not know why. Perhaps Mansur's saddlebags held enough jewels to enable Jason to settle down forever in this evil life. Perhaps it was something else; but she was afraid. She hardened her jaw. She'd stop him.

Inside the grove he followed Mansur, and they were close behind when Mansur said to the old servant, "We'll sleep here, just here, at the foot of this tree."

"Very good, lord," the servant said quaveringly.

Jason led on to a clump of bushes nearby and said, "This will suit us."

She said, "This is only a bush. It won't keep the dew off us."

"This is where we're going to sleep," he said curtly. The old servant was muttering to his master, and Catherine looked in their direction. Should she warn Mansur of Jason's intention? But then they'd seize Jason, and beat him, and perhaps discover his other robberies. Besides, she was afraid.

Jason said, "You can gather firewood tonight. It's everywhere. Just feel with your hands along the ground."

She went off obediently, but, while she gathered sticks, kept looking back into the grove. From this distance she had a clear picture of it. The travelers were scattered about under the trees, though tending to bunch toward the center. The sun had set, and already one fire had been lit. She heard Mansur call, "*Ohé,* friend Jason!"

She worked quickly back toward their place so that she could hear what they said. Mansur went on, "I think we ought to have a man on watch, don't you? It will be safer. All night, by turns. It will keep the evil spirit away too."

Jason muttered something. Mansur said, "*And* a fire burning all night, in the middle there, to frighten off the dwarfs. I hear they're afraid of fire."

Jason said, "Why should they be? They must have fires themselves." Then his voice changed, and he said cordially, "But it is a good idea. I will certainly do my share."

Mansur fussed away toward the center of the clearing, obviously bent on enrolling more volunteer sentries. He gave her an impression of gazelle-like movements and soft, uncertain outlines. But his voice did not match.

Now Jason was thinking how clever he was. As a sentry he would have a right to be walking about in the night. Besides, the travelers would sleep more soundly if they thought they were being guarded. Now at what time of night would he want his duty to fall? It must be late enough for him to be sure that Mansur and the servant would be asleep, early enough to let him get well away from the camp before dawn. He would probably need at least two hours of darkness for that.

She watched him stroll over to the group round Mansur. She had enough wood now. She gathered up the sticks in her arms and walked carefully to their place. Jason returned, and she said, "What time are you to be the sentry?"

His body moved, and he said, "Eavesdropping, were you? The last hour but one of the night. I said it had been laid on me as a penance to say prayers every night at that time—prayers for Molly. God's blood, I wish Molly were here instead of you."

She said, "You loved her, didn't you? I would like to know her. But she wouldn't help you to steal."

"Oh yes, she would!" he shouted. "You don't know anything about her. Go and gather big wood now, and take it to the middle of the grove."

"Yes, lord," she said.

Now what was he thinking of, lying there on his back? Of the robbery he planned? Of the great house where he would live one day? In spite of himself he thought too about other things than money. Once he had asked her, "Why is there so much difference between a statue in England and a statue here?"

She returned and poured oil from a flask into the little bowl of the lamp, and lit the wick. Kneeling opposite him, she asked, "Shall we do our reading now, Jason?"

He said, "Not tonight. I'm tired."

She turned away from him and lit the fire. His voice was on edge. She glanced at Mansur Khan's tree and tried to decipher the wavering picture her eyes presented to her. Usually, she had noticed, master and servant slept side by side, probably with the bags between them. Jason had his knife as well as the pistol. He had not killed anyone yet. That would be a barrier she must not let him pass at any cost.

Suddenly Jason said, "After tonight, if our friend over there has what I think he has, we'll leave the road." He spoke dreamily in English. From the tone of his voice she thought he hardly realized she was there, and he certainly was not speaking to her. Yet he spoke at all only because she was there.

He went on, "I'll live in a big house with a garden and books and music—in Agra, perhaps, where the Great King's palace is. I'll only have to go on the road in the cold weather. It'll be easy. Rich men hear what other rich men are doing. I'll know when the merchants are sending bullion from market to market. I'll learn to play the flute. I'll read and write."

She stirred the vegetables slowly in the black pot. So she had been right, but not wholly right. He had at least learned that wealth was only a key. But he did not know himself well enough to know that for him there would be no wonder, not even the meanest kind of happiness, behind any door that would open to that key.

After tonight. She had no more time to think and worry. Tonight she must act. Tonight, for the first time in many years, she cursed her blindness.

She handed him a leaf-plate loaded with vegetables in a thick, hot sauce. He ate, and she noted that it was already quite dark. The big fire burned merrily in the center of the grove, and its sparks swam up among the treetops. Mansur Khan bustled off toward the fire again, but she thought that the servant stayed by the saddlebags. Most of the travelers began to gather round the fire, as was the nightly custom. They would gossip for an hour while digesting their meal, and then return to their places, and gradually the grove would fall still, and soon the only sounds would be the horses changing their positions and the heavy breathing of the sleepers and the creak of the high boughs. The sentry was supposed to walk round and round the whole encampment, but probably he would stay by the fire, telling himself it was his chief duty to keep it strong and big.

Jason went away for a moment. She felt in the saddlebag, took out the pistol, loaded and primed it, and hid it in her blanket. Jason returned, rolled himself into his blanket, and turned his back to her. She lay down beside him and muttered, "Don't rob Mansur Khan, Jason."

He murmured, "Mind your own business."

She touched his shoulder and whispered, "Please don't. We have enough money to reach the mountains now. How can you think you will be happy as a rich man, when you have to rob and kill to keep rich?"

"I'm not going to the mountains," he muttered. "And I haven't killed anyone. Now be quiet, or it will be the worse for you."

She decided she must try to sleep. Jason would do nothing until his turn for sentry duty came, and then he must awaken her and tell her to be ready to flee, with the donkey. The pistol lay hard against her thighs. She did not know how or when she was going to use it, but she knew she would if she had to. She thought she could hit him in the arm, if she stood close enough, without doing him much hurt.

Just as she was going to sleep she saw the blurred figures of three men coming over from the fire. She heard the servant yawn as the three men passed Mansur's tree—so he was there still, guarding the money.

Mansur was one of the men. He leaned over and said to Jason, "Friend, surely you haven't gone to sleep already? Come to the fire. It's warm there, and the little Hindu clerk from Sagthali has turned out to be a wonderful storyteller—wonderful, quite wonderful." He seemed to be in a jovial mood.

Jason muttered, "I don't think I will, friend. I'm tired and sleepy." He yawned convincingly.

"Oh, come on," Mansur said. She thought he had caught Jason's shoulders and pulled him to a sitting position.

One of the other men, by Jason's head, cried in a loud and cheerful voice, "It's time for a story!"

She heard Jason's startled shout. All the movements about her became jerky and fast. A soft thing encircled her neck. She grabbed the heavy pistol, raised it, pointed it at a black, eye-twinkling shape above her, and fired.

A choking silence fell, the dead leaves thrashed, the thing round her neck let go its hold. Jason's hand seized hers and dragged her away. Gasping, he said, "Run! Murderers! I knifed one. You shot the old servant. He was in it— Stop! Lie down!"

He pushed her down, and she turned toward the unsteady light. That would be the campfire. Two men of the murderous band had not been hurt and would be coming after them. Jason muttered, "Mansur! A murderer! The swine. He's coming now. I can see him against the firelight." Catherine held the empty pistol by the muzzle and hoped she would not strike Jason by mistake.

Jason muttered, "They've stopped now—behind a tree, sixty feet away!"

She whispered, "Can we go on?"

He breathed, "On? The shot must have awakened everybody. We'll wait for some of the men to come out from the camp. Then we have the treacherous devils trapped."

After a time he said, "They're going back to the grove! Quick, get up. We'll follow and shout as soon as the people in the grove can be sure of catching them."

She thought: They're going back? Into the camp? There was something wrong about that, as wrong as Mansur's voice. She said, "Don't follow them. I don't like it."

He said, "Don't be a fool! Come on."

He gave her his hand, and she had to follow him toward the glimmering fire. He muttered, "God's blood, they're strolling along as carelessly as though they don't mind who knows they're coming. They tried to strangle us with black cloths. The servant had one round your neck."

He stopped suddenly, jerking at her hand to bring her to a standstill. She smelled the smell of fear on him and held his hand closely. Then she smelled worms and new-turned earth and became very afraid herself.

Jason whispered, "A pit! Newly dug. Five feet deep and ten feet long. Wide. The fill is hidden under the thorn bushes."

It smelled like a grave. But that was nonsense, that there could be a newly dug grave, enough for a dozen people, here in the empty jungle. Jason said, "Mansur and the other man have gone into the grove. Come on."

But she held him back, her fingers closing in spasms on his hand. She could see the firelight. The people were dancing round it, dancing slowly, with bright colors flowing at their feet. She said, "What are they doing?"

After a long time Jason whispered, "They're— What are they doing? Nine or ten men are moving about, round the fire. They're dragging saddlebags behind them. They're carrying women's shawls. Some— Oh, the wounds of God! Men and women, dead, their hair trailing in the dust—they're dragging them by the feet! Mansur's there in the middle of them. He's their leader. He's pointing and speaking, and they do what he tells them."

Now she saw, before her inner eye; and all about the fire the brightness moved, a slow dance of looted silk and gold and shining hair. All dead—the merchants and the travelers and the old dancer with the jewels, dead.

"They're picking them up." Jason gasped. "They've killed everyone else! They're coming out in a procession. Mansur's at the back with a lamp."

"Quick!" she whispered. "They will bring them to this grave." She jerked at his hand, and he hurried her back farther into the jungle. But they could not go very far, for the twigs went off like pistols under their feet and the murderers were close. They crouched, huddling together in the darkness, and turned to watch.

What she saw ran together with what she sensed, and with Jason's slow, awed whispers in her ear. The murderers laid down the bodies, the naked bodies, and set upon them with stakes and clubs, ripped them open, broke their bones, and threw them into the pit.

They treated the bodies worse than a butcher treats meat on his block—but they were not butchers. These were ritual movements, and the men who were not hacking and battering stood by the side of the grave, as still as priests at prayers. The tall trees arched overhead; from the fire came music, and a man chanting. The murderers stood like men waiting for the sacrament. All about them the forest was tinged with yellow and red and gold, and the blood lay sweet on the air, and they had black cloths in their waistbands.

They finished and began to shovel back the earth. The sacrament was over. Mansur's voice broke out cheerfully. "It is a pity those two escaped." He laughed. "You know, I swear that young man was going to rob *me!*"

Another laughed with him, and Mansur said, "I wish I knew for certain, because I would like to have him in our band. He is quick and careful. So is she. Does she always sleep with a cannon under the blanket? Poor Daud's head is quite hollow now. I don't think they are far away. Shall I call them and offer them membership with us?"

"Just as you wish, Jemadar-sahib," the other said politely.

"It's worth trying." Mansur's voice boomed through the trees. "Ohé, Jason! Come back, and we will make you a member of the band. Your woman can live in one of our villages while you are on the road. We do not permit women to travel with us. Come back now to the fire. Otherwise we will certainly catch you tomorrow and kill you!" Aside he muttered—but she heard it—"We will find them round here in the next two or three days if we look for them." Once more he raised his voice. He shouted, "Come back, and you shall be a great man among us! Six months on the road, six months as a gentleman of leisure!"

Beside her, Jason started. He was sweating like a horse frantic for the race. This power, this wealth, and half a year with the shelves of books and the thin voice of the flute! The wind from the Plain that he always talked about, blowing through his mind. Power like the Romans, like the people of Stonehenge, where, to him, the stones smelled of blood in their places. He leaned forward to call out to the leader.

The pistol was useless. She slipped her hand down his back and drew his knife from its sheath. She stepped close and slipped the point of the knife under his ribs, and pushed. He should not go, and she was not afraid to die with him.

She thought his pale eyes turned down in amazement on her, but he made no sound. Perhaps he did not even feel the knife in his flesh, though the running blood warmed her fingers.

She listened desperately, holding hard to the slippery handle, while Mansur and his men walked back in procession to the grove.

Now he was safe. She wrenched out the knife and flung herself against him, trying to enwrap him in love. She whispered, "I couldn't let you, Jason. I love you."

He turned away from her, and she heard him vomiting and gasping and trying to make no sound in the agony of his disgust. She put her hand under his forehead and crooned gently to him until he recovered. Yet, in all his pain, which she shared, and in all her horror that she had wounded him, she felt a stubborn gladness. It had taken a rougher lesson than any she could have given, and for a moment the temptation had almost overthrown him—but now he was safe. One road was blocked to him forever. He would not seek his goal through violence.

*   *   *

For three days they crept through the jungles, eating what berries they could find. On the fourth day, when shimmering rocks and ghostlike trees stretched forever around her, Jason said, "A road!"

The ground sloped down beneath her feet, and she went carefully. Soon she told Jason she smelled water. He said, "There, a trickle, along the side of the road." They knelt and drank, and when she had had enough she stood up and looked around. The blurred foreground gave way to the focused distance. They were standing on the lip of an escarpment, and to the north the land spread away in a wide plain scattered with hummocky hills. In the middle distance a white city shone in the plain, and beside it she saw the silver flash of a river.

Jason dabbed water on the inflamed sore on her arm and muttered, "I'm tired. How are you? I wonder how far the city is?"

She could not guess. Jason said, "Ten miles, at least."

She smiled at him and said cheerfully, "I can walk ten miles."

He said, "You're as strong as a horse. But you'll need some real food before you can hope to walk that far in this heat."

The tone of his voice refreshed her. When she held the knife under his heart she had done something more than prevent him from joining Mansur's band. Jason respected her now—for the wrong reasons, to be sure—and took extra care of her, as though to prove that in spite of her strength of will she still needed him.

After a moment he said, "Someone's coming from the south. They've gone into a dip now, and I can't see them. They must have some food."

She said, "Give me the pistol." She held out her hand. Jason had forsworn robbery, but hunger knew no law.

He said, "But Catherine, it's empty."

She said, "Give it to me, dear. They might think you were going to threaten them. Perhaps they are as hungry as we."

Grumbling, he handed over the pistol, and she threw it far into the scrub. Jason said, "I can see them again now. They're less than a quarter of a mile away. Two—four—five, with three horses and a donkey." A long pause. She felt him stiffen beside her. He whispered, "The man in front is wearing a blue robe. He rides like—" His hand grabbed hers, and he said, "Mansur! Quick, back into the jungle."

In the shelter of the trees thirty yards from the road he said, "Can you run?"

She said, "Not easily. Could they have seen us?"

Jason's voice steadied. He said, "We were in the shade. They might not have noticed us. We'll hide here. Why did you throw my pistol away?"

She said, "*They* know it isn't loaded."

Then they crouched together and held their breathing to silence until the travelers passed by from south to north along the road. Jason whispered, "Mansur Khan—looking nervously from side to side! The treacherous swine! God's blood, our donkey! They've got our donkey."

Then they waited another half-hour before they crept out to look up and down the road. Jason cried, "They've gone, Catherine! They're going to the city! There will be a king or a rajah there, or perhaps a Mogul governor like the one they had in Sagthali. God's blood, he's not going to get away with our donkey. Hurry!"

They began to walk quickly north, Jason keeping a careful eye on the dust and the now frequent muddy patches, for signs of Mansur's party. She thought: It isn't our donkey, because we stole it. Why are we so anxious to get it back?

She spoke to Jason, and he snapped, "I don't care whose donkey it is. You're the one who didn't want me to rob because it's wicked. You can't tell me now not to get Mansur punished. Why, he's—he's the wickedest man I've ever met."

She said slowly, "Yes, but—" She was still afraid but didn't want to tell Jason so.

When they came to the outskirts of the city she unfastened a gold mohur from the corner of her skirt, and they ate quickly, and Jason found out that the name of that place was Kishanpur and its ruler a rajah called the Rawan. Close to the eating house the square bulk of the Rawan's fortress-palace rose against the evening sky, and they saw the river behind it, and tall trees in a garden under the north wall, and beyond the river the rolling, rising carpet of jungle.

"Are you ready?" he asked.

Now she had thought of a reason with which to cloak her reasonless fear. She said, "But Jason, are you sure that you want to complain to the Rawan? There may be trouble. He may keep us here. Is it worth it, just for revenge?"

He said, "It's not for revenge. We can't leave Mansur free to murder more travelers when we can so easily have him caught and punished. Besides, why should there be trouble?"

She said, "I don't know, but I think there may be." Then her heart softened because what Jason said was true and right, and she smiled at him and said, "But we must go."

Soon the shadow of the huge eastern wall of the fort towered over her and then she saw yellow, moving, and a flash of steel, and behind that a black tunnel. A voice said, "What do you want?"

Jason muttered, "It's the sentry at the gate." He began to explain in slow Urdu that they wished to see the Rawan or his chamberlain. The soldier said, "You can't go in now. The hour of public audience is long past." He paused, and his voice became sly. He said, "I'd get into trouble if I let you in."

She knew he wanted a bribe. She slipped him a handful of small coins and heard the *chink-chink* as he counted them. He said gruffly, "Go on in, then."

Jason said, "But who should we ask for?"

The soldier said, "What do I care? What *is* your business?"

Jason said, "We fell in with a gang of murderers on the road, but by chance we escaped. Their chief is in the town now and can be caught. His name is Mansur Khan."

The soldier's spear flashed, and he said in a changed voice, "Oh!"

He shouted, "Ohé, within!" More yellow blobs floated out of the tunnel and surrounded them. The sentry said, "These people escaped from a band of murderers. The leader of the band was called Mansur Khan, they say."

The other soldiers said, "Oh, do they?" Hands seized her, a sword point pricked her. The soldiers hurried her into the black tunnel. It must be the entry port. They crossed a courtyard where a fountain tinkled, and stumbled down into a passage below the earth. Jason kept shouting, "What's this? What have we done?" But the hurrying yellow blobs only said, "Hold your tongue!" and when he began to struggle she said, "Save yourself, dear."

They were pushed into a dark place. The door slammed, the bolts grated. They stood alone in deep blackness under the fort. After a time she heard the river chuckling and whispering above their heads, beyond the walls of their dungeon. She smelled rats and mildew and old blood. Jason said, "They've taken my knife."

✻   ✻   ✻

Much later men came down the passage, the door opened, and she blinked in the strong glare of hand torches. There were five yellow blobs among the torches, one with white below and a wavering black sail above. That must be his hat. This man said, "Stand up." They stood slowly, holding hands. She remembered what Jason told her had happened in Ponpalamai. She ran her finger along the top of his nail. Not again!

The man in the hat said, "I am the dewan of this kingdom. You are foreigners? From where?"

Jason said, "I am from England, this girl from Portugal. Why have we been—?"

The man said, "The Rawan wishes to see you. He has never seen a foreigner." He spoke a word to the soldiers, who dragged Jason and Catherine into the passage. Then they climbed up many stairs but never saw daylight, and she knew it was night.

The soldiers thrust them through gold gauze, and she saw black and yellow, and moving yellow and white above it, and another black sail-hat, and ranks of yellow and steel on either hand, and pale red sandstone walls in the distance.

There was a long silence. At length a cold voice spoke. "What skills have you?"

Jason said, "I can dance."

A single point of white fire, ringed with red, blazed in the black sail in front of her and moved as the hat moved. It must be an immense diamond in a ruby setting.

The voice said, "Dance? Pah! Can you build the European guns? Make powder?"

Jason said, "No, lord, but—"

A diamond in a ruby setting—only one! But she had seen two, in a smoky corner behind a curtain, in the Sagthali serai.

The voice said, "They are useless to us. The woman is not beautiful. Kill them." The yellow ranks broke; they seized her and began to drag her out. She pulled against them and said quietly, "That is a bright jewel in your hat, lord. Where is its twin?"

The voice said sharply, "Stay! This jewel has no twin, woman. It is unique."

She said, "Lord, I am nearly blind. I can see only a point of white light, surrounded by red. But in Sagthali I became friendly with a dancer who was traveling with us. She showed me her jewels. Those she valued most were a pair of brooches, each a great diamond in a ruby setting. May I look at the jewel in your hat?"

The voice said, "Yes."

She stepped forward, her eyeglass in her hand. She examined the brooch carefully, although a single glance was enough. It was one of the old dancer's pair. Then, while pretending to look at the brooch, she studied the man who was wearing it. He had thin lips and hooded brown eyes, and a thin face. This was a hard man, dedicated to power.

She lowered her glass and said, "It is one of the pair belonging to the dancer."

The sail-hat turned; the cold voice said, "Is the jemadar in the palace?"

The dewan said, "Yes, lord."

"Fetch him."

Then they waited, and there was no sound in the room but the *scratch-scratch* of someone's long fingernails on damask cushions.

She heard footsteps coming from behind. Jason cried, "Lord, that is the chief of the murderers! Mansur Khan!"

She bowed her head in pain. She wanted Jason to have this kind of simple, foolish trust—but how bitter must be the taste of these endless drafts of disillusion! She had allowed him to come to the

Rawan, believing he would find justice here—and the Rawan was the master, or at least the accomplice, of Mansur's murderous gang.

She heard Jason's sharp intake of breath and his whispered "No!" as he realized the truth. The Rawan was saying, "Mansur, this woman has shown me proof that you kept back another brooch, such as this that I am wearing. And also ten thousand rupees in gold bars."

"Ten thousand rupees!" Mansur exclaimed nervously. "Lord, there was no such sum. We took no gold at all."

"And the brooch?" the Rawan said.

"Only the one, lord."

The Rawan said, "Give him the red-hot iron."

Mansur cried, "There may have been another brooch, lord. I will cause a search to be made. My men sometimes hide things from me, in spite of their oath. I will go and search all their belongings."

"Bring me the brooch and the ten thousand rupees, in gold, by dawn," the Rawan said.

Feet hurried out. She thought: This Rawan is as ruthless as Mansur, but cleverer—and it is he who now holds our lives in his hand. But he is greedy too.

The Rawan said, "For two hundred years we've been trying to find a way of making sure that those deceivers give us the agreed share of what they take. It is time you solved the problem."

Catherine's mind raced. Greedy, ruthless—greedy!

The dewan stammered, "W-why—yes, lord. But it is very difficult. What is to be done with the foreigners now?"

The Rawan said, "Kill them. Why don't we send an officer with every band while it is in the kingdom?"

Again the soldiers were dragging her out of the room, and Jason with her. She heard Jason beginning to struggle, and the gasps of the soldiers wrestling with him. She said, "Lord, in my man's waistband there is a greater treasure than any Mansur has taken."

When the Rawan spoke she heard a thin warmth of respect in his voice. He said, "Show me."

She took the folded map from its hiding place in the top of Jason's loincloth and held it out. The Rawan said, "Paper! Do you want to have a dose of the thumbscrew before you die?"

She said, "It is a map, lord. We are following it to find a hidden treasure."

"How much?"

"Countless."

The paper rustled. The voice said, "Can you read it?" The paper rustled for a longer time. The dewan said, "No, lord."

The Rawan said, "You can read it, woman?"

She said, "Yes, lord."

The Rawan said, "Kill the man, then."

She said, "Lord, there is a part that only he can read."

The room echoed with a sudden and surprisingly pleasant chuckle. The yellow ranks stirred; everybody murmured with laughter. The Rawan said, "You will have to divide your share with him—you realize that? There are plenty of strong men in my kingdom. Are you sure you can't read the map without his help?"

She said, "Without him it is impossible."

The Rawan said, "Why did you not say you were skilled in diplomacy when I asked you? I do not need dancers. I have hundreds of them. You shall both live. Answer me one question, and you shall live well. You shall be a secret councilor. Publicly this clod of a husband of yours must be the councilor, because you are a woman. This is the question. How can I prevent Mansur's deceivers from deceiving *me?*"

She said, "Lord, you will gain greater wealth by preventing them from stealing and killing. Your subjects will grow rich. More travelers will pass through your kingdom, spending their money as they go. More—"

Beside her, Jason laughed shortly and said, "Lord, she is a woman. You should indeed prevent them from robbing and killing in your kingdom. And your people will grow rich just as she says. You should give these murderers land, to each a portion according to his skill—but tell them to rob only in the territories of your neighbors, not in yours. Promise to protect them. Then they will rob on all sides of Kishanpur, and, because they can quickly find sanctuary here, they need not pay any part to the kings of the lands surrounding yours. You will get a larger share."

"A marvel!" the Rawan said slowly, and the jewel flashed in his hat.

Catherine caught hold of Jason's arm and cried in English, "Don't! This is worse than stealing with your own hands! Oh, my love, don't be bitter. There are people in the world you can trust."

But Jason went on relentlessly. "Don't ask a percentage, lord. They will always cheat. Charge them a flat sum for the sanctuary—a good large sum. Then let them keep all they make."

"A miracle!" the Rawan said.

"In the winter they will go out to work on the roads. For the rest of the year employ them as tax collectors for yourself. *They* will know where rich men hide their money while pretending to be poor."

The black hat rose slowly, the jewel twinkled. "By my ancestors, this is wisdom such as I have never heard! My friend, you shall be head of my council, and the woman shall be second. Can you think of anything else?"

Jason said, "Not now, lord. Later I will."

She shook herself wearily. She'd think of some way to escape this fate soon. Now she must keep her wits. She said, "Prince, make Mansur give us back our donkey and our books and clothes. And my lord's knife your men have taken."

The Rawan said, "It shall be done. Show them to a good chamber."

She said, "Prince—the map?"

The Rawan said, "I will take good care of it. Is it really genuine?"

Jason said, "No," and Catherine said, "Yes," simultaneously.

The Rawan said, "Ah! He is apt to be a little overcunning, is he? He would like me to think it is not really of any value—now that his neck is safe? Well, well. Is this treasure on my lands, or on the lands of my revered Moslem overlord, the Grand Mogul?" He spat.

She said, "It is beyond your lands."

The Rawan said, "Then we shall have to be careful. And how am I going to be sure that you bring back all you find?"

Catherine said, "Send an officer with us. Send Mansur Khan."

The Rawan cried, "Magnificent! I have gained a diamond brooch, ten thousand rupees in gold—and two priceless pearls. You shall set out in seven days."

The yellow ranks broke up. Hands took her, but gently now, and led her out. They went slowly, one behind the other, along the passages. A yellow coat fussed along in front, murmuring, "This way, lord. Mind the step. Turn to the right here, ma'am."

Jason said, "Now I'm a great man again!" He laughed harshly. "A great man! No one will laugh at me for a time now."

She said desperately, "You promised never to steal again."

"Steal? *I'm* not going to steal," he said. "Not one whoreson farthing! I'm going to see that no one steals. I'm going to stop Mansur from stealing, and Mansur is going to keep rich men out of the temptation not to pay their proper taxes. Look at this beautiful room we are getting."

The officer had thrown back the curtains covering a heavy door. They were looking into a light and luxurious apartment with three wide windows. The moon was high, and she saw the river far below, and across the river the moonlit waves of the jungle. She was exhausted, and the pain of Jason's bitterness overwhelmed her. She sank slowly, trembling, onto the divan.

After a moment Jason came to her, and she felt his hand on her forehead and heard his unsteady voice. "I'm sorry, Catherine. But what else can I do? Perhaps, after all, I am the same sort of person that they are."

        *   *   *

Jason let go of her hands and shouted, "Hey!" and the dance ended.

She sat down, panting, on the divan. It was exhausting, this wild English dance, when you were not used to it. But she could have danced all day and all night with him, if he would let her. He was a good teacher, too, patient and skillful. She felt that he had come immeasurably closer to her since the night she drew his knife on him. He was not happy; he had not lost his bitterness; he had not regained his wonder or his innocence or his trust in the map—all of which she hoped would come together; but, slowly and hesitantly, he was finding her. These dancing lessons, which he had suddenly instituted the day after they reached Kishanpur, were an indication.

She said, "Will I ever be any good?"

"Oh yes," he said patronizingly. "But never as good as Molly or Emily."

"I don't expect to," she said, "but I'd like to be able to dance well enough so that you can dance your best with me."

She heard water gurgling out of the water jug. Then Jason said, "Let's read now."

"Very well."

But someone called from outside the door, and Mansur Khan came in and said, "We leave tomorrow to find the treasure. These are the clothes you will wear." A heavy pile flopped softly to the floor.

"These?" Jason said. "These plain things? Why can't we wear our own clothes?"

"We will be traveling in the lands of the Grand Mogul," Mansur said. "His servants are unconscionably greedy, and often sharp-eyed." He went out, and Catherine smiled, in spite of herself. Mansur hated both of them, especially her, and yet was awed by the skill with which they had saved their own lives, had him fined ten thousand rupees, and made themselves councilors of the Rawan—all within an hour.

When they were alone she jumped up and cried, "Tomorrow we really go to follow your map, wherever it may lead! We'll see the Castle of the Holy Men, and the mountain Meru—and things neither of us has ever dreamed of!"

"Perhaps," he said gently.

"Aren't you excited?" she cried. "I am!"

She reached out tenderly, her arms trying to gather him in, but he leaned away from her. She said, "Please believe in the map, Jason. You want to, don't you?"

After a time he said, "Yes."

"Then do! What harm can it do you?"

He said slowly, "I do believe in it."

"Because of me? Just to please me?"

"No," he said quickly—too quickly. She sighed and turned away. He jumped up. "But I do, Catherine. I've learned how clever, how wise you are. If you believe in it, I do. But what's the good? We'll find the treasure and come back here, and nothing will have changed. We can't escape."

She thought: It's no good going on arguing now. He doesn't really mean what he says. Perhaps it is enough for now that he even says he believes in the map. The old doubt came back to her; *she* was sure the map was false.

She moved her head restlessly. She could only go on hoping that Jason would discover himself before they reached the mountain Meru and found nothing there—perhaps not even a mountain.

Jason said, as though to convince her of his faith, "We never found out who the galloper in the fur cap was. We were going to ask Mansur Khan, do you remember? But we never did." He laughed without mirth.

She said, "I found out. Azeema the concubine told me yesterday— the one who is being sent with us as my tirewoman. The man was a Mongol messenger. The emperors themselves came from beyond the mountains years ago. They are descended from Tamerlane, and they still have many servants from their old homeland—Samarkand! So you see, the map was right again. The picture on it is quite clear, of men in fur hats somewhere beyond the mountains, and now we have seen such a man, and Azeema has told me that he came from beyond the mountains. I wonder what mountains look like—real, big ones. I saw some in Italy once, but they weren't very big."

Jason changed the subject. "Shall we read?"

She had been thinking all the while. They were off tomorrow. Something must be done. Jason had said wearily, "We can't escape," meaning that fate seemed to have chained him to a life of power and wealth, earned by murder, and enjoyed among books and music and dancing. But they could escape—at least from Kishanpur.

Azeema was a strange, hard little thing, no more than fifteen, but old with a kind of cruel wisdom. And she was a devout Mohammedan, while the Rawan and all his court were Hindus. And she had recently been whipped for some minor harem peccadillo.

Catherine said, "Oh, Jason, I promised to talk to Azeema again today. I must go. We'll read later."

She kissed him on the forehead and left him.

❖　　❖　　❖

She sat on cushions in a dim corner of the harem. The air, stirred by a breeze through the arched window slits, smelled of cloying flower perfume and the sharp odor of musk. Azeema sat opposite her—a shape of rustling green and gold, overlarge glowing eyes, and black round them, all smudged and wavering together—so close that she could hear the girl's even breathing.

Catherine said, "Will you do it?"

Azeema said, "Yes. I hate this pig of a Rawan anyway. But I am thinking how to send a message, and to where."

Flies buzzed around them. Below, by the river, a man sang an old love song, and the oars of the fishermen clunked in the rowlocks, and rhythmically a woman slapped wet clothes against a stone.

Catherine said, "Is there not a Mogul post near the frontier—to collect taxes or the like?"

"Yes," the girl said quickly. "That's it." She named the place. "But we won't be going along that road. We shall use a little-known road farther east."

Catherine said, "But if word reaches the post in time, the officer can send to intercept us."

Azeema said, "But how can word reach him? Don't think I am afraid, sister, but I don't know—I cannot go myself."

"Your priest?" Catherine said.

Azeema muttered, "The mullah? He is an old man with a gray beard. How can he ride so far in so short a time?"

"Men tell me you are beautiful," Catherine said with a smile. "Are not your eyes black, and blacker from kohl? Could not tears shine in them, to make even an old man leap on a horse and ride till he dropped?"

Azeema chuckled delightedly. "I think it is possible. I can try, at least, and I *am* beautiful, though this Hindu dog of a Rawan does not think so—more than once every six months. Bah!"

"Will you go tonight, then?" Catherine cut in quickly.

"I will go now, as soon as you have left me. That is one advantage I do have. None of these Hindus know the customs of our religion, and they are so afraid of the Great King—who is, of course, a believer—that they dare not forbid anyone to see the mullah at any time. So I go when I wish."

Catherine rose to her feet and stooped to kiss the girl on the cushions. "God be with you," she said.

"With us!" Azeema amended, and then, shortly: "Don't think I am not acting for myself too. I need a whole man, not the two-hundredth part of a bloodless weasel."

*   *   *

The horses champed in the courtyard, and it was dawn. She counted the uncertain shapes of the party—Mansur; a lieutenant; five soldiers in dirty white, armed with swords; four servants, including Mansur's; Azeema, the concubine; Jason; herself—fourteen in all. They had fourteen broken-down riding horses, and each servant led three pack horses, so there were twelve of those. Mansur sounded more than ever like a nervous merchant, and the pack horses were loaded with opium, cotton, and fine oils. The yellow coat and the black sail-hat leaned over a balcony above, in silence.

Azeema whispered in Catherine's ear, "The mullah found he was not so old as he thought."

She said, "Oh, Azeema!"

"Don't look so shocked. I only had to cry a little. I told you I was beautiful."

Mansur said, "We are ready, lord."

The Rawan said, "Go, then. You know what to do if the foreigners should try to escape—though I don't think they will. And in the name of Vishnu, remember your skill at pretending when you are questioned. And don't use the black cloths."

They wound out of the gate and into the open, turned north, and settled down to a steady walking pace. They camped that night in a mango grove among rich fields; and the next in a thicket of jungle by another river; and on the third day, at a great pillar set in the road, they passed out of the Rawan's kingdom and into the lands of the Great King, the Grand Mogul.

She heard Mansur speaking to Jason. "Now be on your guard. These Mohammedan officials are nothing but pirates. We shall be lucky if we reach the mountains with even half our loads."

They rode on across the flat country, green with crops and ashake in the midday glare. Jason said, "Why is the Grand Mogul the overlord of our Rawan?"

Mansur said, "Because the devil Akbar conquered us in battle fifty years ago. So the Rawan must call himself a viceroy of his own lands!"

A galloping shape bore down on them in a cloud of dust from in front. Catherine tensed as a snaffle chain jingled and a horse neighed. A voice said, "Cavalry ahead, Mansur. By the huts there." Ah, it was one of their own soldiers, ridden back from his place in the van.

Azeema muttered, "The old mullah rode fast!"

Mansur cried, "Cavalry already! Well, just pass by with a salute. If they stop you, whine that we are poor men."

The hoofbeats receded up the road. Mansur began to mutter. "I see them now. A whole troop! There's never been more than a couple of tax collectors here before."

Jason said in disgust, "And we're only just in Mogul territory. I can still see the frontier pillar back there—two miles!" He edged his horse closer to Catherine's and said, "Mogul cavalry ahead! Remember, now—we're from Sagthali."

That was the tale the Rawan had rehearsed them in, in case awkward questions were asked of them. Catherine said, "We'll remember. But, Jason, if anything goes wrong, don't fight! Whatever you do, don't fight."

"It wouldn't be any use," Jason said. "There are about twenty of them."

Now she saw the green Mogul cavalrymen riding out to form a line across the road. On the left, one of them had a golden drum, and on the right another unfurled a green standard, and before the center a green and silver vision danced on a trampling gray.

Slowly, with the thin *taratarararata* of the drum rolling round the wide plain, and the sun glittering on the steel helmets and the chain mail and the drawn swords, the parties came together.

Mansur rode a few paces forward, alone. The drummer beat a final ruffle. Mansur's shape bowed and rose, bowed in the dust, rose again. He stood silent now beside his horse.

The green-and-silver spoke. "I am an officer of the Great King's service. Where are you from? Where are you going? What is your merchandise?"

Mansur cried, "Great Prince, I am a merchant of Sagthali. These are my servants, guards, and women. We have opium, cotton, and fine oils, which we take to Tibet beyond the mountains, to exchange there for gold, salt, and borax." He added something in a low whine which Catherine could not hear.

The officer said, "Are you trying to bribe me, dog? Did you not hear? I am a lieutenant of the *Great King*."

Mansur rose and fell in the dust, chanting flattery and apologies. The officer said, "Get up. We are looking for two foreigners, a man and a woman, who ran away with the Great King's favorite dancer. Stand still, you!"

He came closer and passed down the line of their party. Opposite Jason, he said, "You! You're the man. Get over there."

Jason said, "I'm not! I am the merchant's clerk, I swear it."

Mansur wailed, "Majesty, there is some terrible mistake. I have known this youth for ten years."

The officer said, "As it happens, it is just ten years and three months since the dancer was stolen."

Jason shouted, "You're a liar! God's blood, ten years ago I was only— I was only twelve, and I was in Shrewford Pennel." But two green coats rode up, one on either side of him, and their steel flashed in short, threatening gestures. Catherine had her hand on his arm, and she felt him reach for his knife. He muttered, "I'm not going to leave you now!"

She cried, "Don't fight, Jason. I'm coming with you." But what had he said? *I'm not going to leave you.*

The green-and-silver advanced on her. The voice, six inches from her face, said, "She's another." She went meekly with the soldiers.

The officer said to Azeema, "Woman, show your face."

Mansur wailed, "Majesty, that is a Mohammedan woman, a concubine of—one of my friends."

The officer said, "Lower your veil. You are Azeema, the dancer?"

"Yes, lord."

Mansur screamed, "It's impossible! She's lying! She's never danced in her life! Ten years ago she was only five!"

The officer said silkily, "The Great King trains his dancers young. Search them all."

Jason said, dumfounded amazement in his voice, "They're taking everything we've got! The map! They're taking the map from Mansur's purse!"

Mansur cried, "Don't take that! Majesty, it is a letter, a worthless letter, but important to the writer. A love letter, it is."

The officer said, "Addressed to whom?"

Mansur said wildly, "To—to—to Tilni Bibi, the famous courtesan of Bareilly."

"We will deliver it. Wide is the generosity of the Great King!"

Mansur muttered incoherent praise on the name of the Great King. The officer said, "We will take the foreigners and the woman Azeema to the Great King. The rest of you may continue your journey. The blessings of Allah go with you."

Mansur shrieked, "But lord, our horses! Our merchandise!"

"Those who walk instead of riding live to a ripe old age," the officer replied. "And, as Jesus said, on whom be peace, 'It is easier for a camel to go through the eye of a needle than for a rich man to enter into heaven'! Go—and in future be more careful whom you pick up as servants and slave women."

Catherine hardened her heart. Mansur sounded so miserable that she could almost wish to let him go free. But he was a murderer. She said, "Lord, that man Mansur Khan is—"

The Mongol lieutenant interrupted. "I got the message, woman. I know who and what he is. But wait! There is nothing like an alternation of hope and despair to purge the soul, which that man's soul most surely needs."

Mansur and the Kishanpur officer and the five soldiers and the four servants trudged away down the wide dusty road between the crops. As they receded she saw them more clearly, a forlorn little group in the empty landscape.

The lieutenant waited until they were almost out of hearing. Then he raised his voice and bellowed, "Ohé, come back! The white woman says there is a notorious murderer among you."

The Kishanpur party halted and gathered together in the distance.

The lieutenant commanded, "Three of you, gallop down and make them hurry!" Three of his troopers darted forward, and then, hastily, Mansur's party began to trudge back.

When they arrived the lieutenant examined them all again. At last he said, "The woman was wrong. I see no murderer here. You may go."

They turned as one man and walked south as fast as their legs would carry them. The lieutenant sat quiet astride his horse until they again reached the borders of earshot. Then again he stood in his stirrups and shouted, "Ohé, come back! You have left your opium and cotton and fine oils behind. They are valuable."

Faintly, after a long interval, came Mansur's answering shout. "Please accept them as a gift, Your Majesty. We do not want them."

The lieutenant controlled his laughter enough to shout, "Come back! Are you trying to get me accused of extortion?"

Once more the party trudged back. As they came close enough to blur before Catherine's eyes, a green soldier walked his horse forward to meet them. A sword flashed—a single negligent back-handed stroke. Mansur's head jumped and rolled in the dust. The rest of the party fled, yelling, down the road toward the distant boundary pillar.

At last the lieutenant stopped laughing. He said, "So this woman Azeema would rather serve in the household of His Majesty, as a cook and cleaning woman, than as a concubine in the palace of the Rawan?"

"Yes, lord," Catherine said.

"She is beautiful enough. In fact, she is so beautiful that the empress will probably have her nose cut off."

"Better noseless among the faithful than beautiful among the heathen," Azeema said stoutly.

"There is one God, and Mohammed is the Prophet of God," the officer said devoutly. "All may be well. The empress has a kind heart —sometimes."

"But—" Jason said. "You knew we were coming?"

Catherine groaned aloud. This time it was she who had deceived him.

The officer's helmet moved, and he said, "This fellow is weak in the head, isn't he? What is he—a slave?"

Catherine said, "Yes, lord. He is my slave. May I have the map?"

The officer said, "Oh no. I'll look after that. My captain will want to see it. And if the story that you sent to me by the mullah should be false— Or if the map should be false— Mansur died quickly. The same result can be achieved much more slowly."

They mounted their horses, and the lieutenant gave the order to move. Catherine edged closer to Jason and said, "I had to do it."

"Why didn't you tell me?" he asked sullenly.

She hesitated and then answered, "Because I didn't trust you. You said we couldn't escape, but really you were afraid to. You thought you'd only meet the same kind of bitterness somewhere else."

Jason said, "So we will. I will be offered the post of chief extortioner to the Great King. Or he will have us killed, after playing cat and mouse with us as the lieutenant did with poor Mansur."

"No," she said, "he won't. Because the map is true."

＊　　　＊　　　＊

Five days of travel brought them to the royal city of Agra. Jason's sullenness slowly disappeared as the miles fell away and no new evil befell him. She thought that perhaps his anger had never been much more than masculine pique, because it was she rather than he who had forced a way out of Kishanpur for them.

And then in a brief twilight they entered the city. The houses rose higher, and the noise increased as the cavalcade trotted on. The lieutenant shouted more often, "Clear the road!" and the beggars whined, and the merchants shouted their wares. The sky burned fiercely in a dusty scarlet sunset, and far in the eye of the purple sun she saw wild geese flying north. Gradually a paler red bluff rose up to obscure the sun, and it became a great fortress, larger than any she had seen. They rode on, the trumpet screaming ahead and Jason silent with awe at her side, until the high fortress blurred and the black stone elephants beside the gate dimmed in her eyes. They entered the fort.

The lieutenant said, "We go now to see the captain."

"Now?" Jason asked. "My wife is tired." She bridled self-consciously. He had taken to calling her his wife, where before he had referred to her as his woman. He had said with a surly mien one night that she must not think he really meant to marry her, just because he called her his wife; only he did not want people to think she was a loose woman.

The lieutenant said, "I know she is tired. I am tired too. But I dare not delay in making this report. Perhaps the captain will let us rest when he has talked to you. Dismount here."

Jason helped her down. Though she did not need his hand, she took it and jumped lightly onto stone tiles. "Now," the lieutenant said, "follow me. And if you have deceived me— But you are honest people, aren't you?"

"Yes," she said. The poor man sounded afraid all of a sudden. Holding Jason's hand, she entered a high arch and walked down a passage. The lieutenant ahead turned right, left, entered a small room, stopped. Another green coat rose and said, "Latif! What are you doing here?"

The lieutenant began to explain with voluble anxiety. Jason muttered, "The captain cannot read the map. He is holding it upside down."

The captain sounded pompous. He said, "It is false. Claw them with red-hot pincers till they speak the truth."

The lieutenant cried, "Yes, lord! At once, lord!"

Catherine said quickly, "Blood has already been shed to prove this map is false! Look at my lord's fingernail. But it is not false, and that is why we are here."

She heard the captain cracking the joints of his fingers. He said, "I have reached my decision, and that is—that the subadar shall decide."

They went out of that room and followed along more passages, with scarlet-clad soldiers clanging among them and the smell of oil from the smoky lamps thick in her nostrils. They passed women too— a sudden whiff of languid scent and two tinkling voices. Jason tripped over his cheap sword.

She began to laugh, the gusts of laughter shaking her so that it hurt to keep her face straight and her body upright.

Jason cried, "Lord, please go more slowly. My wife is almost blind." But really it was his sword that was worrying him. Oh, she loved him, and all would be well, somehow, somewhere.

They hurried along, and Jason kept muttering, "Careful now! Steps up here—twenty-five. God's blood, the thoughtless brutes! More steps—seven, eight, nine."

(Blind she was, but she loved him. She had guided him from the coast of Coromandel to the fortress of the Grand Mogul. She had executed Mansur Khan because Mansur had done wickedness—no, because Mansur had tempted Jason to do wickedness. She was sorry that the lieutenant had been cruel about that execution, but that was not her fault. God would be good to her and find a place for Jason.)

This room was large and strongly lighted. The subadar wore blue, and the ranks of blue and steel were thicker about him, and a thin, ancient voice was reading aloud from the Koran in a far corner. The captain began to explain.

The subadar said, "Show me this map, then."

In the corner the old man's high voice piped on above the subadar's grated decision. "It is false. Hang them up by the thumbs till they speak the truth."

Catherine said, "The wazir has word of this map, lord. I am to show it to him when I go to his couch tonight."

She heard Jason gasp beside her, but she felt hilarious and capable of saying anything. She had never met the wazir, but she knew he was a more important man than a subadar.

But the subadar stood up with a cry of astonishment and said, "The wazir! You! This is a miracle! We must take them to the wazir indeed."

She thought: What have I said now? It didn't matter. This was India! Let her speak, then, in riddles or jokes. Let her join the charade, because no one, including the actors, knew from moment to moment whether it was charade or reality. Kisses and blood, gold and cow dung—anything might be pressed upon her at any time. Meantime she was in love, and Jason loved her, though he dared not tell himself so, and this was a wonderful and ridiculous game of wits.

"To the wazir!" everyone cried, and one and all rushed out into the passage—half a hundred now, and she and Jason nearly forgotten in the crush, so that she could say, trying not to giggle, "I love you so," and he could cry, "God's blood! What trouble have you got us into now?"

(She had given Azeema the power to leave the Rawan's palace, where before she had had only the longing to. At second remove, the fire of her will had scorched the mullah's ancient behind so that he had jumped up and onto his horse and galloped off, faster than a fur-capped messenger, to the nearest Mogul post.)

They stormed up and round and down, and, from the shouting, half the hawk-minders and curtain-dyers and zither-tuners in the palace seemed to have joined them. The wazir's room was twice as large as the subadar's, and all white, dazzling white, with lacy reflections on the ceiling and everywhere a secretive smell of flowers.

Jason whispered, "Two boys are stroking his hands!"

Then she remembered the lascivious tales of the old housekeeper in Manairuppu, and knew why the subadar had been so astounded that she was going to share the wazir's bed. She giggled uncontrollably now and could not stop until she managed to turn it into a fit of coughing.

The wazir had a sweet, hoarse voice. It said, "Show me the map, my dear." And the subadar said, "Here it is, Lord Wazir."

After a time the wazir said, "It is false. Force raw red peppers into their rear ends, my dear, until they speak the truth. I will come and help you."

She nudged Jason and muttered in English, "Kiss his hand! Go on!"

She heard the smacking of lips. The wazir said, "*Such* eyes! We must take him to the king's dear son."

Out again—and God knew how many in the mob now. The wazir was there, and the subadar, and the captain, and the lieutenant, and hundreds of soldiers and clerks, and probably the boys Jason had told her about.

(She must have smelled Mansur's true nature that first day in Sagthali. Perhaps she had known all along—because God was good—that something must happen to show Jason the evil of that road. She had known Parvati from the first, too, when everyone else, including Jason, thought she was a common strumpet. Jason hated himself sometimes for the way he treated people who had been good to him; he had told her about the women Emily and Mabel in London. But he could not help it. He hurt them because, in spite of himself, he must follow his dream. They were good women all, but they did not belong in that dream. *She* did!)

The room of the king's son was like a barn, where a squadron of cavalry could hide unnoticed. All around her the men threw themselves flat on the floor, and *bang-thump-bang* went their heads against the stone. She looked over their prostrate, heaving behinds and saw an army of soldiers in green, shimmering on guard, and the flesh of girls glowed gauzily about a pile of cushions, and somewhere a hookah gurgled.

Then everyone rose to his feet, and Jason too. He was silly to have bowed with the rest. He should have stood, to make himself obvious to the king's son.

Jason said, "I can't see a thing. We are at the back now."

A stern official voice beside her said, "What are you doing here? Out, foreigners!"

Jason said, "Yes, lord! At once! Quick, Catherine, let's go while we can."

But from a distance the king's son said, "It is false. Put them in a bath and pour in boiling water till they speak the truth."

Then—"Where are they?" screeched the wazir, and everyone dashed about, shouting, while she and Jason stood still, and soon fifty soldiers fell on them, each holding an ear or a toe, and dragged them forward. The one who shouted loudest was the man who had told them to go away, and he yelled, "Lord, I caught them! They were trying to escape!"

Jason shouted, "Why, you damned liar!" But Catherine bowed before the brilliance that must be the king's son, and said, "Your Majesty, this diamond came from the treasure—so it must exist." And she held up the last of the stones she had brought from Coromandel. The king's son took it from her and said, "Well, then, we had better take them to the Great King, my father."

"*The Great King!*" everyone whispered. Catherine held out her hand for the stone, but the king's son did not give it back.

(She had made Parvati an offer that would have meant sharing Jason with her, although she loved him. There was no other hope at that time, and even that wasn't much of a hope because—oh, he'd been in love with Parvati. Before all that, in the very beginning, she had decided to marry him when she first saw him—no, when she first heard him singing "Greensleeves." That was an impossible thing to decide, but she had done it. He ought to understand. He had bought a map at first sight, and spent all that he had saved, and gone to Coromandel.)

In the court of the Great King a thousand clashing points of color danced a slow dance around a peacock throne, and in the still night air horses neighed and elephants trumpeted salutes, and all the people of the city shouted their petitions. Someone held tight to her, and

231

soon she arrived before the Great King, the Mogul Emperor, Shah Jehan, Lord of the World.

The king's son, the wazir, the subadar, the captain, and the lieutenant all spoke at once. "Majesty! Majesty! There is a map—"

One by one, in ascending order of importance, they fell silent. At last the king's son said, "Your Majesty! My father! . . ." He told the story and gave the map to the king his father.

The Great King said, "Come here."

Quietly the sense of unreality subsided in Catherine. This was a quiet, nasal voice, speaking from the throne above her. The joke had ended. She stepped forward at Jason's side.

There was a long silence, in which she heard the rustle of paper. The people around her seemed to be breathing less noisily.

The king said, "Which?"

No one seemed to breathe at all. The horses in the courtyard ceased their neighing, and the elephants fell silent, and all the vast throng made no sound.

Then the king sighed, and the sound of the people moving and breathing stirred like a wind in the palace. She did not know what had happened, except that it was important.

The king said, "Go and tell your tale to the empress, then. She understands adventurous young people better than I do. Don't be afraid."

When the audience heard this they shouted aloud in a trance of adulation, "Beyond description is the wisdom of the Great King!"

The Great King suddenly screamed, his voice breaking, "Be quiet, you blasphemous dogs! You, lead the foreigners to the empress."

Slowly they were led back through the enormous fortress. Catherine whispered, "What happened—there, in front of the king? Why were the people so quiet?"

Their guide said, "Sssh!" and stopped and called, "Within there! Two foreigners, a man and a woman, sent by the Great King to explain themselves to Her Majesty."

A womanish voice answered, "Wait. Her Majesty will see them now."

"Where's the map?" Catherine whispered.

"I have it," Jason said in a strange voice. "The king gave it back to me."

The guide said sharply, "Be quiet! Go in there."

Jason led her forward. When he knelt she knelt beside him. It was dark here, except for a single blue light. There was a curtain, but she could not tell whether it was behind or in front of the lamp. A woman's clothes rustled richly beyond the curtain. The eunuch rattled his scimitar in the corner behind them.

A quiet, rather high-pitched voice said, "Look at me."

She raised her head, put the glass to her eye, leaned forward, and could not suppress a violent start and a cry. The curtains were parted near the level of her face by a single huge eye, six inches across. A yellow light glowed in it, the blue lamp cast lustrous and ghostly shadows on it, it did not move. Slowly she realized that it was not an eye but a piece of glass that she gazed at—curved and most cunningly shaped glass that caught the light from within and without and magnified just the eye of the empress behind the curtain.

The eye blinked as she examined it, the light chased across the pupil, and the treble voice said sharply, "What are you doing, girl?"

She said, "I can see nothing without my glass, Your Majesty."

"Oh. But you are beautiful in your way, aren't you?"

"Your eye is beautiful," Catherine said.

"And the rest of me?" The empress's voice rose inquiringly.

Catherine said, "I have heard that the Great King thinks so. He is not blind."

The voice trilled delightedly and said, "Come round to the back of the curtain—on the right, my dear."

She got up, putting away her glass. The voice said with sudden suspicion, "You are really blind?"

"Nearly, Your Majesty."

"Come, then. Even the Great King may see no more of me than my eye when I am like this."

Catherine slipped round the edge of the curtain, wondering. As soon as she felt the hand in hers, guiding her down to the cushions, she understood. The empress's hand was fat and puffy—not just the fatness of obesity, but a soft, yielding fatness that spoke of disease. Yet the eye was very beautiful.

"Now tell me," the empress said. "We will leave your young man outside there. He looks handsome, in your European fashion."

"I love him, Your Majesty. It is about a map. Jason, give me the map, through the curtain. . . ."

She told the empress the whole story, from the beginning, omitting nothing except her own disbelief in the map as a guide to hidden treasure. She would have liked to tell the empress that too, for she felt that this was a sensitive woman; but Jason could hear what they were saying.

When she finished, the empress said, "It is a strange and unlikely tale. All the best tales are unlikely, especially the ones that come true. Such a tale is that of my marriage to the Great King, and how I came to be called Mumtaz Mahall, the Treasure of the Palace. I would like to help you if I can. I want to believe in your map, so I do—but that is not enough. Let me think. All the men who have examined this map have been thinking only of money, and I only of the tale you have told. There must be some better way—some man who can judge it with an eye that is blinded by neither greed nor romance." She lay back, only to start forward and cry, "Ishmael! Of Multan! You shall go to Ishmael tomorrow. He shall decide."

"Who is he?" Catherine asked.

"Ishmael is the king's librarian," the empress said. "He is a funny old man—yet he is not funny at all, but wise. He is laughed at sometimes—but when you see who is laughing, you see only oafs and fools. Yes, Ishmael shall decide. But have no fear. Even if the map is false, I shall see that you come to no harm. You are my sister in suffering. I understand much that you do not have to tell me. Do you know that I am a poet? Perhaps that is why I understand. But I am also an empress, and that is why I must send you to Ishmael, instead of coming with you!"

Catherine bent, without disgust, to kiss the pulpy-soft hand.

※   ※   ※

In the morning a eunuch took them to the library.

The door closed with a heavy thud behind them. They stood motionless for a minute, but no one came to them. She said, "Where is Ishmael? Can you see anyone?"

The words went running away from her and were overpowered by silence, and then the silence crept up from the farthest corners and, when it reached her, laid hands on her, first stopping her mouth and then driving out from her the last remains of yesterday's tempestuous hours and all her anxiety. The whirling, darting, bowing memories slowed their circular wheels of movement. The jagged colors faded as the motion died. At last all settled into place. They were in a great room. There was a cool floor, shadowed white light, in the distance a pierced marble screen. She moved slowly forward.

The room smelled of parchment, paper, teakwood, and leather. She drew out her glass and began to examine everything within reach. There could be no hurry here. Rolls of parchment lay stacked on the shelves, and there were other books, of the kind that she knew, standing straight-spined in their places. There were low tables covered with books. There were single sheets of paper, resting alone in lakes of light, whereon three or four arabic letters, graceful as leaping deer, swept across the smooth white planes.

Jason wandered on ahead, feeling the thick parchment between his fingers, stooping to examine the hanging seals, carefully lifting out the brass cylinders in which some of the rolls were kept. Such strange and wonderful worlds were displayed here, yet hidden from him by the bindings, by his ignorance. Surely it was in these worlds that he was meant to wander and wonder.

Jason said, "Oh!" and came to a stop. She joined him slowly, and he muttered, "That must be Ishmael."

"What does he look like? Is he close?"

"Twenty feet off, near the marble screen."

By the dappled light something rose, and white wings fluttered. A man spoke somewhat querulously. "You see, he was as wise as Solomon, yet as eager as a child. He journeyed all over the world, but he had time to notice the flowers and the birds." Then, with vehemence: "And, more important than all, he wrote down what he saw, what he did, what he felt. Nothing like that is being done now, is it?"

He seemed to expect an answer. Jason was obviously struck dumb, so she said, "No, sir. Who are you talking about?"

The man exclaimed, "Why, the Emperor Baber, of course! Who else? But I see you are a foreigner. Dutch? Portuguese? English? I speak them all just a little, and—" He moved quickly and called, "Come and look at this! Hurry!"

She followed him and saw, beyond a blurred forecourt, a stretch of the river, a couple of boats, and then, sharp and still on the opposite bank, small horses and big trees.

"Wonderful," the voice breathed.

Jason said, "What is, sir?"

"Why, didn't you see? The heron, flying upstream—such beautiful wings, such slow strokes, yet it never falls into the river. What keeps it up? It is a heavy bird. But if you don't see, you don't. What have you come to me for? Do you want a petition translated? That's what the Portuguese priests were always wanting, till they learned for themselves."

She thought: He is an old man; during his life he must have seen a hundred thousand birds in flight. Why does he suddenly dart out to see another? Yet of course it *was* wonderful, and why should the hundred thousandth be any less exciting than the first?

Jason said hesitantly, "Sir—you are Ishmael of Multan?"

"Indeed, yes—librarian to His Majesty."

Jason said, "The empress, Mumtaz Mahall, told us to show you this map."

The paper rustled. Catherine waited in painful suspense. Ishmael cried, "Wonderful! Look at this, look at that! The man who painted this was an artist—in his way, in his way. He was a Westerner, of course. Sir Thomas Roe often tried to tell me about your art."

The blood began to pound and her heart to sing. She must see this man. She put the glass to her eye and leaned forward. They were taking no notice of her. She could look without being rude. He was old indeed, but red-bearded. A green turban was pushed to the back of his bald head, and a pair of spectacles pushed to the front of his long nose. She stooped closer. The beard had been dyed with henna. She chuckled aloud with delight; he was a scholar, but he dyed his white hairs to show the woman of his house—and perhaps other, younger women—that he had not buried all his power in books. She looked more closely yet at his face. It was not a scholar's face like those she had sometimes examined in drawings and paintings. His was thin and strong, and scarred by old wounds.

And Jason stood there, leaning over the map, wonder like spring in his face. He must have looked like that when Voy sold it to him; when he lay on the floor of his room in England and looked at it, his sister beside him. His eyes sparkled.

She put away the glass. God *was*, after all and in spite of all, good. This old man was Jason. Wherever Jason had been, this old man had been, in his own way and his own time. Wherever Jason wanted to go, this man could go with him. She had led far enough, and had known for some days that the end of her capacity to lead was near, because also the end of her experience and understanding of this man she loved. She had known from the beginning that Jason was a deeper, stranger person than herself. Now she could hand over, and Ishmael would take the charge.

Ishmael was saying, "Look at this! See, these men in fur hats—

Tartars. This mountain is marked Meru. Hmm! Everyone who makes a map shows Meru somewhere up there. *I* don't believe it even exists. I'll prove it to you."

The white wings fluttered and bent down. She sought Jason with her eyes. Though she could not bring him out of the pearled mist before her, she knew that he was looking at her. She held out her hand.

Chapter Five

Ishmael was saying, "Look at this! See, these men in the fur hats—Tartars. This mountain is marked Meru. Hmm! Everyone who makes a map shows Meru somewhere up there. I don't believe it even exists. I'll prove it to you." He darted round and began to rummage energetically in a chest full of papers and books.

Jason took a deep, incredulous breath. This old man was as excited as he had been when Voy first mentioned the map. This old man behaved as though the map were true—not quite that, certainly not in respect of the treasure, which he hadn't even mentioned yet, but as though, true or not, the map was a wonderful thing to have and to look at and wonder over.

Catherine was looking at him, the sun in her eyes and her hand outstretched. God's blood, it was lucky that she'd been so tired she'd flopped asleep as soon as the empress dismissed them last night. Otherwise she'd have asked again about that tense moment in the king's council chamber. He had to remind himself that she was blind. It was hard to realize that she had known nothing of that critical pause, when the king had said, "Which?" and he alone had had to decide.

She looked so happy now that he took her hand and kissed it. She held the hand to her cheek, and he flushed with awkward pleasure.

Last night the Great King had said, "Come here," and they had stepped forward together, he and Catherine. The king had the map in his hand and a moody smile on his face. A great black man, black as pitch, almost naked, with a red turban and green pantaloons and a black, naked, hairy belly, stood at the king's left hand, a long sword on his shoulder. A fat and hairless man, all in yellow, stood at the king's right hand. The king was in the middle, with the map. Grouped all round in a close circle were the wazir and the king's son and the rest of them.

The king raised his little finger. The fat man held out a bag of money, the neck open so that Jason and everyone else saw the gold coins glittering inside it. The black man brought down the sword, and the long, shining blue blade, with ugly little nicks in it, rested across the map on the king's hand.

Then the king said, "Which?"

No one seemed to breathe. The horses ceased their neighing, and the war elephants arrayed across the far courtyard, steel spikes in their head harnesses, fell silent. The king smiled still—that menacing, harassed smile.

He was offering them an ordeal: take the money and bother him no more with the map; or cleave to their silly tale and risk the sword if it was false. "Which?"

But it was not to *them* that the ordeal was being offered, but only to *him,* Jason Savage, because Catherine could not see. On him alone rested the decision, and he did not truly believe in the map. The sensible thing to do was take the money and get out. All would have been achieved—escape from the Rawan, escape from violence, escape from lying. He had only said he believed because Catherine believed, and he did not want to hurt her. It was madness to risk that sword. This was not a charade. The king smiled, but the sword would sweep down if he gave the signal. This was India.

He glanced once at Catherine waiting placidly beside him. Madness! But he reached out his hand and, looking straight at the king, touched the map and the sword, laying his hand across both. Then it was that the king sighed, and the sound of the people moving and breathing stirred like a wind through the council hall.

Jason had thought of the ordeal, and his choice, all during the time that Catherine was closeted behind the curtain with the empress. He had decided he was a fool. Now, in the library, listening to Ishmael of Multan, he was not so sure.

Ishmael straightened his back from the box and said, "I can't find it. You'll have to take my word for it; there is grave doubt among scholars as to whether this famous magic mountain Meru actually exists. Do you know what the trouble is?" He waited, his eager eyes behind the scratched lenses fixed on Jason.

Jason muttered, "No, sir."

"I'll tell you! The trouble is that those who dream, don't do, and those who do, don't dream—except Baber and perhaps Jehangir and a few others. Love, war, peace, the beauties of repose—it's always the same! Passionate love lyrics are written by nervous little fellows who've crawled home every blameless night to their shrewish wives. Old, bearded clerks curdle their own blood with epics of battle.

Kings pour out poems about their gardens and their nightingales! Do you know what *I* dream of? Exploration of the earth and the people in it. And what do I do? Sit here and explore old books. Why don't I do both? Why don't I try to relate the wisdom of the study with the fierceness of the mountains? Why don't I try to find what men have thought in the past and compare it with what they actually do now? Why?"

He demanded an answer. Jason was no longer afraid or worried. He had no desire but to help. He said, "Because you think you're too old."

Ishmael leaned back slowly, the tips of his slender fingers dragging across the map on the table.

He said, "Ah! You are wise. Yes, I do think so. And I have no follower, no son or disciple or friend who can go on where I must stop." He brushed his hand wearily across his forehead and spoke in a more subdued tone. "I'm sorry, my friends. I have been alone a long time in this library. I get excited. Now about this map—what do you want me to say?"

Jason glanced at Catherine, waiting for her to speak. She said nothing. He realized that she was waiting for him. Very well. He was ready now to assume the leadership.

He said, "We want to follow this map to find the treasure on it. Here." He thought he saw a small crease of worry flit across Catherine's face. What was the matter now? What else could he have said?

"Treasure?" Ishmael said sadly. "You're after money, are you? Then I'm afraid the map is useless, as a map. Look at this. Look at that. Hills—here? There are none. The man who made this map had never been near India. He had heard of the Himalayas. He has marked them here—not bad, not bad. The Castle of the Holy Men? I wonder what that might be." His voice lost its gloom and began to quicken and sharpen. "Badrinath might fit, though it's five hundred miles from where he's shown the castle. The Hindus have a temple at Badrinath because it's near the source of the Ganges. If you went that way you would cross into Tibet over the Mana Pass."

He turned suddenly to stare at Jason. He said, "The Mana Pass! Come and look at this!" He dived into the chest again, but this time came up with a small, thick manuscript. He dumped it on the table. "Look at this!"

"What is it, sir?" Jason asked.

"Diary, my boy. Mmm. *Crossed the pass on such-and-such a day.* Mmm. Diary of an ambassador sent to Lhasa by the emperor about forty years ago. *Weather cold this day and the Lady Fatima complaining that the wind, which never stops, will ruin her skin. What am I to do?* Ha! *Met a monk.* Ah, here we are. Listen, now. *This infidel monk, who seemed nevertheless to be a man of taste, told us that, some two days' march to the north of where we then were, a scholar had died in olden times. No one knows the name of that scholar. He was buried where he died, at the edge of a salt lake near the foot of a great mountain which has two peaks, and all his knowledge was buried with him. Later the king of that land is said to have caused a tomb to be built over his grave. The monk told us that the winds had blown sand over the tomb, or 'stupa,' as he called it, for hundreds of years, and no one now knows exactly where the scholar lies. Ishmael of Multan—that's me—has instructed me to dig up any such place I heard of, but the monk said there would not be any treasure buried in the stupa, so we did not waste time searching for it. What would I find, even if by the grace of Allah I came upon the tomb? The Lady Fatima complains that—* Bah!"

The old man's eyes blazed. "No treasure! But the scholar was buried *with all his knowledge.* Books, inscribed tablets—what may not lie hidden there? I have never forgiven that fool of an ambassador."

Jason thought: Twin peaks! There was a mountain, then, even though it might not be Meru; and there was a treasure, though not a treasure of money. He said, "Father, I will look! I will find the stupa!"

Ishmael said, "What do you care about knowledge?"

Jason began, "Father—" then stopped.

He wanted to say that now he cared about nothing else. In this library only his four books, of all that he owned or had ever owned, seemed to have any value. But Catherine was standing at his side, and the map was her guiding star. All her strength came from it. He could not say that the map meant little to him now, any more than he had been able to say it to the king yesterday.

He said, "Father, can we not dream of gold and look for knowledge? Or dream of knowledge and look for gold?"

Ishmael said, "*Can* we? I don't know. But we can try. We shall go together. I shall come with you."

Jason said, "But you are—you have said you are not young."

Ishmael said energetically, "Sixty-nine. And you are—twenty-two?

241

And the lady about the same? That makes us each thirty-seven, for we must share alike all that we have of experience and skill and muscle. An excellent age. Now, the king will not wish to let me go. But he needs money. It is, after all, possible that there is a treasure of money on Meru—if Meru exists. Or on some other mountain, if it does not exist. I think His Majesty will let us go, provided we do not ask him for guards and traveling expenses. As to that, I have a little saved up. So, we shall go! And what shall we see?"

He wandered over to the stone screen as he talked, and now gazed through it, the birdlike eagerness of his movements stilled and his voice quieted. He spoke as Voy sometimes used to, so that his words took the power of wings, and Jason rose with them. He knew the unknown scholar. He *was* the unknown scholar, dying among foreign mountains. The hard light dimmed. Death came to him as a wild bird across the plain. Must he leave all his knowledge behind? No, because he could leave it buried there with his body, and yet take it. There was nothing else in the world, except love, that could be shared and yet possessed. They were burying that body by the salt lake, and the wind blew stronger. Jason was at peace. He knew where his life must go. He would be a scholar.

Ishmael's voice ended. Jason said, "We shall find him! Then we shall know everything!"

Ishmael took his hand and shook it gently. "Not everything, my young friend. Only a little, and that perhaps of no great importance."

"When can we start?" Jason said eagerly. The sooner they started, the sooner they would return.

"Patience, my son," Ishmael said, leading him outside. "Will the lady join us? How should I address her?"

Catherine said, "Please think of me as your daughter, and so call me by my name."

Ishmael nodded, and with his hand brushed a few specks of dust off a marble bench. They sat down there on the terrace above the river. The shadow of the pink walls laid its careless shelter over them, and the sun beat at the stones beyond their feet. Ishmael said, "Tell me your story, from the beginning. Wait!" He stood up.

There was no heron this time, but Jason did not need to ask, What is it? A man stood in the shallows on the far side of the river, a net over his shoulder. So they watched; and two saw the sudden curve of light along the fisherman's back and thighs as he flung the net, and the sweeping arc of the net in the air, flying, unfolding, falling, and the circle of splashes where the weights, all together, struck the face of the Jumna; and one saw nothing, because she had closed her eyes and fallen asleep, her head on Jason's shoulder.

Then Ishmael said, "Now—begin."

* * *

Jason groaned, turned over, and tried to close his ears.

Catherine said, "What is it, Father?"

Ishmael said, "Come out, children."

Jason struggled out of the blanket and crawled toward the opening of the tent. The old man's enthusiasm knew no limits. What would it be this time?

Once in the open, he stood up and stretched. The camp was in a grove, the night's fires were dying, and the first splash of yellow light warmed the eastern horizon. Ishmael tugged at his hand, and he at Catherine's, and they hurried through the grove, over the sheeted travelers and among the ranked trees. At the farthest edge Ishmael stopped and exclaimed, "There!"

Crops sloped gently away in front. An opal-starred mist hung over the ground. A cock crew from a clump of feathery trees. Jason yawned, rubbed his eyes, and looked.

He blinked. His eyes widened. His knees began to buckle, and he sank to the earth with his fingers locked on his chest and his breath altogether stopped.

Above the crops spread the white mist. Above the mist green hills climbed slowly upward. Above the hills the air was hazily blue and dense with distance. Now out of that blue sea of air rose the golden battlements of heaven. Their walls swept down in falls of pearl. Their diamond towers soared up from oceans of sapphire. From their black portals unseen archers streamed red arrows at the paling stars. A thousand cathedrals thrust up thin golden spires.

The light changed; the colors ran down from dazzling white cones to purple deeps. The sun rose, and for a moment the miracle hung, all gold and black above the abyss, stretched from the rising sun to the setting moon, and from earth to heaven.

Catherine whispered, "I see the City of God." Jason closed his eyes.

When he opened them the mist had risen, and all was gone. He stood up slowly and said, "Father, what have I seen?"

The old man said, "The Himalaya—a hundred and fifty miles away.

We are going beyond that. We had better get back and eat. See, they are packing up the camp already. Oh, look at those ducks!"

But Jason did not want to look at anything. He wished he might be struck blind at that moment and never see anything again. Or sit here for a year, at the edge of the grove, facing north, and every morning at dawn watch the light lift that City of God out of the darkness. No, he would rise two hours before dawn, and wait alone through those last chilly hours in contemplation, thinking. Sometimes the mountains would not be seen, because of mist or cloud or rain. In a way, that would be better, because he could imagine them.

Still, he could not do it now. He had to go on, following the map and Ishmael and Catherine. He walked pensively back through the grove to their tent. Catherine busied herself over the fire. Jason sat down, cupped his chin in his hands, and stared into space.

Ishmael said, "What's the matter with you, Jason? You have been very quiet all the time. Are your bowels loose? Are you constipated?"

Jason said, "I was thinking. I understand why the Hindus think that most of the gods live up there in the Himalaya. I could watch them all my life."

Ishmael said cheerfully, "Many people do exactly that and nothing more. They are mystics. I'm hungry!"

An hour later they trotted out onto the road and continued their journey. Toward midday Ishmael drew up to Jason and said, "There see! There's a man such as I told you about—a mystic."

Jason reined in. He had seen these ash-smeared figures from Manairuppu to Agra, but he had never before understood them. Now he thought he did understand, at least a little. It was a life of inward and outward contemplation. It was not his life, but it was nearer to it than any other he had known.

He rode on thoughtfully. Yes, he could understand. He could live that life, exploring ever farther among dreams and visions. Then farther still—what would there be? Would dreams become thoughts and thoughts, facts? Did they change their nature as you followed them? So that what you thought, was? Or perhaps came back on themselves? Or returned to God? He closed his eyes momentarily. There was a rare exhilaration in this contemplation, almost like danger, or temptation to a great evil.

But supposing he turned his back on the world, one way or another, as either scholar or mystic, what would happen to Catherine

She and he had gone through many perils together. He thought back over their long journey. She was a woman of action. She was determined and forceful. She loved traveling and the smell of campfires and the stamping of the ponies in the hour before dawn, and dancing. . . . He had used to like dancing. This was not her life.

Tenderly, in his reverie, he touched her hair, and tenderly told her to go and leave him and find her happiness. He was not worthy of her. Nor was his life hers. He would sit under a peepul tree and explore in the mind. He would sit in a library and travel among books. Ishmael did not understand that he, Jason, had already exhausted the shallowness of desire and lust and action.

But he loved her. He said it twice to himself: *I love you.* Yes, he loved her, but not with earthly desire. She must go and find her happiness. He rode along, bathed in a warm, satisfying glow of self-abnegation.

Ishmael rode up alongside him, slapped him on the back, and cried, "What *is* the matter with you? I'm sure you need a purgative. There are a thousand things to see, and you moon along like a stuffed duck. Look, the hills! This is where the Ganges comes out into the plain."

Jason shook the reins, and smiled soulfully. "It is beautiful, Father," he said. "Tell me about it."

Catherine turned sharply toward him, and he smiled at her too; but of course she could not see. She could not know how much he loved her. Perhaps it was as well. When she set her mind on something she was like an elephant in persistence and strength.

Next day they entered the foothills. In the plains the heat had been spread over the whole large horizon. Here in the river valley the hills enclosed it, the sun glowered overhead, and no air flowed, except that sometimes the cooler air above the river spread out so that a tendril of it lay across the path. When they came to such a place they stopped and stood for a minute, believing themselves cool, until Ishmael cried, "On!"

Their horses plodded on and up the gradual rise of the rocky trail. The hills rose higher on either hand. One by one the heavy trees gave place to pines; the smell of hot resin filled their nostrils, and brittle pine needles crackled under the horses' hoofs. Lone pines stood like sentries on the shoulders of the hills; the gray rock thrust up through the grass; the river began to make a sound of bells. Always the pilgrims, struggling toward the source of the holy river, climbed with them. Sometimes they recognized people they had passed farther back—a hillman now hurrying past, his energy doubled by the sight of snow; a rich man changing horses. Usually it was only the backs that they saw, the anonymous, dragging heels, the heavy load. Sometimes one turned to watch them go by, and then they saw the exhaustion, the illness, or the strength of that traveler—and always the shining hope, whether it was a man squatting against a pine while he smoked, or a woman bowed under her palsied son.

Each day they lifted themselves a little higher. At any moment, round any corner, they might be given a single passing sight of far snow; or the mountains would stride from hiding at a pace as slow as their own. As the path climbed, far ahead they would see a slope of trees; then, hour by hour, the lesser hills fell back, the slope soared, shedding in turn trees, grass, and rock, until at last it stood out white and unencumbered against the sky; then, hour by hour, the hills closed in and ate away the sides of the mountain until they had altogether swallowed it.

On the fourth night Jason shivered from the cold and spent the night huddled close against Catherine's back. On the sixth day Ishmael bought blankets and long-skirted sheepskin coats from a Hindu store beside the trail. On the tenth day the river roared down beside them, all young and white and foaming, and that day every pilgrim on the road seemed to have left his weariness at the night's camping place and stepped out with the river's power flowing in him.

Jason said, "They are near the end now." And Ishmael answered, "Near the beginning. They are traveling backward, to the source!"

Jason's horse began to trot out, blowing jets of crystal air from its nostrils. It trotted over a pass; the wind blew strong in Jason's face from sloping snowfields, and he saw in the distance, under the mountain wall, a huddle of stone buildings and a thousand rude tents.

Ishmael said, "Badrinath!"

Catherine cried, "The Castle of the Holy Men!"

Jason examined the place thoughtfully as he rode forward. Perhaps it was here, or in some similar shrine, that his life would lie. A temple would be a good place to combine scholarship and contemplation. A balance must be struck. He had thought more about the mystic surveying the Himalaya, and decided that that life was ot for him. The man who only thought did no good to anyone else, because he did not share his discoveries. Besides, there might not be enough inside himself to provide sufficient food for contemplation. What if, after examining it for a couple of years, he found he had reached the bottom of his soul, and there was nothing more here? Then what?

No, he must put something in—ideas and facts he would find in books—and *then* contemplate, and then write books himself so that others could profit from his work. He might think about the world, for instance, and God and Man. And then write a history of the world!

They reached the camping site. As soon as the tent was set up and the small fire lit—wood was scarce and expensive here, every faggot carried up the valley four days on the backs of the hillmen—Jason wandered away toward the temple.

At the main entrance a priest greeted him impassively. Jason asked to be shown round. The priest said, "You may not see the sanctuary. The rest I can show you."

Jason said, "Please."

He followed the priest, speaking little, hardly listening while the priest rambled on about the uses of the various parts. Books he saw —yes, they had books here. And men at prayer. A priest writing— good! And idols. He wouldn't like the idols. The priests were taking money for the idols. The pilgrims were paying the money. Not quite right; money was unnecessary, if not evil, in the contemplative life. Still, this was a stage closer to the goal he sought. Not a library, not a peepul tree, not a Hindu temple—something combining all those; but bigger, more glorious, more awful. He would go on looking and thinking. Soon he would find what he wanted, or it would find him.

Outside again in the twilight, and having paid the priest, he saw Ishmael wandering round the temple, peering at the carvings. He did not want to talk with Ishmael just now, so he walked round the other way and returned to the tent.

As he approached he heard low singing.

> "*Alas, my love you do me wrong*
> *To cast me off discourteously,*
> *And I have lovèd you so long,*
> *Delighting in your company.*

> *Greensleeves was all my joy,*
> *Greensleeves was my delight.*
> *Greensleeves was my hart of gold,*
> *And who but my lady Greensleeves?"*

She was lying on a blanket in the mouth of the tent. She did no
stop her song as he sat down, though she had heard him coming. Sh
turned her face to him and sang softer, looking at him.

She finished, and he said, "You have a beautiful voice."

It was not so beautiful—small and clear and true, that was all. Bu
he loved her with a pure, empyrean love, all passion and vilenes
purged, and all that she did was beautiful.

She said, "Come and sit close to me. It's cold round my back.

He moved over, and she lay back against him. It was warmer in
deed then, and the dusk fell silently on the high snowfields, and
hundred fires twinkled, and the river sang beside them. She leane
her head against his chest. He stroked her hair, just as he ha
dreamed he would. Pure love flowed in his fingers, the love of
scholar, of a monk. They must part. They would turn, like angels, i
mid-air, and, loving, go their ways.

She said softly, "Don't you love me yet?"

He said, "Yes."

She turned her head and kissed his shoulder. Half muffled agains
him, she whispered, "I'm your wife, then."

Mechanically he stroked her hair, down the back of her neck. H
remembered what she had said on the sand dunes by the pearler
cove. Now she would lie with him. Now he must not. Now h
did not even want to. What hurt had he done, to how many womer
by that act! There could be no lying with women in a world of th
mind. He would say nothing now, but wait till a time and a circum
stance came when he could tell her she was free of her promise

She said, "Ishmael won't come back for a time yet. It's dark."

He got up quickly. He could not resist this much longer. He said, "
love you—too much." He began to blow up the fire, puffing furiousl
until he felt his eyes starting from his head, until the nag of desir
had gone.

Catherine began to sing "Greensleeves" again, and later Ishmae
returned.

The next day they set out for the Mana Pass and Tibet.

❊   ❊   ❊

Ishmael gripped with his knees and leaned back as the pony scrambled down the steep. One enormous plain lay behind them, and another, but a little smaller, in front. This land was all plain, split by ridges where the horses had to climb wearily up and carefully down. The Himalayan snows rose out of India a hundred miles back; nameless peaks glittered along the horizon in front. The air came thin into the lungs here, and in the shadow it was always cold. He felt better than he had for many years. Why didn't he come to live up here? Or go off on such a wild journey every year? But that wasn't the reason; it was the young people, the wonderful Jason and his wife. In some ways she was even more remarkable. She had no genius, as Jason had; but she had the wisdom. The young man would not be happy without her. That reminded him. He must talk alone with her and find out what was the matter with the boy.

He screwed up his eyes against the glare and peered forward. He was looking for the black tents of nomads, for a caravan or a wall or crops—anything that would show the presence of other people besides themselves. They needed information about twin-peaked mountains. They needed butter and more of the ground barley called sampa. The horses were thirsty and walked sadly, their jaws drooping open.

But it was good up here on the high plateau. There were marmots beside the trail, and stone walls in the middle of a forty-mile plain, and on every stone the same inscription: Om mane padme hum—"O hail, the jewel in the lotus"; and, all day and every day, the howling wind; and swirling herds of the wild ass; and a long column of sheep, each hurrying, with a sack of salt or borax across its back, toward India; and men with fur caps turning their horses at full gallop beside an icy lake where the wind rippled the salt water and a thousand ducks whirred up from the reeds as they approached. That time—when he had cried, "The fur hats!" and Catherine shouted, "Let's catch up with them and speak to them!"—Jason had said, "We had better not. They may be bandits."

True enough, the old man thought. Tibet was full of bandits. But he thought Jason had said no because he did not want to continue the search for the mountain Meru and the treasure it might hide. He was more interested in the scholar's tomb, but even there his enthusiasm seemed to have waned or been diverted.

They had reached the level plain. Ishmael said, "Jason, ride ahead, try to run down one of these hares."

Catherine said, "Yes, go on, Jason. I'm hungry! Go far, where can see you galloping."

Jason hesitated, then cantered off. When he was half a mile ahead Ishmael said, "My daughter, I want to talk to you. That's why—"

She said, "I know. What do *you* think he's thinking of?"

Ishmael adjusted the leather thong around his head. He kept hi spectacles in place with it, for fear he might miss something if he ha to stop to put them on. He said, "Why, Catherine, I don't know. I ha thought he might have told you."

She said, "He hasn't. You would have noticed if you hadn't bee so intent on the country and the people and the scholar's tomb." Sh spoke with unusual sharpness, and Ishmael thought: Goodness me she's upset. It must be serious.

She said, "I'm sorry, Father. But I am worried. He hasn't told me but I think I know what's in his mind. He's going to shut himsel into a library or a temple or a mango grove, and leave the world.

Ishmael started. "Impossible!" he cried. "Why, that would mea he'd leave you too." But, by Allah, the woman might be near th heart of the matter in spite of that. He thought of Jason's recen actions in this light and said slowly, "It is not impossible. But it i folly. Did I not tell him, about doing and dreaming? I had though he understood."

"So had I," she said, "but he didn't. Or if he did he didn't agree But what can we do? He needs me, and I need him. Father, I lov him."

"I know, I know," Ishmael said. "I've been in love, even though am sixty-nine." He spoke testily. Women—he had loved them ever way it was possible to love them; and books; and the whirr of th sword unsheathing; and wine in the cup. The young were annoyin sometimes, reminding you of the past.

Now she said again, "I'm sorry, Father. I know you have been i love. That's why I was so happy when Jason met you. I thought: Her is a man who can lead Jason the way he should go. Jason is of th world. It is not right for him to shut himself away from it. He onl thinks it is because we—he and I—have seen so much killing an struggling for money and power. He is impressionable—very. I ar sure he has sworn never to kill again. I don't want him to kill withou need, and there are people who must live by such a rule. But he' not one of them. He's a hunter. Do you remember how he misse that great pheasant below the Mana Pass, when you told him to tr kill it because we were hungry? He never missed before. And look here! Hasn't he started a hare?"

Ishmael looked ahead under shaded eyes. Jason's horse galloped and turned across the plain half a mile in front. As he watched, the horse swung sharply, and Jason fell off.

He cried, "He's fallen!"

She said, "Do you see? He'd rather kill himself than kill a hare."

Ishmael said, "I can't believe it—neither that nor the other, that he is going to become a recluse. He is thinking—about you, about how to get enough money to buy a house, about what he is going to do with his life."

She said, "I do not think so."

Ishmael rode a long time in silence while the wind tugged fiercely at the skirts of his coat. By Allah, the boy needed a smart whipping! Or a fight—something to warm his blood, make it run hot and fast in his veins. Disgraceful to brood on solitude and the contemplative life while this young wife longed for him and was neglected! Passionate thighs that young woman had, and a hungry mouth, and a mind to travel beyond the physical ecstasies of love.

He himself was in the way, of course. How could they make love, or even thrash out their problems with kisses to help at the difficult places, when he was there? No shady corners here, nothing but the enormous sweep of nothing. He'd better go out from camp a long way, say he was looking for stones or something, make it clear he would not return till midnight. Damnably cold for an old man at midnight . . .

Catherine said, "I see something moving beyond Jason."

Ishmael looked up. Fur hats! He wouldn't be put off a second time. A good furious gallop was just what he needed, to shake up his liver and clear his head. He beat his horse into a weary canter. His beard flew back all over his mouth and nostrils, and angrily he brushed it away so that he could shout, "Jason, fur hats! Catch them!"

Jason wheeled alongside, shouting, "Father, come back! They may be bandits."

Ishmael yelled, "I don't care. Come on!"

The three men ahead had trotted out of the rocks where the plain met another ridge. They wore fur caps and carried long bows slung across their shoulders. Now they turned. All three unslung their bows, fitted arrows, and fired. The arrows whistled past Ishmael's head and stuck, quivering, in the earth.

Ishmael's heart leaped, and the old scars tingled in his cheek. A fight! Better and better! He drew his sword, leaned low along his horse's withers, and thundered on, shouting defiance. Another flight of arrows droned past him.

He yelled, "Dogs! Pigs! I'm coming! Ishmael of Multan!" He turned and shouted, "Draw your sword, boy!" But Jason galloped alongside with one hand upraised in the sign of peace, and his sword bounced about, undrawn, in its scabbard.

Two arrows sizzled by, but the third hit Ishmael's horse in the chest. The horse screamed in sudden pain. The three bandits wheeled their ponies round; for a moment he saw the flat sunlight splash yellow on their brutish, terrified faces; then Jason cried, "We are men of peace! Do not be afraid." But the bandits fled.

Catherine arrived at a gallop. Ishmael roared, "Men of peace! What do you mean? I'd have cut their damned heads off!" Breathing hard, he dismounted, adjusted his spectacles, and pulled the arrow from his horse's chest. It was a Tartar arrow. Very interesting. Now what wood might those fellows use for their bows?

The bandits had disappeared round a shoulder of cliff. It was no good trying to catch them. Jason said, "I will clean your horse's wound."

Ishmael said, "I'll do it. We'd better camp here. That's what those rascals were doing when we disturbed them." He noticed that the grass under the hill was a darker, richer green than elsewhere. A stream trickled out of the hill a little farther on, and then ran eastward along the foot of the ridge. After a few yards it disappeared again into the fine loess soil.

The bandits might return, but that couldn't be helped—in fact it would be fine; then there'd be a real fight. Jason would have to fight. There was definitely something wrong with the boy. Ishmael decided to ride forward with him tomorrow and give him a good talking to.

The sun sank, and all warmth left the harsh landscape. They hobbled the horses and unrolled their blankets near the stream. In Tibet there could be no sitting round a great campfire, because there was no fuel. Sometimes they had found dried yak dung at a camp site, but here there was nothing. They worked a little butter into a little tsampa, kneaded water into the whole, and ate the cold, soggy mess with their fingers. They drank from the stream and lay down to sleep.

Ishmael thought: I'll talk to him tomorrow, without fail. Or I'll ride ahead and leave Catherine to talk. Something's got to be done. This wild journey ought to have been so wonderful—even though their map is as unreliable as my ambassador's diary. Have to tell them about that soon. But there must be a twin-peaked mountain somewhere around here. Jason was a good young man, perhaps the best he'd ever known. What to tell him, how to show him, so that he wouldn't keep going off at dangerous tangents? It had happened all his life, from what he'd said about England and London and Manairuppu. The woman, his wife, was probably the answer. Jason needed anchoring to a firm piece of earth—wise, beautiful, understanding earth that recognized the glory of the dream, but knew which dreams were good, and which evil. Catherine . . .

❀ ❀ ❀

Darkness did not come quite so suddenly here. For half an hour Jason watched the pale slope of the hill blacken against the sky. The stars came out, and Catherine's flank moved warm against his through the blankets. He marveled at the fiery brilliance of the stars. Again, as at Badrinath, the wind left the plain, so that the blades of grass stood unmoved and silent by his ear, but high in the sky, between earth and stars, he heard the drone of the wind in its long passage.

The bandits might come back, and then Ishmael would want to fight. But fighting never did any good. He, Jason, would go out to them, his hands upraised and love in his heart, and they'd all sit down together and be friends. When he got back to India he'd be careful never again to put himself in the way of such distractions.

Molly saw those stars, and Emily and Mabel in London by the Thames, and Parvati outside the temple. He had loved them all, in their ways, and they were all unhappy because he had loved them. It had been the wrong kind of love.

The stars were fierce as the eyes of queens tonight, and the air flowed like ice round his ears, and Catherine snuggled against him. How could a man contemplate in this world of ice and fire and women?

Ishmael said, "Catherine, there are at least six horses."

Jason smiled. The old man was talking in his sleep again. But Ishmael said, "At least six. Nearer eight."

Catherine started up and said, "I'll put down the tent." Ishmael scrambled out, and his sword blade flashed in the starlight. He whispered, "The bandits have come back. Draw your sword, Jason. Get down the stream bed a few paces, and then—"

Jason sat up. He had heard the clatter of a horse's hoof against a rock. That was all. The loess soil buried all other noises the approaching horsemen might be making. He said quietly, "No. We mustn't fight. I will go and tell them we are men of peace." He set off toward the faint sounds.

Ishmael muttered, "Come back! They'll kill you!" But Jason walked slowly on along the bank of the stream. The unseen strangers had reached a stony outcrop among the loess, and their horses made a continuous low clatter. The starlight painted all things equal, whether light or dark—rocks and men, some moving, some still.

A tremendous whinny ran like maniacal laughter along the hillside. From startlingly close, two other horses answered the whinny. For a moment many horses cackled together in question and answer. A voice called sharply, but in a language Jason did not know.

He found himself in the middle of a group. There were six men altogether—three riding, three walking—and several pack horses already grazing, the sound of the tearing grass and champing teeth very clear in the silence. The men wore long-skirted coats, high boots, and cowled cloaks that came to a point above their heads. A light flared up, and the circle of faces took color and form—bronze-red hairless faces, fiercely tilted eyes, no eyebrows, expressionless. The riders dismounted and let their horses wander.

Jason said, "We are men of peace. Welcome to our camp." He tried to feel peaceable, but he thought they were a dangerous-looking crew and was guiltily glad he had his knife.

Ishmael was at his side, the sword in his hand and his old face alert and wary. He whispered, "They are going to try to surprise us when we've gone back to sleep. But we're going now. Too many to fight. Catherine's unpicketing the horses."

Jason said, "Very well." Better run than fight. A scholar had no business even thinking of fighting.

Ishmael said, "They don't understand Urdu. I have a little Tibetan. I'll tell them we must go. Then be ready. If they mean harm they'll try to prevent us."

He turned to the newcomers and broke into another language, speaking slowly and with obvious difficulty.

The leader of the strangers was a small old man with a face like a dried apple. When Ishmael finished speaking this man answered

254

Ishmael translated. "He says, blessings be on us. He doesn't seem to care whether we go or stay."

Jason thought: They are certainly bandits. What else can they be, moving about over this featureless plain in the middle of the night?

The old man's followers set about unloading their pack horses. They had brought fuel with them, and already a small fire glowed near the stream. The small wrinkled man spoke again.

Ishmael said, "He wants us to drink with them! By Allah, there will be poison in the wine. Get ready!"

The old leader clapped his hands. One of his men came running with a small goatskin under one arm and a pile of nesting cups in the other hand. He poured out the liquid into the tiny cups and handed one each to Ishmael, Catherine, and Jason. The little old leader made a courtly, obvious gesture— *Drink.*

Jason said, "Please to drink first," and held out the cup to him. His mind began to move fast and with a resentful desire to fight. But he must not fight. But was this fighting with words and wits any better than fighting with swords and arrows?

Ishmael said, "He never drinks spirits." He sniffed his own cup. "Barley brandy. It smells good. I don't think it is poisoned, after all."

Jason said, "Don't drink!" He saw another goatskin among a pile of rolled cloth and silver pots on the ground nearby. He said, "Tell him we'll drink from that."

Ishmael spoke, pointing to the goatskin on the ground.

The man holding the other cups dropped them. The murmuring in the background ceased. The little wrinkled leader spoke slowly.

Ishmael translated. "You mean—*that?*"

Jason nodded.

The leader picked up the goatskin, and then Jason saw that there were two, one slightly larger than the other. The small one had a leather case tied to the outside of it. The leader held them up, one in each hand.

Ishmael said, "Which?"

Jason said, "The small one." It would make no difference, because neither of them was likely to be poisoned. He had been too clever for the bandits.

The leader opened the leather case and lifted out a jade cup. It was very small, and there were black veins in the stone, which was so thin that the lamplight shone through from underneath it. He poured spirit into it from the small goatskin and gave it to Jason.

255

Jason took the cup in his left hand. His right hand slipped back to rest on the rough, comforting handle of his knife—just in case. But violence was not for him. He let go of the knife and drank.

The strangers sighed. The spirits burned in Jason's throat and chest. After a time he said, "It's not poisoned. Don't forget you have the spirits from the other goatskin, the first one. Throw it away."

But the leader seemed to have forgotten that Catherine and Ishmael existed. He stared only at Jason, his dark old eyes full of amazement.

Jason handed back the little cup and said, "Thank you. Now tell him we're going."

Ishmael spoke. Simultaneously the old leader began to speak rapidly. He beat his hands together in anguish. He conferred with another, larger man, almost as old as himself. He kept staring at Jason.

Ishmael said, "He wants to know where you were born, what your house looked like."

Jason said, "God's blood!" He forced himself back into his new-loved calm. If he were patient all this excitement would pass away. He described the farmhouse under the Plain.

Catherine said, "The horses are ready."

Ishmael translated, even more slowly than before, for the idea of an English farmhouse under the Plain could not be easy to explain.

The leader began to speak. Ishmael said, "Jason, they're not bandits! They are monks. The leader is called Tendong, and he is the chief abbot of Tsaparang monastery. He doesn't want you to go. He must give you another—I think the word means 'examination'!"

Jason looked at the old leader with new interest. Tendong, an abbot of a monastery! There was a monastery down the Vale, four or five miles from Pennel—a big ruin with no roof and stinging nettles in the forecourt. A monastery used to be something like a temple. He'd like to go and see this Tsaparang. Probably it would still have a roof on it, if all these men lived there.

With his own hands Tendong unrolled a carefully tied bundle. He spread it out beside the lamp and stood back. On a large sheet of yellow silk lay three brass cylinders, three squares of yellowed paper, three silver handbells.

Ishmael said, "You know what those cylinders are? Prayer wheels. And the papers have the Wheel of Life painted on them. Beautiful!"

He hurried forward, adjusting his spectacles and murmuring apologies to the abbot. Tendong gravely held him back and spoke a few words.

Ishmael said, "Jason, he wants you to touch one of each—one prayer wheel, one painting, one bell."

"Why?" Jason said.

"He won't tell me."

Jason bent down and touched his finger to the prayer wheel on the right, the painting in the center, the bell on the left. He waited tensely. This was a queer, exciting examination.

The Abbot Tendong stood up and seemed to grow larger. The light glowed in his bronze-red face, his men fell away from him so that he stood alone, and his voice rang like a trumpet. He spoke a long time, using small gestures, powerfully controlled. He pointed to the east, the direction whence he had come with his followers. He pointed to the west. He pointed at Jason.

Ishmael kept looking at Jason with a more and more startled expression. By the time the abbot finished, Ishmael had turned pale and begun to tremble. Catherine left the horses to wander at their will and came to Jason's side.

Ishmael said huskily, "My daughter, our talk this morning was so much wasted breath. Jason may be the reborn Lama of Tsaparang, for whom the abbot is searching."

Catherine said, "He's no such thing!"

Jason stood away from them. He found it difficult to breathe, though the night air was like ice in his lungs. Something large, larger than he had ever imagined, something like an enormous red bird, hung over him with slowly beating wings. He looked at Catherine and noticed that her eyes were wet. He said, "Let the abbot explain further."

Ishmael said, "Tsaparang is a big monastery with two thousand monks. Some of it is very old. There are three abbots in charge of the monks, but the head of the monastery is the Lama. The Lama of Tsaparang is not chosen, like the abbots. He—" Ishmael's voice became suddenly sarcastic and angry. He said, "But you know all this, lord. Why am I telling you?"

"Go on," Jason said without anger.

Ishmael said, "The Lama never dies. When he *seems* to die the abbots go out to find the boy in whose body the Lama has chosen to be reborn. The monastery oracle tells them where to look. This time it said: in the west. And what kind of a house to look for—it said: a house under a hill."

A house under a hill. Yes, the farm lay under the Plain and in the west.

Ishmael said, "It always takes the abbots several years to find the new Lama, this time much longer than usual—twenty-two years— because several candidates were found to be impostors when they took the final tests at Tsaparang. In truth, Jason, there is intrigue among the abbots, I expect, each putting forward his own candidate. It is not real, this thing! It is a kind of folly—a divine folly, Jason, but a folly. *It is not real.* You must understand that. The searching abbots carry with them relics of the Lama's last time on earth, such as his prayer wheel, his bell, and his cup. Obviously the Lama will recognize his own belongings. That is what you have done!"

Ishmael went on. "The abbot is disturbed that you were not born into the Lama's religion. Also he fears that you look like a man of blood—of flesh and blood, Jason—with your bleached skin and pale eyes. There are the other tests which you must undergo in the monastery before he can be sure. But so far the signs are unmistakable. You would not drink from any but the Lama's cup—"

Jason said, "Yes."

Ishmael snapped, "But it was the goatskin that you were pointing at. . . . You drank with your left hand, as the dead Lama used to, though he was not left-handed."

Jason said, "Yes."

"You used your left hand because you had your right on your knife. I saw. . . . You limp, as the dead Lama did."

Jason said, "Yes."

"You fell off your horse today! . . . You picked the dead Lama's prayer wheel, bell, and Wheel of Life."

Jason said, "Yes."

Ishmael growled. "Pure chance! . . . And of course your age is right. Why didn't I tell the fools you were only eleven? You are behaving like it."

Jason stared at the Abbot Tendong. So I am the Lama. I always wondered what I was. The lamp gave out an oily smoke in the clear night. The stars were a long way up, where the wind blew. He walked unsteadily up and down. He was a Lama. He had been a Roman. He had built Stonehenge. He had climbed the wall of the

Spanish galleon before he was born. He had lain with queens, strangled tigers with his bare hands, played melting music on the flute. He had been a seagull and a fish. He had inhabited Shiva and taken the god's lawful wife, Parvati. Who knew what happened when a man died, if all this happened while he lived?

He looked down into Catherine's eyes. He thought: I am a blur to her, but she can see the stars. She has never seen my whole face and never will. She has looked at me, piece by piece, her spectacles an inch away, and laughed and smiled. . . . He would never see her again. This was what he had been waiting for, not solitary contemplation, not the taking of alms before an idol, but this—books without end, two thousand monks under his orders. The work should be done. What work? A history of the world, to begin with.

Catherine would never reach the end of the map now. He could give her money, though, to enable her to go wherever else she wanted. He said, "Tell the abbot I will come to the monastery, that they may test me." But really there was no need for tests. It *was* so. But let it be disclosed in due form, that Catherine might see the truth.

Ishmael spoke. The Abbot Tendong hid his hands in his sleeves and bowed.

❋ ❋ ❋

They traveled two days eastward, Jason in a near-trance the whole time. He saw nothing of the road or of his companions until in the middle of the third day a slow perception reached him that he was approaching a great house—no, a city.

He reined in his horse and, when his eyes came into focus, examined what he saw. He was in the center of a circular plain, perhaps twelve miles across. Black mountains rose out of the plain on all sides, and snow dusted the serrated line of their peaks. The sun shone in a cloudless sky. A small river flowed silently with him, at his left hand. Men and women were working in the fields; the tassels of the barley waved in the wind; and three women were bathing in an irrigation channel. The women sat in the shallow water with their clothes hanging in thick bundles round their waists, and splashed one another's naked bodies and laughed shrilly with delight.

The city stood against the farther wall of the mountains—a white city, brilliant, its feet in the plain and its summit high against the black rocks behind it.

"The monastery of Tsaparang," Catherine said.

Jason rode on, now never taking his eyes off the monastery, for that was to be his kingdom.

They reached it at sunset, a towering city such as the Himalaya itself, but of a dimension sufficiently smaller for men to understand every detail of its vastness. Its walls rose in tiers to a height of three hundred feet above the plain. Tall golden cylinders stood like an army on the topmost roofs, and below them, along the upper wall, were fixed a thousand gold shields. There were balconies and terraces almost hidden by black and gold cloth which fluttered in the wind, and in the walls the rows of windows gaped like square black gunports in the side of a monstrous ship. Atop the gate ten red-robed monks blew into the mouthpieces of ten long trumpets. A little shaven boy stood between each pair of trumpets, a yoke over his shoulders supporting the two bell-mouths. The hollow, booming drone shook the air so that the massive wall itself rattled and the great gate buzzed.

They entered the courtyard and dismounted. There were stalls here, and women selling vegetables and milk, and on each side a row of doors such as Jason had seen in many Indian caravanserais. The double-bass throb of the trumpets began to quake like a fever in his body, and his head throbbed in painful sympathy.

A door opened, and they entered the lowest level of the monastery. To right and left stood a row of monks, some beating gongs and some rattling drums made of human skulls. They climbed a ladder and walked through a darkly echoing hall. Gods and devils, all hung with silk scarves, necklaces, and ropes of jewels, towered gloomily against the walls. They climbed another ladder, its rungs black and slippery —another chamber, longer, narrower, and darker than the last. On in smoky darkness—up, up ladders, and past idols; past wooden pillars like a forest, their lower parts swathed in dull red cloth; past smells of sweat and rancid butter and incense; through great halls with a hundred doors, all alike, and dim corridors alive with the sound of gongs and bells and trumpets.

The abbot opened the door of a large, plain cell, stood aside for them to enter, and silently closed the door behind them. There were two padded couches, a window, a lamp, a table. Jason lay down slowly on one of the couches and stared at the dark beams of the ceiling.

After a time the throbbing drums marched out of his head. He said, "Can we make tea here, Catherine?"

Ishmael said, "She stayed behind in the serai by the outer gate."

Jason sat up. "What! Stayed behind? Why?" He looked round the bare cell, but she was not there.

Ishmael said, "Women are not allowed inside. We told you on the road that she would have to stay outside. I told you many times. She cannot come in, ever."

Jason muttered, "I remember."

This was the biggest building he had ever been in—bigger than the fortress at Agra—and soon he would be the lord of it—lord of two thousand monks, lord of knowledge beyond reckoning. Several of those great chambers they passed through had been full of books, and each chamber larger than Ishmael's library. Catherine liked books.

But she wouldn't be here. There was no place for her. She wouldn't want to be here and share this life, even if it were possible. He'd never seen a female recluse or a girl yogi.

Ishmael said, "Tonight they will take you through the monastery in procession, Tendong told me, and there will be many tests on the way. Then you will spend tomorrow and tomorrow night locked in the dead Lama's private apartment. It has been kept just as it was when he died. When they come to fetch you on the second morning they will see what you have done in there and what you have used. Then they will decide. This must be one of the older parts of the monastery—*gompa*, in Tibetan. It was founded seven hundred years ago by the first Lama. They call him the Great First."

Jason said, "Did the Abbot Tendong talk at all of the dead Lama's habits?"

Ishmael peered at him across the ill-lit room. He said sharply, "Why do you ask? Ah, you're not so sure of yourself, after all. That's a good sign."

He strode agitatedly up and down the cell, tugging at his beard. He stopped by the couch and bent so quickly over Jason that his spectacles fell off. He swore and fastened them on again. He said, "Jason, my son—I'll tell you. If you are meant to live the rest of your life here—even if you have made up your mind that that is what you want—that is what will come to pass. Perhaps this *is* the life and place you are best fitted for. Tendong thinks so. He is a wise old man, as wise as I. He told me things, on the road, that he meant me to pass along to you. He believes you are the Lama, but after all he's an agent of God too, isn't he? I'll tell you. But it's your decision,

Jason, not his, or the oracles', or even God's. God sometimes leaves it to us to decide. That's why he's God. The late Lama was the eighteenth reincarnation of the Great First—that makes him the Nineteenth Lama, eh? He was a quiet and peaceful man. He liked to drink barley spirit, but never very much. He had dreams and visions, which he wrote down in books. He loved birds and animals, and never harmed one in all his life. You are a hunter, aren't you? But you don't need to tell them that, do you? I won't tell them, nor will Catherine. It's up to you. Of course no Buddhist may take life, but the Nineteenth was especially careful. He liked music."

Jason listened, relaxed and at ease now. He was the Twentieth Lama of Tsaparang Gompa, who had been the Nineteenth and the Eighteenth, and the Great First, and would be the Twenty-first and the Twenty-second . . .

Ishmael said, "They will come for you in a moment, Jason. Don't pretend. Be yourself; then they will see what you truly are. Don't deceive them. Tendong will be sad if it turns out that you are not the Lama, because already he loves you. But I love you too, and I am sad now. Catherine—"

Jason jumped up and said harshly, "Be quiet! I must be what I am."

"That is all we ask," Ishmael said with dignity.

Then the door opened. The Abbot Tendong waited in the passage, flanked by two other old men. Behind them stood three gigantic monks in bright scarlet robes, each carrying a golden mace, and on top of each mace rested a high orange hat shaped like a crested helmet. Behind again stood an even bigger monk, this one's scarlet robe almost hidden by white scarves, and his mace surmounted by a larger hat—a very old, shabby hat, its orange color faded to the dullest terra cotta.

Jason stepped forward slowly, his eyes fixed on the faded hat—the Lama's hat, *his* hat. From a distance he heard Ishmael's murmur, "Good-by." Then he took his place in front of his proctor and behind the three abbots. He forgot Ishmael.

Twenty shaven-headed monks formed the procession. One had a small conch horn, two carried hand gongs, nine had flaming tapers, and eight bore sacred scrolls. They struck the gongs and sounded the conch. The procession moved off.

After a long way and two ladders, Tendong opened a door on the right. Jason passed through into a small chamber. Heavy robes, white scarves, and jeweled rings lay neatly arranged on a couch. The three abbots fell back. The proctor took the hat off the mace and laid it beside the clothes.

They wanted him to put on the robes and the faded hat. If he was not the Lama boils would burst out all over his flesh. Painted hells writhed on the walls here, full of demons and screeching monks.

But he could not put on the robes until his head was shaved.

He touched his hair and said, "Cut it." The abbots sighed.

He stood silently while they went slowly round him with a razor-sharp knife. His hair fell to his shoulders, and they brushed it with their hands to the floor. Tendong sank to his knees and with a tiny brush swept the hair into a wooden box.

His head felt cold now. He put on the robe and the hat. The gongs boomed in front, and he walked out into the passage.

Slow, slow steps. It was dark and lined with more hells, dark and furious with grimacing. The abbots fell back, and he stopped. Three doors faced him, each of black wood, each barred with gold and hung with paintings on silk screens. He waited, but none of the doors opened.

The Abbot Tendong breathed asthmatically behind him. Tendong was an old man, and tired. His feet dragged as the responsibility that had given him strength was lifted from him. He, Jason, was lifting it and taking it on himself. He could carry it. The old abbots needed a rest. They needed to be told what to do instead of having to worry.

Jason walked to the left-hand door and rapped on it. It opened at once. He strode through, Tendong's feet shuffling more wearily now behind him. Nineteen portraits hung in a row along the left side of the room which he now entered. There were no windows. The light came from a row of lamps, one under each painting. Jason walked down the line. Every portrait was of a man. Some were crude, some delicate and finely detailed. Some of the men wore ritualistic expressions, some were as sharply seen as a beggar scratching his ear. One had soft dark eyes, a long chin, and in his hand a stringed instrument. Jason touched that portrait, and again the abbots sighed.

He followed the abbots down more ladders, and the monks followed him. Another door—but Tendong flung it open with a crash, and Jason strode into a blare of sound. Two thousand devils filled the enormous hall, the walls writhed somberly in smoke and scarlet, twenty long trumpets boomed. He paced forward among the devils, who opened their prancing ranks for him. The monkish robes swirled about their legs, but their faces were hideous black, white, and red masks, with gnashing fangs and yellow tongues and scarlet horns.

He took his seat on the wooden throne at the far end and turned to face the dancers. The abbots stood in a row behind him. The mouths of the trumpets were at his ear; their bellowing deafened him, then drove out all sense of reason. The robes of the devil dancers swirled, the masks dipped and rose. . . .

Ah, white cross-garters, down and up! The monastery shaking under the heavy feet—the wind drumming across the Plain.

He stepped forward and held out his hand. Someone must have the thing that he wanted. The Abbot Tendong handed him a mask of black and gold in the shape of a horned demon. They fastened it to his head, and he began to dance.

This mask held a glaring power in it. Or was it his pale eyes seen through the slits that made the other dancers drop out and squat cross-legged on the floor as he whirled among them? The trumpets boomed like the ocean on the shores of Coromandel, but it was the Wiltshire wind that soughed in his ears. The devils that fell away before the power of his eye, of his dance, were the devils of Stonehenge, and greater than these masked impostors of Tsaparang, for he came from the beginning. He had danced two thousand years longer than they. This was the Oak and Horn.

He danced alone, across the floor, among the cloth-draped pillars, out through the door.

He stopped, breathing hard, and waited for the procession to join him. Then he handed his mask to his proctor, who lowered the hat onto his head. The abbots strode off, and all the two thousand devils followed with trumpets and gongs and bells and the rattling of skull-drums.

In a gloomy cavern, deep in the belly of Tsaparang, all noise suddenly ceased. The shuffling of feet died away down the tunnel behind him. He looked into a square room, unlit, unwindowed, totally bare. A dark orange sheen and a low droning sound came out of it. A little light from the tapers crept past his body where he stood in the doorway. After a time he saw that four monks were kneeling in a row in the middle of the room. They were speaking, sometimes all together, sometimes by question and response, as in a litany. He took a step forward to enter the room.

He was kept out. He stood a moment, feeling the gentle pressure against the front of his body. No one was touching him.

264

He peered into the room and longed to enter, but he could not. Four monks passed by him, went in, knelt, and joined the litany. The first four moved over, shuffling on their knees. The new four shuffled into their places. For a second Jason saw the floor where the monks knelt. In four places the granite was grooved to the shape of a man's knees. The grooves were six inches deep.

He turned away, the great hat nodding forward as his shoulders drooped. Men had prayed in there, without ceasing, for seven hundred years. The room was so full of prayer that there was no place for him—no place for the Twentieth, the Great Twentieth.

No place for Jason Savage.

On, on—two thousand pairs of feet tramping behind him, climbing the ladders, pacing the corridors; and the gongs beating and the trumpets blowing and the monastery speaking with the voice of timber and stone.

The abbots stopped in front of him. His eyelids drooped, and his head nodded. No place for Jason Savage.

A door opened; he stumbled inside. It was a big room, with six lamps burning, and the walls were splashed with gold and white. He flopped on the couch and fell asleep.

❋   ❋   ❋

As the sun rose he looked out from the highest room of all, a quill in his hand, the plain like a carpet of pearl below, his servants no bigger than ants down there as they ran to do his bidding. Of course he might be dreaming. If he was, it might be a sight into the future, rather than a dream. . . .

As the sun set he rode in toward the great gate. Tsaparang rose in triumph against its mountain to greet its master. The vivid light burst over it, and they were blowing the trumpets for him.

Parvati knelt to worship him. She understood. There was also another woman he had once known. She would not kneel. He could not see her face or remember her name. Parvati said, "Jason, you can swallow the sea." "No, I can't." "You can. Try." He tried. The sea rushed down his throat and was all, all gone. The seabed looked like hell and smelled of smoky butter. She smiled at him, suddenly lascivious.

Parvati would believe in him, the Great Twentieth. Ishmael—no. Jane—no. Emily—no. Old Voy—no. Molly—sadly he had to admit—no.

One day there would be a place for him in the room where they said the prayers. Meantime he had better set out again on a long journey to perfect the contemplative state of mind. . . . Dawn, ten thousand monks behind him—*tramp-tramp-tramp,* their shaven heads like cannonballs in the sunlight, and the crops waving: Good-by, come back soon to us. Ishmael's stupa was under the sand—here. He said, "Dig! Dig here!"

He awoke, his voice echoing round and back to him. "Here!" Slowly he got up off the couch. The sun was high, and he could walk out of the room onto an open terrace. This was not the cell he had set out from.

"Ishmael," he called. "Ishmael!"

No one answered, but there was a wavering and a whistling in the air, like fifty flutes. They did not make a tune but all sang together, every note that God had ever given. The terrace was twenty feet square, and the edges were guarded by a low balustrade. Scores of pigeons circled round, flew back and forth, came in to land with their legs forward, their bodies back, and their wings fluttering to throw the air forward. Little bamboo tubes were tied to their legs. He muttered, "*They* are the flutes." It was a beautiful idea. The pigeons allowed him to stroke them.

He walked into the room and opened a brassbound box just inside. It was half full of parched barley. He took out handfuls of it and scattered it over the terrace for the pigeons. They cooed down in thick multitudes and in a minute were fluttering all round him and under his feet.

Glancing at the sun, he realized that the terrace jutted out over the southwest corner of the monastery. He had a long view from here, toward the mountains and over the plain. Staring suddenly, he raised his hands to shelter his eyes from the sun and peered into the northwest. A mountain with twin peaks stood out there, distinct among formless fields of snow and rock. He had the map in his loincloth, under the robes.

He rubbed his hand over his head and listened to the crackling of the stubbly hairs. He sighed and turned back into the room.

He remembered. This was the Lama's apartment, which Ishmael had told him about. They were going to leave him here until tomorrow morning, when they would come and decide finally whether he was or was not the true Twentieth.

So he was not the Lama—yet. But how could that be? *Yet* was the word that made it impossible. He was, or he was not, now—whatever they said tomorrow. He would like to ask Ishmael to explain that. But Ishmael was not here, and they had locked the door.

Yes. Bolted and barred.

Early afternoon. He must have slept like a dead man. The apartment had several rooms, and everything he could need. Here was a carved box. Ah, spare flutes for the pigeons' legs, and golden thread to tie them with. The pigeons must wear them out quickly, fluting from dawn to dusk, landing, flying up, probably pecking at them sometimes.

This was no cell. There were books by the hundred—but he could not read them. Several low tables. Jade ornaments. Prayer wheels. Six statues of the Buddha, all draped with scarves and necklaces. A pen case. Ink. Paper. Two jars. He removed the stoppers and sniffed —barley spirit, rather like brandy. A metal pot with a spike on top and a flame burning under it, and a jar of oil under the table. Tea leaves. Tsampa. Butter. The Lama's jade cups with the black veining.

He made himself some tea, lifted down a parchment roll in a brass case, and began to unroll it. This must have been the Nineteenth's favorite. It had lain easily to hand. It was full of pictures of gods, wheels, and dragons. He studied it for a time, then laid it on the table. When they came for him they would know that he had read it.

He told himself that he was calm, confident, and happy. He felt restless.

Now the Nineteenth would probably have done some writing at this time of day. The Great Twentieth should do the same. He'd write down some of *his* dreams and visions. Well, he could write a letter or a lot of swear words, and the abbots wouldn't know the difference, because they could not read English.

But first . . . He washed out a tiny jade cup, filled it with brandy, and drank, using his left hand.

It could hardly be tasted, the cup was so small. He refilled it and drank again. Careful. The Nineteenth never drank more than two.

But they were *so* small! He refilled the cup, sat down, took paper and pen, and prepared to write.

He wrote: A HISTORY OF THE WORLD.

This was foolish, that he thought so quickly and wrote so slowly. He laid the pen down and stared across the terrace. If he had two thousand monks, *and* all of them must do what he told them, he could divide them into parties of, say, ten each. That would make—two hundred parties. But they couldn't all go out searching for knowledge at the same time. Some would have to stay here to put into books what the others saw. Probably one hundred parties would be out and one hundred in. The brandy jar made a pleasant, gurgling sound as he lifted it.

He needed more monks—another two thousand, at least. And more abbots to control them. He took another drink. The pigeons fluted melodiously, and he thought he heard a tune—but no, there was none.

God's blood, now he'd lost his train of thought.

He went out to the terrace to examine the view. Evening was on its way but not yet come. The sky to the west burned orange-red like one of his monk's robes; all day it had been pure and as coldly blue as the northern ocean.

He could see a hundred miles—a thousand. Not far enough, by half. The pigeon orchestra, nothing but flutes, never stopped its music. He'd better feed them again before they went to their lofts. He scooped up a handful of grain and threw it out. They swooped in whistling dives, landed, and ate and clucked and cooed. He took a little drink.

God's blood *and* bones, where did the whoreson brutes go at night? Couldn't see a pigeon loft anywhere. He leaned far over the balustrade to look. It was a long way down, and at once he knew what it was like to be a pigeon. Tie a bamboo pipe to his leg, and he'd jump over there. It would have to be a big pipe, though, and make a drumming noise like one of the twelve-foot trumpets. He'd been a seagull on the water once. That was in Simon's log boat.

He was looking down into the forecourt of the monastery. Some monks were unloading yaks after a journey. Two hundred feet from him to the yaks' backs? Three hundred? A long way. He couldn't tell whether the manlings down there were men or women. They'd mostly be men, even though it was the serai that he was looking into. No woman ever came into the monastery.

Never. Tendong had not raised his eyes to a woman along the road—not even to the half-naked ones bathing in the irrigation ditch. Tendong was old and wise; he, Jason, was young and wise. He'd looked. He remembered the shapes of them very clearly. And Coromandel! The women carried polished golden pomegranates in Coromandel, and the tips stood up like soldiers when it was cold in the morning.

He thought sensuously of women. Now there was not a woman he knew within a thousand miles of him—ten thousand miles. He took a drink.

Women. The devil take them for so many bags of flesh! They didn't matter. It didn't matter. He would get over it, and he had a history of the world to write.

Women were nothing in the balance against this—knowledge, two thousand monks, music, books. He breathed deeply, standing with legs braced and the brandy jar swinging in his hand. This was perfection! The air ran cold as ice and pure as water into his lungs. He felt like a hundred men, because he would never think of a woman again. The mountains glittered in the fire of evening. The trumpets boomed, throbbing-soft in the distance. In his room were gold and silk, and gods about whose necks hung necklaces of great red stones. Perfection! The end of the road! The Great Twentieth!

His shoulders sagged. No room for him in the place of prayer. He took another drink.

The pigeons fluted without ceasing. He couldn't think properly with that noise going on. But he must treat them well. The Nineteenth had liked pigeons. The Great Twentieth *loved* pigeons. He had always treated pigeons properly. He had never done a pigeon harm in all his life. Never thought of it. But they were making too much noise.

He took a silver bowl from before one of the statues, threw out the tsampa and butter in it, and filled it with grain. He poured brandy into his jade cup and emptied it over the grain. He stirred the grain with his finger. Useless. That had hardly wet one piece. They would be disappointed. They would think he was miserly. He had never been miserly with pigeons. He emptied the second brandy jar into the bowl of grain. That was excellent too, because it would prevent him from drinking too much, in case he should be tempted to do so through his joy and happiness in the perfection of this place. He mixed the grain and the brandy into a mash and took it out to the terrace.

He called, "Ohé, pigeons! Come along, pigeons. Nice food for you, pigeons!"

They descended on him in thousands, fluting in his ears and hair and flapping their wings about his head. As many as could dived into the bowl and pecked greedily. Others strutted around, awaiting their chance to get at it.

"Good pigeons," he murmured. "Good pigeons. That ought to keep you quiet, you poxy, puffed-up sparrows."

The pigeons pecked and fluttered furiously, and walked up and down, cooing. Why couldn't a piegeon walk without nodding its head? Nod-walk-nod-walk-nod-walk. It was enough to drive you mad. If he ever found himself in that state he would go to see a surgeon at once, or at least an apothecary. Some pigeons were staggering about the terrace now, and the sun was setting. Time they went home to bed.

He shouted, "Shoo! Shoo! Go home!"

A few pigeons lurched off the balustrade into space and flew erratically away. The rest clambered over one another to get at the bowl. One sat down on the floor and looked at Jason with its beady little eyes slowly disappearing under its eyelids. Another lay on its back and stretched up its legs.

He wanted to sleep or read or write, or something. How could he, with a flock of drunken pigeons fluttering over his bed and swaying on the head of every Buddha in the room? They weren't allowed inside the apartment, and they knew it. Damned mutinous pigeons they were, staring and nodding and slyly winking as if they had secret information about him. They knew where the brandy had gone.

But he would treat them well. That was necessary, and in his nature. He shooed and shooed.

Some lay down, some nodded sleepily, some became full of energy as though a new dawn had come, and flew rocketing past the terrace about thirty feet out, right to left and left to right. Or they soared to a great height, turned over, and dived toward the courtyard with the wind shrieking in their flutes.

"Drunken devils!" he shouted. "You wait."

He ran inside, fell down, got up, tore a heavy necklace off the nearest Buddha, snapped it. He held the stones loosely in his left hand. He got his slingshot from his sack and ran back to the terrace.

Now—must be just, give the pigeons a fair chance in spite of their mutinous drunkenness. He picked out two that were soaring on rapidly beating wings against the twilit sky, and kept his eyes on them. A hundred feet above the highest roof of the monastery they turned and dived. He swung the slingshot easily in his hand, round and round and round. No pigeon could expect more than this—and the light so bad! Faster, faster! The left-hand pigeon.

They raced past the terrace, and he let fly. The red carbuncle struck true. The left-hand pigeon wobbled in flight; the rushing air folded back its wings, and it raved on down, its flute screaming. Jason ran to the balustrade and leaned over. Down, down, smaller and smaller, the note wailing downward in pitch.

Thud!

He hurried back to the far side of the terrace. Must be fair. He chose a pigeon flying from right to left among a bevy of its drunken friends. Missed, and the stone flew God knew where.

He began to shoot fast. The Great Twentieth did everything better than other people—dancing, drinking, making love, writing books, dealing with mutinous pigeons. He began to hit more often. The flutes shrieked down, a succession of thuds rose up faintly from the courtyard.

Getting too dark now. He leaned over and dimly saw a crowd of monks down there in the forecourt—shaved heads, upturned faces, much scurrying and alarm. He cupped his hands and bawled, "I don't want them back. You may eat them. The Great Twentieth says so."

Now he had used up the necklace, and it was nearly dark. Carefully he swept up the drunken pigeons from his floor and off the heads of the Buddhas and laid them in a row under the balustrade. There they would be in no danger of falling over the edge. Nidnod—one or two of them still walked up and down in spite of his frowns. Well, he had done his best for them. Let them fend for themselves now.

Back in the apartment he upended each brandy jar in turn and sucked. Empty as two drums. Damned pigeons.

He went out to the terrace and heard the murmuring of many monkish voices from the well of darkness. Let them go to one of their own painted hells and eat tsampa if they didn't like pigeon.

Suddenly he knew exactly what he wanted. There was someone in the monastery whom he must see, though he couldn't for the moment remember her name.

He stepped over the balustrade and walked along the west wall of the monastery on a ledge a few inches wide. The wind tugged at his robe, and his shaved head felt like a cold turnip. A couple of times he paused to look down. It would be a long way to fall, but not enough to worry about—only a mile or so. He raised one leg and shook his foot over the abyss to show himself he didn't care. He spat out into the darkness and listened. Couldn't hear anything but the wind and the gongs.

After a time he came to a window and climbed in. The cell was empty and the door open. He walked through into the passage and strode slowly on, his head bent in meditation. The gongs thundered louder here, and heavy feet were running in the distance. Most of them would be down in the forecourt, blowing trumpets to avert the rain of pigeons. Fools. They'd do better to smell the pigeons' breath.

He climbed down seven ladders. Many monks hurried past him, but he held to a studious silence. At the top of the eighth ladder he stopped. The great chamber below was full of monks, buzzing like a swarm in June, and in the middle the junior abbot was holding up a pigeon. Jason turned back and climbed out of the first window he came to.

Walking on air—how wonderful! But he would be killed, his skirts flying up round him and the air shrieking by!

A jarring shock rattled his teeth. He waited for the flat destruction which must follow such a fall. Nothing more came. He got up, took a pace forward, and fell down. He could not walk because he was waist deep in glue. He felt round with his hands. Manure. Yak manure, horse manure, ass manure, all sorts of manure. How wonderful the smell was, good and rich and like Shrewford Pennel on a spring morning—lots of straw and all steaming warm. He would like to lie here, rest a bit, and think. But he did not know what to think about.

He scrambled down the immense midden and at the bottom turned to look up at the monastery. He could not be sure which window it was that had deceived him. He might have fallen twenty feet or a hundred. What difference did it make, among the terrible dangers of drunken pigeons and buzzing monks surrounding him?

He had to be careful now, keep cool, hug the wall, look narrowly from side to side. They were after him, and the Golden Fleece was wrapped round his waist under the terra cotta robe.

He crept to the corner of the building and peered round. Now he knew where he was—in the forecourt. It was empty—no monks, no pigeons. The serai was just through that gate. He went, crouching low, across the forecourt and stood against the side of the arch. Ten doors against each wall of the serai, but which was the one he wanted? The trumpets boomed inside the monastery, and the golden cylinders on the roof stood up like sentries amongst the crackling stars.

One of the doors opened, and a woman came out. She put a small lamp beside the jamb and went in again. She had not thought he would come so quickly. She did not know that he could fly as well as any damned pigeon.

The little lamp burned quietly there. He smiled lovingly at it. Time to go now.

He crossed the courtyard, pushed the door open, went in, closed it behind him. It was dark, but he knew she was there in the darkness. She walked past him without a word, brought in the lamp, bolted and barred the door. He stretched and yawned and looked with blurred interest around the little room. She came to him and put her arms about his neck. She began to laugh and whispered, "Jason, you smell like a farmyard."

Someone else had said that to him—a girl, with her arms round his neck too—and he had resented it. But this was Catherine, and it was very funny that he smelled like a farmyard.

He began to kiss her slowly, the kisses haphazard and mixed with gurgling laughter and nothing like any kissing he had known before. Even when he lay down with her the joke stayed with them and got mixed up with the lovemaking as it had with the kisses. Jason felt the joke, and the ecstasy, and love, and the future years, and all the discoveries that lay hidden for him in those years.

They slept an hour or two at last, tight-locked and trustful.

✤   ✤   ✤

Jason awoke with the sourness of last night's brandy in his mouth, and a strong sense of guilt in his mind. A thin sliver of light was creeping under the door, but there was no sound except the whine of the wind high above the monastery.

Catherine opened her eyes and kissed him. He jumped up and began to dress in his own clothes. Looking away from her, he said, "I only escaped because I wanted to lie with you. It wasn't love, then. I was thinking of some women I'd seen bathing, nearly naked, in the water channel up the valley. Then I thought I couldn't live without you." No, God's blood, he must be honest! He said shamefacedly, "Without a woman, I meant."

She said, "I should hope not. Ishmael thought that if it wasn't one thing it would be another. I'm glad it was that—and me."

He ran over and hugged her breathlessly. He asked, "Is Ishmael down here?"

She said, "Yes. In the next quarter. He came down as soon as the monks came for you. It was he who brought your clothes. He told me all about that. He was worried, but we cheered each other up and decided in the end that—you were Jason Savage, and that you knew it better than anyone." She stretched and slowly began to dress herself.

Pulling on her high felt boots, she said, "What now?"

He said absently, "Follow the map."

She said, "Yes. Of course. I didn't mean that. Afterward, when we have found Meru and the treasure and the scholar's tomb, and come down from the mountain, what then?"

He said, "I don't know." He was no longer unhappy about it, but he did not know. He said, "I've learned here what I am not. I still do not know what I am, where my work lies."

She finished her dressing and came over to him, her eyes widely unfocused in the half-light, her face a pale shadow tinged with the night's color, and her lips dusky red. She said, "We won't think about it for a bit. Perhaps the answer is hidden on Meru!" She laughed and added, "I don't think anything else is. Do you?"

He said, "I don't know."

She said, "I know the map is false. That's not the word—I know the map is not an exact fact. I'm sure it will not lead to any money. I said once I'd tell you what the Latin means—the line on the map— when you needed to know."

"Yes."

"*Quae visa, vera; quae non, veriora*—'What you see is true; what you do not see is more true.'"

Jason considered the statement carefully. It was a good statement, true to what he felt and what he had experienced. Written on the map like that, it might mean many things. It might be a warning not to take the map seriously. It might imply that it was better to look at the map and think of the treasure then to go and find it. Then the map would be true after a fashion, but not as true as the treasure shining and glittering in an imagined cave on a nonexistent mountain. Or suppose there really was a treasure—and you saw it. Then the other, what was not seen, would be the imagined things beyond the treasure—the farther mountains, your wonderings about the man who amassed that treasure and carried it up the mountain. Or . . .

He gave up. With Ishmael to teach him and Catherine to guide him, he was content. He said, "First we must follow the map to the end. I knew there was something I had to tell you. From my room up there, the Lama's room . . ." He described the twin-peaked mountain he had seen on the northwestern horizon.

"There are many mountains with two peaks," she said cheerfully. "This may be ours, or Ishmael's, or neither."

"Or both!" he said, and then the door rattled, feet shuffled outside, and voices murmured.

Jason started up. "The monks! God's blood! We should have escaped while we could. They'll kill me for what I did last night. Those damned pigeons!"

She said, "I don't think so. They believe it is wicked to take life."

"Except people's, probably," Jason said gloomily. He unbolted the door and stepped out, blinking in the strong light, Catherine's hand in his.

Ishmael was there, his face twisted into a ferocious frown and his eyes sparkling, and the three abbots, and about a hundred monks. Eleven dead pigeons lay in a row, feet up, in front of the Abbot Tendong.

Jason said, "Hello, Ishmael. Are they angry?"

Ishmael said, "The abbot wants to know if you killed these pigeons, and whether you lay with the lady last night."

Jason said, "I did."

Ishmael said, "They will believe you if you say you didn't. Tendong loves you as much as I do. They need a Lama."

Jason said, "Thank you, Father." Ishmael was giving him another chance, now that he was sober and that Catherine might be presumed to have taken the edge off his earthly appetites. Old Tendong looked very tired. The long search would have to begin again. Tsaparang Gompa towered above him, and up there was the Lama's terrace. The pigeons cooed and fluted.

He said, "Tell him I'm sorry, Father. I am not the Twentieth."

Ishmael spoke. The old abbot's shoulders shrank. He held up his hand, and Jason saw that he was crying. Ishmael said, "You must give back the Lama's robe."

Jason said, "It is in the quarter here. I left the hat in the monastery."

The huge monk who had been his proctor stepped forward, laid down the rest of Jason's belongings, and went into the quarter. He returned with the robe folded carefully over his arm. Another monk gathered up the dead pigeons. Tendong turned away. The abbots and monks formed a procession behind him, the robe and the pigeons in front. The trumpets sounded, the inner door of Tsaparang opened, and the procession wound through and out of sight. The door closed.

Jason cried, "Load up, saddle up, as quickly as we can. Father, buy food from the women outside the gate!"

Ishmael cried, "Almost ready now, my son. See what Tendong gave me as a present." He held up a beautifully painted Wheel of Life.

Jason said, "They gave me something better still—two presents. Catherine—and myself, for her to find a use for!"

Catherine laughed, and they set off.

✻   ✻   ✻

They breasted the last pass and stood a moment to let the panting horses gain strength for the descent. Heavy tendrils of vapor blew round them; a few snowflakes drifted gently down. A slate-colored lake lay in the plain below, and, beyond it, the twin-peaked mountain. Clouds hung like curtains round the lower part of the mountain, and it did not seem high. A wand of icy light passed over it and made it, in that wilderness, a magic mountain.

Ishmael said, "Meru! Let us hurry on."

The clouds boiled up, and they began to scramble on down toward the lake. The snow fell steadily now, blown into their faces by a north wind. When they reached the lake they and their horses were draped in snow, and all the ground was white. Jason dismounted and tested the water of the lake. It was bitter. He remounted, and they trotted on. Catherine said, "We must find shelter soon. It is evening."

They rode along a level shore between the lake and the low bluff on its western side. After an hour a tiny stream crossed their path, flowing black across the snow from the bluff to the lake. Again Jason dismounted. He said, "Fresh." They turned left and groped through the blizzard toward the bluff. They rode up and down and soon found a place where a ridge of rock protected them from the north wind and a cleft in the ridge made an overhang that was almost a cave. They hobbled the horses, made a rude shelter from their blankets and coats, and huddled inside it.

Ishmael said, "Children, I'm hungry. I'd like a good pot of tea now. Even Tibetan tea would taste good—even with rich tsampa in it and rancid butter floating half-melted on top."

Jason said, "I'd like a Multani pilau like the one you gave us in Agra, with some of the Lama's brandy, mulled and spiced." He felt warm and cheerful. The weather would improve soon—tomorrow or the next day—and the end of the map lay so close there beyond the lake. He could not see the lake any more, nor the reeds by its shore, though they were only fifty yards away. The snow fell silently, and it was not very cold yet.

He opened one of the saddlebags and got out a sack of tsampa. He said, "But today we have a rare treat for dinner—tsampa, snow, and butter." He found the biggest bowl and mixed the mess into it for all of them to share.

"Eat up," he said cheerfully. "Tomorrow we shall start searching round the shores of the lake for the tomb of the scholar. Do you have any notion which side it will be, Father? It is a big lake, and we do not have much food."

Ishmael choked on a piece of tsampa. Snow lay thick in the folds of his turban and sprinkled his beard, where the henna dye had begun to fade, with brighter strands of white. When he had recovered himself he said, "No, boy, let's go up the mountain first. There may not be time to do both. Your cave is more important than my tomb."

"But we've told you about the Latin on the map," Jason said. "We must find the tomb first, because that is more likely to exist."

Ishmael succumbed to another fit of coughing, and his face went purple. Catherine beat his back anxiously until he wheezed, "All right, now. Mmm. There's something I ought to tell you about that. Ought to have told you before, really. You see, the ambassador who wrote that diary was something of a practical joker. I was the favorite object of his jokes. A coarse fellow, but I liked him. He's dead now, may his soul rest in peace. I started out twenty years ago to find this same tomb. Got as far as Badrinath. Then a message reached me from the ambassador. He'd retired by then. He'd invented the whole story."

"But why?" Jason asked, puzzled.

Ishmael took off his *kulla* and turban, all in one piece, and irritably beat the snow off them. He said, "Because he thought I'd like to believe it. I did, too. I was never so miserable as when the emperor made him send to tell me he'd made it up. *Quae visa, vera . . .* what was the rest of that?"

Jason said, "And then you wanted to go so much that you persuaded yourself it was true after all and came with us?"

"No, boy!" Ishmael roared. "I'm not a lunatic. Once I knew it was false, I knew. Your Voy had more sense. He didn't tell you."

Catherine bent over and kissed Ishmael quickly on the cheek. She said, "There! We love you, Father. Do you think we ought not to go any farther, then, so that we can be sure of believing the map for the rest of our lives?"

"No," Ishmael said. "That's being a coward. We must go on as soon as the weather clears. One thing is certain—this mountain is not Meru. The legends say that Meru is much higher than this. Look, I think it's going to clear."

They twisted round. The snow had stopped, and the clouds were rising fast. Soon the twin peaks of the mountain appeared, very close across the bitter lake.

*   *   *

At dawn of the second day they left their next camp, on the shoulder of the mountain, left the hobbled horses to find what grazing they could among the rocks, and began to climb. Jason hummed "Greensleeves"; Catherine hummed with him; Ishmael saved his breath.

They struggled up, at first across loose shale, then to rock, then to fields of sloping snow. According to the map, the treasure was hidden in a cave on the eastern peak. After two hours they came to the saddle where the mountain split. They faced the bare rock ridge leading up the eastern slope.

The western peak rose beside them, receding in distance as it climbed. They came to the base of the clouds, trudged on upward, and were alone on their mountain with the wet stones clinking under their boots. Jason sang aloud, and the swirling vapor echoed his song.

Ishmael said, "Go slower, my boy. I'm not as young as I ought to be."

Suddenly there was no more mountain. Jason said, "We must look for the cave. 'Forty-eight paces below the eastern peak, toward the north.'" He began to walk north, counting aloud.

At forty-eight paces, his heart beating fast and the mist thick in his lungs, he stopped.

If there was a cave here, he could not see it. It was almost impossible, from the shape of the mountain and the pattern of the rocks, that there could be a cave, certainly not one large enough to hide a considerable treasure.

He sat down slowly on the wet stones.

No cave, no treasure, no tomb. In fact, nothing. Yet he was smiling. Exhilaration enwrapped him like a—like the Golden Fleece! And he had found nothing and should have felt nothing but disappointment.

So that was it. The Golden Fleece was inside you rather than at the end of any road or map. A great discovery! He supposed some lucky people were born knowing that. He laughed. It was more exciting to be unlucky, to undergo the adventures of the journey.

Catherine and Ishmael groped toward him, looming up like giants out of the mist. He said cheerfully, "Nothing."

Catherine whispered, "Jason! Father! Look!"

The cloud blew thick about them in strange and thinning patterns, now rushing up with a current of wayward air, now whirling in ghostly circles, swooping downward, blowing into their faces, standing dense and vaguely translucent over the mountain.

Jason peered in the direction of her pointing hand. "I saw something," she insisted, "far away, or I wouldn't have seen it so sharply. It was black and gold."

"The treasure?" Ishmael cried, jumping to his feet with such force that his turban flew off.

"No. There, there!"

Jason saw a nearby cone of black rock, momentarily sharp among the drifting cloud. He said, "That's the western peak."

"No," she cried. "I can see that. Higher, farther to the left."

Jason looked, and saw.

A pyramid of black and gold hung in the sky immeasurably far to the northwest. It fell steeper to the left than to the right, and a plume of snow trailed from its peak, like a pennant across the horizon. The face of the pyramid was all black, for the snow could not lie there, so steeply did it fall into the clouds at its feet, but the sun poured gold onto the sides of it.

The clouds began to rise with unbelievable rapidity from the base of the distant golden pyramid. They soon tarnished its gold and, after half an hour, hid it altogether.

The three waited a long time more, but the vision did not come back to them.

Jason got up. He wished almost that he had not seen the distant mountain. Now he would never forget it. Nor would he ever be able to reach its base, let alone climb to its summit.

Ishmael wiped his spectacles free of mist and put on his turban. He said, "*That* must be Meru. So your map is still true! We have not reached the end of it."

"We never will," Jason said. "Did you see that tangle of snow and ice between here and Meru? Not even a goat could find a footing there."

"We might. You might!" Ishmael said. "If not you, then your son, your grandson—someone you've never heard of, any more than the first person to draw your map had heard of you. You must make a map, boy, a better map. Make it and keep it. One day someone will reach Meru. You must leave wonders for other people as well as using the wonders others have left for you."

Catherine said, "We had better start down now."

They started down, going very slowly in the cloud. Jason said, "I still don't know what I am to be. I thought somehow there'd be a sign here. I've been traveling so long."

Ishmael went more slowly yet, using what little breath he had in urgent question and answer. "Could you see Meru from your home in England, where you began?"

"No."

"Or from Coromandel?"

"No."

"Or from the topmost roofs of Tsaparang Gompa, even?"

"No."

"No. You had to struggle to the summit of this twin-peaked mountain. And what have you learned here?"

Jason said, "I don't know. Except that I am content."

Ishmael gasped triumphantly. "That's—what—you've—learned!" Then his breath gave out.

But Jason thought: It's more than being content. I am excited. Soon we'll all be back in Agra. I don't know what will become of me nor what I will do, except that I will live my life and find it wonderful.

I may be an equerry in the household of the poet-empress. I can set myself to explaining the English to the emperor, or the emperor to the English. I can find out why the Hindus, who are so wise, worship foolish idols. I can be a scholar or a general or a merchant or a physician, or all of those at once. I can make maps and write books! Whatever happens, people will find me easy to deceive—God be praised—because I want to believe, because I know now that the magic mountain is always the one beyond the one you have climbed, the coast of Coromandel is always over the horizon. If it were not so, magic would be at an end and a man could only dream, or only do —but never both.

He gripped Catherine's hand more firmly, and she began to hum.

Due